Problems
in
Measuring
Change

Proceedings of a Conference Sponsored by
the Committee on Personality Development in Youth
of the Social Science Research Council, 1962

Problems
in
Measuring
Change

Edited
by
Chester W.
Harris

The
University of
Wisconsin
Press
Madison
1963

Published by

THE UNIVERSITY OF WISCONSIN PRESS
430 Sterling Court, Madison 6, Wisconsin

Copyright © by the
Regents of the University of Wisconsin

Printed in the United States of America
by the George Banta Company, Inc., Menasha, Wisconsin

Library of Congress Catalog Card Number 63-19211

List
of
Participants

CARL BEREITER
  University of Illinois
  Urbana, Illinois

R. DARRELL BOCK
  University of North Carolina
  Chapel Hill, North Carolina

DONALD T. CAMPBELL
  Northwestern University
  Evanston, Illinois

RAYMOND B. CATTELL
  University of Illinois
  Urbana, Illinois

JOHN GAITO
  Kansas State University
  Manhattan, Kansas

CHESTER W. HARRIS
  University of Wisconsin
  Madison, Wisconsin

WAYNE H. HOLTZMAN
  University of Texas
  Austin, Texas

PAUL HORST
  University of Washington
  Seattle, Washington

HENRY F. KAISER
  University of Illinois
  Urbana, Illinois

FREDERIC M. LORD
  Educational Testing Service
  Princeton, New Jersey

FRANCIS H. PALMER
  Social Science Research Council
  New York, New York

LEDYARD R TUCKER
  University of Illinois
  Urbana, Illinois

HAROLD WEBSTER
  University of California
  Berkeley, California

DAVID E. WILEY
  University of Wisconsin
  Madison, Wisconsin

Preface

On April 30, 1962, the participants listed on page v of this volume gathered in Madison, Wisconsin, for a three-day conference on problems in measuring change. The participants had prepared in advance papers dealing with various aspects of this problem, and the conference was devoted to the reading and discussion of these papers. Following the conference, the participants revised their papers to whatever extent they deemed necessary in the light of the discussion. It is these revised papers that appear in this volume.

The idea for the conference grew out of discussions within the Committee on Personality Development in Youth of the Social Science Research Council. This committee had been engaged since 1957 in stimulating research dealing with the development of personality—broadly defined—of young people. One illustrative activity of the committee was the conference held at Andover, Massachusetts, in March, 1959, at which a large number of persons representing various disciplines who were carrying out research on personality development during the years of college attendance met to discuss problems of measurement and design and to report results. As the committee came in contact with a large number of such studies—often voluminous studies in terms of the amount of data being gathered—it became evident that a wide variety of practices could be identified with respect to what was taken as the evidence of change or development. It seemed reasonable to believe that not all these many procedures were equivalent, and that these procedures were not always unambiguous in what they defined as change. Gradually there developed the suspicion that the deceptively simple question of how to describe or measure change in such young people needed further examination.

The Committee on Personality Development in Youth of the Social Science Research Council considered ways in which it might assist in clarifying the technical problems associated with studies designed to describe change or development in young people, and in communicating to persons interested in making such studies the results of these attempts. It was decided that one appropriate step would be that of stimulating a critical review and, if possible, an extension of presently available techniques for describing change. A set of topics was planned, and individuals whose work indicated interest in these aspects of the problem were asked whether they would be willing to contribute. Titles of papers were negotiated, and the conference was scheduled. At about the same time, the interest of the University of Wisconsin Press in the publication of the papers was made known and communicated to the participants.

The selection of participants and of topics discussed in the conference was guided primarily by me. It is evident that I drew heavily on persons whose special competence may be labeled psychometrics. This was deliberate: first, because the interests of the committee have centered on personality development; and second, because—apart from econometricians—psychometricians probably have devoted more attention to the problem of measuring or describing change than has any other group. Essentially, I saw the conference as a starting point that could appropriately focus first on psychometric aspects of this problem; certainly I hope that in time the focus can be enlarged, possibly through further conferences and publications, to include the contributions that can be made by many other groups. The problem of describing change seems to me to be pervasive. Many—perhaps all—of the social sciences attempt to develop statements of some generality that incorporate the notion of change or development or decay. Insofar as these statements are based on observations, their development necessarily raises issues that are considered in this volume.

To my colleagues—both past and present—on the Committee on Personality Development in Youth, I wish to express my pleasure in their support of this conference. These are Ralph W. Tyler (Chairman), Lee J. Cronbach, Robert E. L. Faris, Dana L. Farnsworth, Nicholas Hobbs, T. R. McConnell, Donald G. Marquis, Lloyd N. Morrisett, Theodore M. Newcomb, C. Robert Pace, Francis H. Palmer, Nevitt Sanford, and Robin M. Williams, Jr.

It is customary for the editor of a volume such as this to discuss, in the preface, the papers, their relationships, and their meanings. I shall forgo this custom; these authors can speak for themselves.

Chester W. Harris

Madison, Wisconsin
January, 1963

Contents

Problems
in
Measuring
Change

One | Some Persisting Dilemmas in
the Measurement of Change

CARL BEREITER

Although it is commonplace for research to be stymied by some difficulty
in experimental methodology, there are really not many instances in the
behavioral sciences of promising questions going unresearched because of
deficiencies in statistical methodology. Questions dealing with psychological change may well constitute the most important exceptions. It is
only in relation to such questions that the writer has ever heard colleagues
admit to having abandoned major research objectives solely because the
statistical problems seemed to be insurmountable.

Such faint-heartedness is easy to forgive. Procedural decisions in the
measurement of change assume, with discouraging insistence, the character of dilemmas, of choices between equally undesirable alternatives.
The purpose of this paper will be to describe these dilemmas, tracing out
their implications for various kinds of research questions, and to suggest
some ways that they might be resolved.

Although they are found in numerous guises, it appears that the dilemmas encountered in change measurement can almost all be identified with
three basic ones. The first of these may be called the *over-correction–
under-correction dilemma.* It originates in Thorndike's (1924) observation
that there is a spurious negative element in the correlation of an initial
score with gains on the same test, because of the sharing (with opposite
sign) of the same errors of measurement, and that hence some kind of
correction is called for. The present state of the dilemma may be fairly
illustrated by Garside's (1956) article in which three methods of solving
for the regression of gains on initial scores are discussed, his own and two
others. All three methods have a certain plausibility, but with one method
the regression estimate increases as the correlation between pretest and
post-test increases, with another it decreases, and the third method is indifferent to this correlation.

In practice these differences have far from negligible implications. Two examples will suffice. The writer had the privilege of working with the Vassar studies of personality and attitude changes during the college years. Most of the quantitative data were obtained from two administrations of the same test battery, once in the freshman year and once in the senior year. Some pronounced general changes were observed, and a natural question to ask was whether these changes occurred at an even rate throughout the four years or whether they were mostly accomplished during the first years. Since yearly retesting of the same persons would probably have a serious contaminating effect, samples of one class were retested at various times—some at the end of their freshman year, some at the end of their sophomore year, and so on. As often happens, however, the subjects, though invited at random, did not accept randomly and it turned out that samples retested in different years differed significantly in freshman scores. What to make of this? We could ignore the discrepancies between initial scores and merely plot the retest means for the various groups as a function of time of retesting and try to fit a continuous curve of change to it. Or we could, by any number of devices, attempt to adjust the retest scores to compensate for differences in initial scores. Depending on the decision, we could get the curves to look almost any way we liked—linear, negatively accelerated, S-shaped, or what have you.

The second example comes from another part of the Vassar studies that was concerned with differences among curricular groups. Two questions were of interest: (*a*) do different fields attract different kinds of students? and (*b*) do students change differently during college depending on their major field of study? The answer to the first question was unequivocally "yes" (Bereiter and Freedman, 1962), and this made it difficult to answer the second question. Several related measures of "attitude growth" were available. When raw change was used, it turned out that the lower groups were initially, the more they gained during college (though these differences were usually not significant). When the initial score on any one measure was partialed out, it was found that the *higher* groups were on related measures, the more they gained. This complete reversal of findings when the switch is made from raw to corrected change scores seems to be typical, and it is difficult not to be suspicious of it, to suspect that it represents a switch from one kind of error to another. As this paper will attempt to show, such a suspicion is well justified.

The second dilemma, and the one that is perhaps most widely recognized as a dilemma, may be called the *unreliability-invalidity dilemma*. It originates in the only too well-known fact that, other things being equal, the higher the correlation between pretest and post-test, the lower the reliability of the difference scores. Accounting for the other horn of the dilemma is the even more elementary fact that the lower the correlation between two tests, the less they can be said to measure the same thing. Thus writers such as Lord (1958) have warned that when dealing with change scores, one had better watch out that conditions haven't changed so drastically that the test doesn't measure the same thing on the two occasions. If so, it would be meaningless to talk of change on the test.

The full force of this dilemma came upon the writer when he was trying, again in connection with the Vassar studies, to apply some new techniques of item analysis in order to develop scales that would yield more reliable change scores. The techniques seemed to be working. The reliability of the change scores was climbing with each successive item analysis. But the correlation between freshman and senior scales was declining at the same time and when, on one highly reliable scale, it dipped below .50, the realization came that all we were doing was building a scale that didn't measure the same thing in freshmen as it did in seniors. So a new tack was taken, endeavoring to squeeze out some gains in change score reliability while maintaining the test-retest correlation at a moderately high level. This recollection is a particularly bitter one, because, as later insights revealed and as this paper will attempt to show, the *unreliability-invalidity dilemma* is an utterly false one, and the intelligent course would have been to go blithely ahead increasing the reliability of the change scores, letting the test-retest correlation drop to zero if it so happened.

The previous two dilemmas are ones with which all reasonably enlightened researchers have attempted to cope. The third dilemma is one which researchers instead have tended carefully to ignore, probably because in facing it one sees psychometric theory totter. A not-very-adequate name for it is the *physicalism-subjectivism dilemma*. It is better illustrated than defined. Suppose, in the example cited above about the plotting of attitude changes across the college years, that the unpleasantness about differences between initial scores had not come up and that a perfectly satisfactory graph of changes in test score as a function of time had been obtained—say a nice negatively accelerated curve. Could we say that change in the particular attitude involved occurs mostly during the first years of college? Not unless we assume that equal score changes at various points on the scale account for equal changes in whatever the attitude is.

One has the unpleasant option of sticking with the particular scale units given or some rather arbitrary transformation of them (physicalism), or else abandoning the given units in favor of others that seem to conform to some underlying psychological units (subjectivism).

Because the dilemma has been generally treated as one entirely of choice of scale, it has been possible for researchers to take an attitude of "Ho-hum, there's no way to tell, and so we'll assume everything's linear." The objections to this seemingly widespread position are two: (*a*) the cost of being wrong is much greater in dealing with change scores than it is in ordinary correlation analysis, and (*b*) it misses the more fundamental question of whether, and in what sense, a functional relation between observed scores and some underlying change can be said to exist at all.

In order to stay within reasonable bounds, the following discussion will be generally confined to consideration of three variables: a pretest, an identical or parallel post-test, and some independent variable. Many of the other papers in this conference deal with multivariate problems, but the relevance of the issues treated here to these more complex problems will be evident without having to extend the discussion beyond the three-variable case.

The following notation will be used throughout:

$$X = \text{obtained pretest score,}$$
$$Y = \text{obtained post-test score,}$$
$$Y - X = \text{obtained change score,}$$
$$W = \text{obtained score on independent test,}$$
$$X_t = \text{true pretest score,}$$
$$G_t = \text{true change score,}$$
$$e_X = \text{random error on pretest,}$$
$$e_Y = \text{random error on post-test.}$$

The following expressions follow from conventional definitions:

$$X = X_t + e_X,$$
$$Y = X_t + G_t + e_Y.$$

Note that there is no special symbol for obtained change, it being always expressed as a difference. This is to avoid the implication that observed change has the same relation to true change that other observed scores have to corresponding true scores.

The over-correction–under-correction dilemma

The spuriousness of the correlation between initial score and raw gain, first noted by Thorndike (1924), is easily seen from the expression for their covariance:

$$C_{X(Y-X)} = C_{(X_t+e_X)(G_t+e_Y-e_X)} = C_{X_t G_t} - S^2_{e_X}.$$

Formulas worked out by Thomson (1924) and Zieve (1940) all amount to adding $S_{e_X}^2$ back in. The general properties of their formulas as well as some other possible ones can be seen from

$$(1) \qquad r_{X_a(Y-X_b)} = r_{X(Y-X)} + \frac{S_X(1 - r_{XX})}{S_{(Y-X)}},$$

where X_a and X_b are randomly parallel forms of the same test. This formula gives the correlation that would be expected between X and $(Y - X)$ if they did not share errors. The above formula can be modified to yield $r_{X_t(Y-X)}$, r_{XG_t}, or $r_{X_tG_t}$ by the usual corrections for attenuation, *but the corrections must be applied to both terms.* Consequently, these correlations will all have the same sign, though this sign may and indeed often will differ from that of $r_{X(Y-X)}$.

The mechanics are simple enough, but there is some perplexity about which coefficient is appropriate where. It would seem that for most questions of the form, "What is the relation between initial status and change on ———?" the appropriate correlation coefficient should be $r_{X_a(Y-X_b)}$. Most similar questions, after all, are answered with uncorrected correlations. But to the writer's knowledge, all researchers have used either the wholly raw correlation, $r_{X(Y-X)}$, or one of the correlations corrected for attenuation.

Further complications are introduced if, instead of correcting directly for attenuation, one uses regression estimates of true scores. Wiseman and Wrigley (1953), for instance, used as their estimate of the correlation between gains and initial status, $r_{\hat{X}_t(Y-X)}$, where $\hat{X}_t$ is estimated from X and Y. Alternatively, one might use $r_{X\hat{G}_t}$, where $\hat{G}_t$ is estimated from X and Y by the formulas of Lord (1956) or McNemar (1958). These correlations turn out to be complicated expressions which will in general lead to different results from the other correlations discussed.

The choice among these correlations becomes critical when it is desired to correlate change with some outside variable, holding initial status constant. The practical importance of such correlations has been explored in the work of DuBois and Manning (1961). The conclusion of this work, and one that seems to be widely endorsed in practice, is that in studying the relation of an independent variable, W, to change, one should use $r_{WY \cdot X}$ or $r_{W(Y \cdot X)}$, the correlation of W with Y, partialing X out of either Y or both Y and W.

Lord (1958) presented a most persuasive illustration of the superiority of partial correlation over the correlation of W with raw change. He showed that in an experiment where, for any value of X, an independent treatment variable correlated positively with Y, $r_{WY \cdot X}$ would always be positive, while $r_{W(Y-X)}$ might be zero or even negative.

In the same paper Lord pointed out another important fact about the use of partial correlation, but this is one that seems to have been largely ignored in practice. It is that the zero-order correlations entering into the partial correlation must be corrected for attenuation beforehand. Although this procedure is advisable with any partial correlations, failure to do so with correlations having to do with change leads to a special and predictable kind of error. Moreover, it appears that it is this error which gives rise to the over-correction–under-correction dilemma pointed out earlier.

The critical point is that when X is partialed out of Y, Y becomes uncorrelated with X but not with X_t. Specifically,

$$
\begin{aligned}
(2) \qquad C_{X_t(Y \cdot X)} &= C_{X_t(Y - \beta X)} \\
&= C_{X_t Y} - \beta C_{X_t X} \\
&= S_{X_t}^2 + C_{X_t G_t} - \beta S_{X_t}^2 \\
&= (1 - \beta) S_{X_t}^2 + C_{X_t G_t}.
\end{aligned}
$$

Since the beta weight will normally be less than one, it can easily be seen that where the correlation between true initial status and true gain is zero, the correlation between true initial status and Y, holding X constant, will be positive. To the extent, then, that an independent predictor, W, correlates positively with X, it can be expected to correlate positively with $Y \cdot X$.

This seems to be what lies at the bottom of the over-correction–under-correction dilemma. Referring to the example of the study of changes in attitudes related to major field of study, the situation seems to have been this: When raw change scores are used on a measure of authoritarianism, negative correlations are obtained between change and other scales which measure in part initial level of authoritarianism. Raw differences thus, in a sense, overcorrect for initial level. Partialing out initial level, we then obtain positive correlations between change and other measures related to initial level of authoritarianism. As far as true initial level is concerned, we have undercorrected.

Although it may be desired to correct all measures for attenuation, the crucial thing is to correct for unreliability in X. What is needed is $r_{WY \cdot X_t}$, which may be obtained by

$$
(3) \qquad r_{WY \cdot X_t} = \frac{r_{WY} - r_{WX} r_{XY}/r_{XX}}{\sqrt{r_{XX} - r_{WX}^2} \sqrt{r_{XX} - r_{XY}^2}}.
$$

In the numerator this coefficient differs from $r_{WY \cdot X}$ only in that the second term is divided by the reliability of X, but it can easily be seen that this could lead to the two coefficients' having different signs.

It might reasonably be argued that Y should also be corrected for attenuation, so that what is obtained is the correlation of W with true gain, holding constant true initial level. Somewhat surprisingly, the effect of correcting for attenuation in Y is to alter the numerator not at all, but merely to replace r_{XX} with $r_{XX}r_{YY}$ in the second factor in the denominator, thus increasing somewhat the absolute magnitude of $r_{WY_t \cdot x_t}$ over that of $r_{WY \cdot x_t}$. Thus the choice between these two coefficients is not critical.

One would like to be able to claim that this solves the over-correction–under-correction dilemma. Actually, the best that can be claimed is that it pushes it back one step, to the point where the dilemma is in the choice of reliability estimates. An overestimate of r_{XX} can make the correlation spuriously positive; an underestimate can make the correlation spuriously negative. The only consolation is that the error is likely to be smaller in magnitude than that found in other correlation coefficients.

A word should perhaps be said at this point about another approach to the analysis of the correlates of change, which can be traced back at least to Woodrow (1939b). In this approach, change scores are not explicitly involved at all. Instead, the correlation of W with X is compared with the correlation of W with Y. Presumably, if W correlates higher with Y than it does with X, W contributes to growth on the dimension involved. If W correlates higher with X than with Y, W is negatively related to growth. Needless to say, such comparisons make sense only if the correlations are corrected for attenuation; therefore we may examine them in terms of error-free measures. We may accordingly think of X as made up of uncorrelated components X' and W', and $Y = X' + W' + G$. It can then be shown that

$$(4) \qquad r_{W'Y} - r_{W'X} = r_{W'G}\frac{S_G}{S_Y} + \frac{S_{W'}}{S_Y} - \frac{S_{W'}}{S_X}.$$

This expression shows that the difference between the two correlation coefficients depends on several other factors in addition to $r_{W'G}$, the datum of interest. For instance, although $r_{W'G}$ was positive, (4) might take on a negative value if S_Y were sufficiently large. For this reason it would seem preferable to use formula (3).

The unreliability-invalidity dilemma

Undoubtedly the best-known "fact" about change scores is that they are unreliable. It is also quite well known that this unreliability has two sources: unreliability in X and Y, and positive correlation between X and Y. Hopes for the attainment of more reliable change scores rest mainly on hopes for the attainment of greater reliability in the pre- and post-measures, but there are realistic limits to the gains that can be made in this way. Consider a test where X and Y have reliabilities of .80 and correlate .70 with one another. Assuming their variances to be the same, the reliability of their difference will be .33 (Gulliksen, 1950, pp. 351–55), a fairly typical result. In most psychological tests, the realistic upper limit of reliability is about .90; but, since increasing the reliability of X and Y will also increase their correlation, raising the reliability of X and Y to .90 will increase the reliability of their difference to only .53. On the other hand, leaving the reliability of X and Y at .80 and reducing their correlation to zero would raise the reliability of their difference to .80. This tempting prospect is marred by two considerations: (*a*) can it be done? and (*b*) is it a reasonable thing to do?

It is not obvious how one might go about modifying a test to lower its test-retest correlation, and it seems that any method that produced this result would be likely to do so by lowering the reliability of the test on either or both of the occasions. But there is a procedure by which lowered test-retest correlations can be achieved as a by-product while perhaps even raising the reliability of the test on the two occasions. This is a procedure developed by the writer for dealing with change measures at the item level in order to operate directly on the reliability of change scores.

A single item administered on two occasions yields an item change score which is the difference between the item scores on the two occasions. If the item is scored dichotomously, +1 or 0, on each occasion, then the item change score may take any of three values, +1, 0, or −1. Alternatively, these scores could be considered as being directly assigned to changes revealed on the item, +1 indicating a positive change, −1 indicating a negative change, and 0 indicating no change. Operationally there is no difference between treating change at the item level as a difference between two scores or as a directly assigned score since identical numbers result, but conceptually the latter view has an important advantage.

We may define a *change item* as an item that is administered to the same persons on two occasions and scored directly for direction and perhaps amount of change. Although this is only a practical rather than a necessary restriction, we shall consider only change items that are scored in a manner that is equivalent to scoring the item separately on the two occasions and taking the difference. Change item scores may be treated like any other item scores, summing them to get a molar change score. Most important, conventional item analysis procedures, using the variances and covariances of change item and scale scores, can be employed to increase the internal consistency of a scale made up of change items.

Thus it is possible to work directly toward improving the reliability of a measure of change.

Under the restriction that change items are scored in a manner conformable to a method of scoring the items separately on each occasion, everything that is done by way of altering the parameters of the change scale can be translated into changes in the parameters of the pre- and post-test. Letting d stand for an item change score and D stand for the change scale score, a well-known expression for the reliability of a scale may be written alternatively as

$$r_{DD} = 1 - \frac{\sum S_{d_i}^2}{\sum S_{d_i}^2 + \sum_{i \neq j} C_{d_i d_j}}$$

$$= 1 - \frac{\sum S_{x_i}^2 + \sum S_{y_i}^2 - 2 \sum C_{x_i y_i}}{S_X^2 + S_Y^2 - 2C_{XY}}.$$

Thus gains in r_{DD} obtained through gains in the change item covariances will surely be reflected in decreases in r_{XY}.

In applications of this approach to the development of scales to measure change in attitudes over the four-year college span, it was found possible to make substantial gains in the reliability of the change scores. Just what levels of change score reliability could have been attained was never found out, however, because, as was mentioned above, the approach was drastically altered when it was feared that it would lead to meaningless results. It was not that the scales began to look meaningless or anything like that. It was just that it seemed that the change scores would have to be meaningless if they were obtained from a scale on which freshman and senior scores had almost no correlation with one another.

At the bottom of this dilemma is a paradox: When scores on a test are observed to change, how can one tell whether it is the persons who have changed or the tests? If the correlation between pretest and post-test is reasonably high, we are inclined to ascribe change scores to changes in the individuals. But if the correlation is low, or if the pattern of correlations with other variables is different on the two occasions, we may suspect that the test does not measure the same thing on the two occasions. Once it is allowed that the pretest and post-test measure different things, it becomes embarrassing to talk about change. There seems no longer any way to answer the question, change *on what?* To the layman and to many psychometricians there is no genuine problem here. It is obvious to them that only the persons can change, and that the test as a clearly specified set of operations does not change unless the operations themselves change.

There does seem to be a problem here, however, but it is not the problem which the preceding discussion and others like it suggest.

A few examples will show the general locus of the difficulty. A test that measures arithmetic reasoning ability in children may measure only computational accuracy in the same children when they are older. Scores on a test in electronics given at the beginning of an electronics course may reflect mainly differences in prior acquaintance with electronics; by the end of the course these differences may no longer matter and scores will depend on learning ability in that subject. In these examples there is every reason to say that the tests measure different things on the two occasions. Nevertheless, the tests might give reliable scores on both occasions and, since there would be little correlation between pretest and post-test scores, change scores calculated from them would also be reliable—reliable and meaningless.

In talking about the meaningfulness of change scores it is necessary to distinguish between the meaningfulness of average changes and the meaningfulness of individual differences in change. In both the examples above there would undoubtedly be large average changes in test scores that would be unambiguous in meaning: They would show that on the whole, subjects gained in arithmetic reasoning ability and learned some electronics.

It is the individual deviations from the mean trend that are meaningless or, as we shall prefer to say, of no interest. The person showing high change in the first example will likely be one who had low arithmetic reasoning ability when young but who was very careful in his computations when older. The bright but careless person could be expected to show less than the average amount of change. Similarly, change scores on the electronics test would favor the people who knew nothing about electronics to begin with. Yet, as dimensions of individual variation these are real enough and sufficiently specifiable. One could study them if he wished, and the tests would furnish fairly precise measures of them. It is just that no one is likely to want to study dimensions that are messy in this particular way.

There are, however, "messy" dimensions of change which one may be interested in studying. Suppose we have a collection of attitude items which yield reliable scores when administered to freshmen or to seniors, but freshman and senior scores show little correlation. We may, nevertheless, be interested in finding out what accounts for individual differences in change. If it should be found that freshman scores depend largely on social class background and that senior scores depend largely on intelligence, this would not render the change scores meaningless. On the contrary, such a finding would contribute substantial meaning to the scores. It would suggest that what goes on during these four years of college *changes the persons* so that their responses to the attitude items cease to depend on social class and become instead a function of intelligence. Such a result is identical in form to the finding that electronics pretest scores depend on prior knowledge and post-test scores depend on learning ability. Why, then, should one kind of change score be of interest and the other not?

It would appear that the critical question is not whether a test measures the same thing at time one and time two. The critical question is whether, taking into account whatever we know about the meanings of scores at time one and time two, individual differences in change on the test are of any interest to us. In the examples of the arithmetic reasoning test and the electronics test, the answer would almost surely be no. If we are interested in growth in arithmetic reasoning ability, we shall need a test with a higher ceiling or else must deal with a more restricted age range. In the electronics course, interest would center in final attainment rather than change. But attitude change is a matter of interest in its own right. Social scientists are interested in what causes attitudes to change; and if some people's attitudes change in one direction and others' change in the opposite direction under similar conditions, this makes the subject more interesting—at the same time that it lowers the test-retest correlation.

In a recent note on test validity, Jordan (1962) put forth a notion that is germane here. According to Jordan's argument it is senseless to consider a test as a valid measure of an attribute that is not clearly conceptualized independently of any instruments supposed to measure it. To apply this reasoning to the present topic, we may say that when all persons are put through a fixed course of study in electronics aimed at bringing them all to the same level of knowledge, there is no conceptual entity of change to which data from such an experience may reasonably be expected to pertain. A conceptual entity called "change in knowledge of electronics" can be conceived of, but data relevant to it would have to come from a situation that permitted people to start from their prior level of knowledge of electronics and progress at their own rate. Change scores obtained from such a situation could be relevant to the conceptual entity of "change in knowledge of electronics" regardless of the correlation between pretest and post-test or any correlational evidence as to what the test measured on the two occasions.

Viewed in this way, many of the situations in which people change are not situations in which change is a meaningful variable. Situations involving uniform training procedures aimed at bringing subjects to a certain terminal level of performance are of this type, as are situations where so much time has elapsed or so many events have intervened that no direct causal link between pretest and post-test performance could be reasonably predicated. The arithmetic reasoning example illustrates the latter type. Even if there were substantial correlation between test scores at age eight and at age eighteen, it would be absurd to suppose that a high score at age eight represented a lead in the attainment of mastery of arithmetic reasoning that was maintained for ten years over persons who learned at the same rate but started out at a lower level.

Within reasonable time restrictions, changes in personality and attitude characteristics can probably be most legitimately treated as change variables. When, in a given situation, people start out at widely differing points and change in different directions and amounts, one is likely to be more interested in the variables that account for the changes than in the variables that account for the final level.

There are other situations where it cannot be known in advance whether one ought to study change or not, and it is only here that test-retest correlations become of any relevance. In a study of the effects of a relaxant drug, for instance, it might not be known in advance whether the drug reduced tension to some level that was characteristic of the individual or whether it produced some characteristic decrement in tension so that the resulting tension level depended on the pre-existing level of tension. In such cases the correlation between pretest and post-test would be one among several kinds of data that would contribute to an answer. Note, however, that this is quite a different question from whether pretest and post-test measure the same thing; the latter is a question that would have to be answered with still other data.

Interestingly enough, it may make no difference in the analysis of results whether one decides he is measuring change or final status. If, in the electronics course, there is correlation between pretest and post-test, one may well decide to partial out the advantage or disadvantage which pretest scores reflect. This is a straightforward partial correlation problem and the idea of change need never enter in. But if, as in the attitude measurement example, one is studying change, he may decide to correct the changes for initial level and will end up performing the same statistical operations.

Where it becomes crucial to decide whether or not one is measuring change is in the selection or construction of measuring instruments. If one is measuring change, then it is as measures of change and only as measures of change that the validity and reliability of his instruments have any importance. The approach mentioned at the beginning of this section is, it would now appear, an admissible one for increasing the reliability of measures of change. The problem of the validity of change measures is explored in the next section.

The physicalism-subjectivism dilemma

Up to this point "true" change, G_t, has been treated abstractly, as a residual standing for whatever true variance in Y cannot be accounted for by variance in X. So long as G_t is treated abstractly, there is no need to worry about the units in which it is measured, since these have been adequately specified by the units of X and Y. As soon as one attempts a substantive interpretation of G_t, however, the problem must be faced as to what antecedent conditions it may reflect and what its functional relation to them may be.

An immediate semantic difficulty arises, because gains or changes do not fit nicely into the traditional language of traits and individual differences. It becomes necessary to speak of change *in* some trait or characteristic, and then one is immediately back in the dilemma of the preceding section: What do you do when the trait seems to be a different one at the end from the one it was at the beginning? As far as this writer is concerned, this difficulty cannot really be cleared up within the language of differential psychology. This language, it seems, consists of a set of locutions that have no applicability beyond a rather limited realm of discourse which does not include differential changes in persons.

A necessary and sufficient proof of the statement that two tests "measure the same thing" is that they yield scores which vary together over changing conditions. P-technique is the logical technique for studying the interdependencies of measures. Now it will generally follow that at any given time relevant antecedent conditions will vary for different individuals who may be tested at that time. Thus correlations between measures over individuals should bear some correspondence to correlations between measures for the same or randomly equivalent individuals over varying occasions, and the study of individual differences may be justified as an expedient substitute for the more difficult P-technique. Viewed in this way, however, the fact that measures on the same individuals may not correlate the same way on different occasions must be taken as evidence for the inadequacy of individual differences analysis as a substitute for P-technique analysis. Woodrow's (1932) concept of "quotidian variability" is relevant to this issue. Briefly, Woodrow found in a number of instances, in which groups of persons were retested on a number of occasions, that the between-occasions variance was about five times as large as the between-persons variance. This could be taken as an index of the relative inefficiency of individual differences analysis as a substitute for P-technique.

This argument, incidentally, is an alternative way of dissolving the paradox of changing persons versus changing tests. In P-technique tests are necessarily considered as constant over time and it is only those interdependencies that persist through all manner of changing conditions that may be taken as a basis for inferring underlying common factors.

The fact remains, however, that we should like to be able to talk about change in the language of individual differences. This, indeed, seems to be the logical rallying-point of this conference. We should like to be able to say that this individual changed more than that one in such-and-such a way, or that this kind of person changes more than that kind, or that this kind of change is related to that kind of change. To do so requires that there be some way of quantifying hypothetical constructs of change.

The two opposing approaches to this problem, which were labeled earlier *physicalism* and *subjectivism*, can in the final analysis be reduced to a very small and specific point of difference. A single change item, a test item repeated on two occasions, can be scored for change in an unlimited number of ways. The restriction was rather casually introduced that the formula for scoring the change item conform to some method of scoring the item separately for the two occasions. Precisely, the requirement is that, to the scoring of d_i, there correspond a formula for scoring x_i and y_i such that

$$\sum d_i = \sum y_i - \sum x_i.$$

The difference between physicalism and subjectivism, as here used, turns upon whether the above restriction is or is not imposed. If it is imposed, then change is necessarily operationally defined as some function of X and Y. If it is not, then change is an independently defined hypothetical construct which has no necessary functional relation to measurable pre-test and post-test performance.

The implications of this difference are far-reaching. Under the physicalist restriction, change can, and indeed must, be treated in terms of the constructs accounting for test behavior on single occasions, that is, in the terms of differential psychology. Without this restriction, the way is opened for a whole new order of hypothetical constructs which might be called "traits of change." The anarchical trend need not stop there, however, for one may easily imagine change items defined over three occasions which would generate yet another set of constructs, and so on in indefinite expansion. Thus the physicalist restriction is not one that should be lightly abandoned.

The term *physicalism*, whose inadequacy is freely admitted, is meant to indicate that, under the restriction given above, test scores are treated as if they were physical measures—in other words, that the problems in measuring psychological change are no different in kind from the problems of measuring change along physical dimensions. Historically, the most impressive work within this restriction has been that of Courtis (1950). From a wide variety of sources Courtis collected instances supporting his contention that the ratio of attained growth to growth-to-be-attained was, when submitted to a loglog transformation, directly proportional to the time over which growth was measured. If the universality of this relationship is granted, the way was opened for a measure of rate of change which was comparable over individuals who differed in initial level, asymptotic level, and progress toward asymptote at the time of testing.

Although Courtis' approach is a far remove from the simple business of subtracting raw scores or solving linear regression equations, it is nevertheless wholly dependent upon the metric of the raw scores and is thus within the physicalist restriction. Any nonlinear transformation of raw scores would lead to rate measures which order individuals differently than do the rate measures obtained from the raw scores (even though the loglog transformation might still yield constant rates).

At one time the writer fancied that the approach to developing reliable change scales reported in the preceding section could overcome the scaling problem in change measurement. This lapse of critical judgment may be worth recounting here because it does furnish some insight into the inherent difficulties of change measurement. The line of reasoning was this: Change items are conceptually no different from any other test items. The time interval is an integral part of the item in the same sense that stopping to examine a map is an integral part of a map-reading item. The change items are scored for change (either with or without the physicalist restriction). We may not know what the change item score means, but if we have a set of change items which are substantially intercorrelated, we can infer that they measure the same kind of change. Accordingly, we are as justified in adding up these change scores as we are in adding up item scores on any other kind of test, and the assumption that the change scale score is monotonically related to some underlying dimension of change is just as reasonable as the similar assumption that is made about other test scores.

This line of reasoning still does not seem to be patently false. The weak spot is in the initial assumption that change items are conceptually equivalent to other kinds of test items. Closer analysis will show that they are indeed conceptually equivalent to a certain kind of test item, but the kind they are equivalent to is a very bad kind of item.

Suppose one were collecting items for a scale to measure anxiety and considered an item like "I often put out a cigarette after taking only a few puffs." This might be a valid index of anxiety—but only among people who smoke cigarettes. Such an item belongs to the class of what might be called "biased" items, items which are valid only given certain conditions which are not met by all subjects. In the same class are problem-solving items which require some special information not possessed by all subjects, the possession of this information itself not being a valid index of the trait in question.

Now consider a change item like "I am often tired." Such an item might be a valid index of improvement in psychological adjustment among people who originally answer yes to the item, but it would not be among people who initially answer no. Conversely, it might validly indicate worsening among people who originally answer no, but not among people who originally answer yes. The item is thus biased in the same sense as the item about cigarette smoking.

Testers make every effort to exclude biased items, or to include only ones in which the bias itself contributes valid variance (as would happen if cigarette smoking in itself were an indicator of anxiety). But because change items are always biased in two directions, this latter way out is barred. Change scales are thus inevitably committed to pernicious kinds of bias.

The insight which this line of reasoning leads to, therefore, is that the difficulties in the scaling of change are not of the kind that can be erased by transformations at the level of scale scores, for they are substantively imbedded in the items themselves.

A "trait" of psychological change, then, is a trait which can only be tested by invalidly biased items. This raises a question as to whether a trait that can only be objectively measured in this way can justifiably be considered as a distinct conceptual entity. Partial confounding is a familiar visitor to behavioral science. It is handled by contriving in some way to have the confounding factors cancel each other out save for the one in which we are interested. With measures of change, however, there appear to be no operations which can accomplish this—nor indeed is it even conceivable. Thus traits of change appear to be consigned to eternal bastardy within the province of differential psychology.

Now if there were some unambiguous, objectively measurable dimension of change, matters would be different. Change items could be selected and scored so as to conform optimally to this criterion. The physicalist restriction on the scoring of change items could be removed, and measures of change could be developed whose relations to other trait measures could be freely studied.

This brings us to the subjectivist approach to change measurement. All sophistry aside, we can, all of us, recognize differences in change that are divorced from all measures of status. We can look at two students in a class, one bright, one dull, and in some instances at least agree unanimously and confidently that one has gained more from the course than the other. We can look at two psychiatric patients, one badly disturbed, one only slightly disturbed, and judge whether one has progressed more in therapy than the other. These are value judgments, pure and simple. There may be related objective score continua, but there need not be. At any rate, we can form our judgment without its having to be isomorphic with any of them.

Judgments of this kind bear a very close similarity to the judgments persons make on a scale like the Semantic Differential (Osgood, Suci, and Tannenbaum, 1957), where they are asked to rate the fastness or slowness of an umbrella or the color red. There is no implication of an objective continuum to which these ratings conform. The continuum is in the ratings themselves.

Rating dimensions of psychological change so defined—dimensions of learning, of attitude change, of change in adjustment—can occupy a natural and potentially useful place in the conceptual realm of differential psychology. Objectively derived change scales might be developed which would provide expedient approximations to ratings, but there would be no implication that the objective scales operationally defined the dimensions. The ratings would do that, just as they would define the scale properties.

The distinction between objective and subjective continua of change may be made clear with an example. The amount of money that a person has gained or lost in a poker game can be precisely stated in dollars and cents as the difference between his total financial assets before and after the game. It is clear that only the difference is important; the total assets before and after are immaterial except as they yield up a difference measure. Here, then, is objective continuum of change. What is vital to note about this kind of change is that, although it may be expressed as a difference between X and Y, total assets before and after play, it does not have to be. By simply keeping track of the exchanges of money during the game, we can arrive at the identical change measure without ever knowing the person's total wealth.

This is not, however, a psychological continuum, nor is it necessarily closely related to one. A dimension of "psychological loss" might be defined. Objective losses would be correlated with it, but so too would initial amount of money. Nor would these together account for it. To account fully for "psychological loss" we should in addition need data on personality factors, past history of gains and losses, marital status—indeed an unlimited host of antecedent variables. These antecedent variables do not, in any meaningful sense, *define* "psychological loss." It is defined by the ratings of the losers: their psychotherapists, ourselves, or whoever it is that we designate as the raters. It is in designating the raters and the rating procedures that we operationally define "psychological loss"; and other variables, including such objective ones as monetary loss, qualify as measures of "psychological loss" only as they are validated against the ratings as criteria.

Of the three dilemmas considered in this paper, the physicalism-subjectivism dilemma is the only true one. A choice must be made between objective measures of change that are meaningless within the province of differential psychology and meaningful measures that carry the stigma of subjectivity. Though it is a dilemma, there can be little question as to which is the preferable choice.

Summary

Three dilemmas in the measurement of change have been considered. The first, the over-correction–under-correction dilemma, concerns the radical reversals of findings that often occur when one turns from raw change scores to residual change scores. The difficulty was traced to the failure of investigators to correct for unreliability in pretest scores. The second, the unreliability-invalidity dilemma, stems from the fact that high reliability of change scores usually requires low test-retest correlations, with the implication that in such a case the test may not measure the same thing on the two occasions and the change scores will therefore be meaningless. It was concluded that the meaningfulness of change scores does not depend on a test's measuring "the same thing" on two occasions, so that the dilemma is a false one. The final dilemma considered was that of the choice between attempting to measure changes objectively as differences between scores on two occasions (physicalism) and measuring changes directly as subjective dimensions which do not necessarily have underlying physical continua. The latter alternative, despite its obvious drawbacks, was seen as the only one that permits interpretable comparisons between changes on psychological dimensions for individuals with different initial standings.

Two | Elementary Models for
Measuring Change

FREDERIC M. LORD

Suppose an *initial* measure, *x*, and a *final* measure, *y*, are obtained on each *individual* in a group. The difference $g = y - x$ will be called the *observed change*. For convenience, positive change will often be referred to as *gain* or *growth*, negative change as *loss*.

The fact that the observation $y - x = 0$ is (in the absence of errors of measurement) to be described as "no change" implies a direct correspondence between the scale of measurement used for *x* and that used for *y*—identical scores on the two scales are to be interpreted as having identical meaning, at least for the dimension that is under study at the moment. This direct correspondence between the scales of measurement will be assumed in all that follows.

Regression effect

The *x* and *y* measurements may be conveniently summarized in the form of a scatterplot. Consider for a moment the simple case, to be referred to as a *dynamic equilibrium*, in which the group statistics for *x* (mean, variance, skewness, etc.) are the same as those for *y*, and the correlation between *x* and *y* is considerably less than perfect. For concreteness, let us talk about the weight of individuals in pounds. Consider the well-known but paradoxical regression effect. If the group displays dynamic equilibrium, this automatically means that (*a*) most heavy people are about to get lighter, (*b*) most heavy people have been getting heavier. In fact, if initial weight and final weight have a normal bivariate distribution, we can predict with virtual certainty that a sufficiently heavy person will necessarily lose weight, not gain it.

The situation is illustrated in Figure 2.1, which represents a scatterplot showing the relationship between initial weight and final weight for some group. In the particular case illustrated, the mean initial weight is 500,

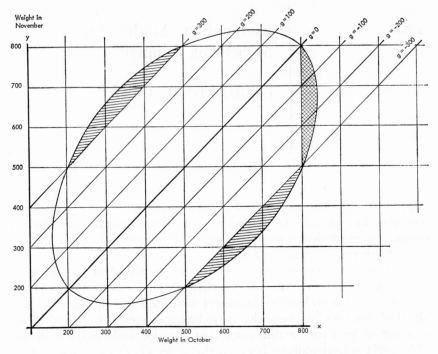

Fig. 2.1.—Hypothetical scatterplot showing change in weight.

and this is the same as the mean final weight. This coincidence is irrelevant for present purposes—the entire discussion could equally well be based on a situation where most individuals showed a real change between initial and final weighing.

For the individuals lying on the line marked $g = 0$, the initial and final weights are identical and there is no change. All the individuals lying along the line $g = 100$ have final weight 100 units above their initial weight, and so forth.

Consider the crosshatched area at the upper right of the figure. If the ellipse is drawn to enclose all the cases in the scatterplot, then it appears that every individual with an initial weight above 800 lost weight during the period covered. This is not a statistical artifact of some sort. It is not a result of the unreliability of the weighings. This phenomenon is an accurate description of what may be expected actually to happen in such a set of data.

Suppose, next, that we are interested in finding variables related to gain in weight. A fairly standard approach would be to select two extreme groups, one showing large gain and the other showing large loss in weight, and then to investigate various possible predictor variables, looking for variables on which the mean scores of the two extreme groups are substantially different. Suppose, for example, that we select all those individuals who gained more than 300 units—we can call these the "gainers." Similarly, let us select those who lost more than 300 units—the "losers." These two groups are represented in the figure by the shading.

We now look for variables that discriminate sharply between gainers and losers. It just so happens that all the gainers in this group had initial weight below 500 and all the losers had initial weight of more than 500! Clearly, if we investigate, we will find that initial weight is a variable that discriminates very effectively between gainers and losers. We thus learn again that heavy individuals are losers and light individuals are gainers.

This relationship is an actual fact, but it interferes with our search for variables that have an interesting relationship to gain in weight. The procedure outlined will turn up many variables that are related to gain in weight only because they are related to initial weight. This confusing outcome can be avoided if we define "gainers" and "losers" in relation to the line representing the regression of final on initial weight. The actual regression line should be used, especially so if it is curvilinear. At each level of initial weight, the "gainers" and "losers" should be defined so that the proportion of gainers at that level is equal to the proportion of losers at that level, and also equal to the proportion of gainers and losers at every other level. This is especially important if the actual data display heteroscedasticity or other irregularities. When extreme groups are chosen in this way, then the embarrassing relationship between gain and initial weight disappears; in this method we are investigating the relation of other variables to gain with initial weight effectively partialed out—in other words, held constant statistically.

In the homoscedastic case with straight regression lines, the foregoing is equivalent to the simple use of deviations from the regression line. Such a use of deviations is by no means new; however, studies still fall into difficulties by failing to use this procedure.

All this has led some people to assert that deviation from the regression line is the real measure of change, and that the ordinary difference between initial and final measurements is not a measure of change. This can hardly be correct. If certain individuals gained 300 ounces, this is a definite fact, not a result of an improper definition of growth.

The real point is that, if we are interested in finding other variables associated with gain in weight, it is convenient to hold initial weight constant statistically while making the search. This guarantees that the variables we find associated with gain are not found simply because they happen to be associated with initial weight. Suppose, for example, that all the people with initial weight of less than 500 ounces were girls and all those with initial weight above 500 were boys. Clearly in this case, sex would be a variable highly related to gain in weight. This cannot be doubted, but this relationship occurs only because sex was highly related to initial weight. If we define our extreme groups in terms of deviations from the appropriate regression line, then half of the girls will lie above the regression line and half below, and similarly for the boys. Thus sex will not be found as a variable that discriminates between extreme groups set up on the basis of deviations.

This last result does not mean that sex was unrelated to gain in weight. What it means is that, in the hypothetical case studied, sex was unrelated to gain in weight when initial weight was held constant. This latter sort of information is usually what we are seeking.

The regression effect is one of the two main reasons why studies of growth may become confusing or confused. As just described, it may seem obvious, so let us consider a less obvious situation.

Suppose that a sample of 6 individuals has been split at random into two groups of 3 individuals each. Each individual is weighed (x), the two groups are maintained on different diets for a time, and then each individual is weighed again (y). Suppose it is found that the mean weight of each group remains unchanged after the treatments. Clearly the average gain for either group is $\bar{g} = \bar{y} - \bar{x} = 0$.

The obvious conclusion would seem to be that both diets were ineffective, or at least that one was no more effective than the other. However, this conclusion will usually not be the most reasonable one to draw from the data.

Suppose that, simply by chance, the mean x for the first group happened to be appreciably larger than the mean x for the second group. In view of the regression effect, under the null hypothesis of no treatment effect, the average weight for the first group should have decreased and the average weight for the second group should have increased. The fact that this did not actually happen requires us to suspect that the diet fed to the first group may have counteracted the regression effect, preventing a loss in weight that would otherwise have occurred; and similarly, that the second diet may have prevented a gain that would otherwise have occurred. Thus the experiment must in this case cause us to suspect that the first diet is superior to the second, even though both diets actually produced the same zero gain.

The general conclusion to be drawn from this illustrative example is that a common-sense consideration of the simple difference scores may be misleading. What is needed is to compare the data actually obtained with the data that would have been obtained under the appropriate null hypothesis of no treatment effect. Any significant discrepancy can then be attributed to some deviation from the null hypothesis.

From a logical point of view, such a comparison provides a very clear and straightforward procedure. It is frequently difficult in practice to obtain highly comparable data with and without treatment effect, however. In the example given, for instance, one would like to know what would have happened if these same individuals—not some vaguely similar individuals—had all been given the same diet. Since this cannot be determined empirically without giving up the original experiment, the statistician may try to estimate what would have happened if the null experiment had actually been carried out. This is done by setting up a mathematical model specifying what would have happened under the null hypothesis. This model can be checked and verified by trying it out in advance on other individuals like those to be used in the crucial experiment. If the model is found to hold to a sufficient approximation, the experimenter may use it to increase greatly the effectiveness and sensitivity of his experiments. If he is not satisfied that the model holds, he must determine empirically whatever he cannot predict theoretically, regardless of the loss in efficiency.

Since models appropriate for the last illustrative example tend to be a little complicated, discussion of these will be deferred to the last section.

Errors of measurement

The second major source of confusion in studies of change is the presence of errors of measurement. A variable containing errors of measurement is called *fallible*. If the expected value of the error of measurement for any individual is zero, the errors are called *unbiased*. If the errors are biased, the measuring instrument is not measuring properly; this must be remedied before proceeding further. Unbiased errors of measurement will be assumed hereafter.

If it is possible to make many replicate measurements on the same individual, the mean of these measurements ordinarily approaches a limit as the number of measurements increases. This means that the errors of measurement are being averaged out; thus the limit is the *true value*, to be denoted by X, from which any particular observation, x, differs because of an error of measurement, e_x. In other words,

$$(1) \qquad\qquad x = X + e_x.$$

It is assumed that e_x is unbiased no matter what value of X characterizes an individual, and no matter what other characteristics he may have. This means that e_x is uncorrelated with and totally independent of X and also of any other variable, excepting such obviously experimentally dependent variables as e_x itself, x, and other variables that are functions of these two. These assumptions about the errors of measurement are considered to hold in all that follows.

If it is not possible or practical to make replicate measurements on the same individual, the concept of true value is still a very useful concept. Even though the true value cannot be determined operationally, nevertheless use of this concept leads to predictions that are both valuable and verifiable. No well-known physicist has insisted that all concepts used by physicists should be operationally definable, and it is time that social scientists stopped trying to impose such a restriction on each other. In many situations, the individual or object measured behaves, at least to an adequate approximation, as if a true value actually existed. This is enough to make the true value a useful practical concept.

Consider a practical example. We are interested in Mary's spelling ability. We administer a spelling test requiring her to spell 20 selected words, and we find that she spells 15 of these correctly. The number 15 can be considered as a measure of her spelling ability, but it must be considered as a fallible measure. We know, for instance, that there are many other sets of 20 words that would have made an equally suitable spelling test, and we know in advance that she would not consistently score 15 on each of these other tests. Very likely her scores would range all the way from 11 to 19, say.

As social scientists we ordinarily cannot be concerned with all the minute circumstances that lead Mary to score 14 on one test and 16 on another. We are interested not in all the separate scores that Mary gets, but in something common to all of these, which we call her "spelling ability." This is what we previously called a *true value*. Mary's actual score on any one test probably differs from this true value, but it is the true value, not the actual score, in which we are interested. Thus we wish to treat the difference between true and observed values as error of measurement.

It is a widespread fault in speech and in thought to substitute the observed value for the true value. We say that we hired the most able applicants when we actually hired those with the highest test scores. We speak of the correlation between verbal ability and spatial ability when actually what we have is the correlation between two test scores. We think we have matched two groups on intelligence when what we have really done is to match them on intelligence-plus-error.

This sort of thinking can frequently be used without serious results because of the fact that in a group the rank order of the observed measurements often provides a reasonably good approximation to the rank order of the true values. This approximation usually falls down, however, when we are dealing with measurements of change. It is for this reason that a consideration of errors of measurement is specially important here.

For those who like a common-sense, operational approach to problems, for those who dislike the use of hypothetical constructs, problems in the measurement of change should provide a special challenge, since the usual common-sense notions can be shown to be inadequate here and models involving unobservable variables seem to be of great practical use.

Estimating change for an individual

Consider a typical study of change. An initial measure (x) is obtained on each individual in a group, a "treatment" is given, and a final measure (y) is then obtained. Can the observed change, g, be used as a useful approximation to the thing we are really interested in—the true change?

If x and y are measured without error, then g *is* the true change. But if x and y are fallible, the conclusion is different.

Suppose that it is possible to determine empirically or from some acceptable mathematical model what the scatterplot between x and y is like when the two measures are administered with no intervening treatment. It is effective to compare this "no-treatment" scatterplot with the one that reflects the effects of the treatment. Any differences between the two scatterplots are, or should be, attributable to the treatment.

Suppose, now, that the two plots happen to be identical. The conclusion that the experimenter ordinarily draws in such a case is that the treatment had no effect whatsoever. Clearly, in this special case, any study of the changes, g, for particular individuals will be totally misleading, for the g's appear to be mere errors of measurement.

Suppose, next, that the two plots are identical except for a translation of 10 points along the y-axis. This is just the result that would be expected if every individual had gained exactly 10 points during the treatment. Thus each examinee's gain would ordinarily be estimated as 10 points, regardless of his actual value of g.

In all this, we are attempting to estimate the true change, G, for each individual, as distinct from the observed change, g. In order to do this, some estimate must be made as to how much of the observed change is simply chance fluctuation arising from errors of measurement. How are these estimates to be made in case the no-treatment scatterplot cannot be obtained empirically?

A simple mathematical model assumes that the true change,

(2) $$G = Y - X,$$

has a rectilinear regression on x and y. An alternative but more restrictive model asserts that the so-called *latent variables* X, Y, e_x, and e_y, $(y - Y)$, have a normal multivariate distribution. The second model implies the first. Under either model, the true change can be predicted from observed values by means of an ordinary multiple regression equation. In standard notation, the estimated value of the true change is

(3) $$\hat{G} = \overline{G} + b_{Gx \cdot y}(x - \bar{x}) + b_{Gy \cdot x}(y - \bar{y}).$$

From (2) and (1) it is clear that for a sufficiently large number of examinees,

(4) $$\overline{G} = \overline{Y} - \overline{X}$$
$$= \bar{y} - \bar{x}.$$

The usual assumptions about errors of measurement, as outlined in the preceding section, lead to the following formulas for estimating the partial regression coefficients needed in (3):

(5) $$b_{Gx \cdot y} = \frac{(1 - r_{yy'})r_{xy}s_y/s_x - r_{xx'} + r_{xy}^2}{1 - r_{xy}^2},$$

(6) $$b_{Gy \cdot x} = \frac{r_{yy'} - r_{xy}^2 - (1 - r_{xx'})s_x r_{xy}/s_y}{1 - r_{xy}^2}.$$

The symbol $r_{xx'}$ represents the correlation that would be found between two replicate initial measurements of x, assuming that the individuals measured remain unchanged during the measuring process; the symbol $r_{yy'}$ represents the correlation that would be found between two replicate final measurements of y. These correlations are called *reliability coefficients*. If the variance of the errors of measurement is known or can be estimated, then, as Gulliksen (1950) shows, in a sufficiently large group of individuals,

(7)
$$r_{xx'} = 1 - \frac{s_{ex}^2}{s_x^2},$$

$$r_{yy'} = 1 - \frac{s_{ey}^2}{s_y^2}.$$

If $r_{xx'}$ and $r_{yy'}$ can be determined, then formulas (3), (4), (5), and (6) allow us to estimate the true change for an individual from observable data. Detailed derivations leading to these formulas are given by Lord (1956), who treats the case where $s_{e_x}^2 = s_{e_y}^2$, by McNemar (1958), and by Davis (1961).

ILLUSTRATIVE EXAMPLE

Figure 2.2 presents a scatterplot showing for a class of 95 students the relationship between the scores obtained in seventh grade on the Stanford

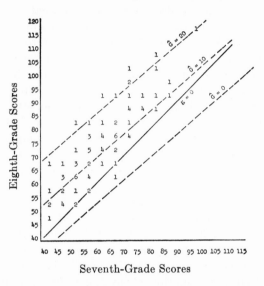

Fig. 2.2.—Scatterplot showing growth of 95 students in one junior high school class. Courtesy of Dr. William E. Coffman.

Achievement Test and those obtained in eighth grade. The raw data are $\bar{x} = 61.5$, $\bar{y} = 73.4$, $s_x = 11.6$, $s_y = 14.2$, $r_{xx'} = .933$, $r_{yy'} = .955$, $r_{xy} = .876$. The data were gathered and analyzed by Dr. William E. Coffman, who has kindly allowed them to be used here for illustrative purposes.

After the necessary computations for the present data, it is found, for example, from equation (3) that all students in this class having an estimated true gain of $\hat{G} = 10$ lie along the oblique line so labeled. The lines for $\hat{G} = 20$ and for $\hat{G} = 0$ are indicated on the plot; also the 45-degree line along which there is zero observed gain, the line $g = 0$.

A number of points illustrated by the figure may be mentioned:

(a) The 5 students who showed approximately zero observed change ($g = 0$) from seventh to eighth grade are estimated actually to have a positive true gain, as indicated by the fact that they all lie above the line

$\hat{G} = 0$. The fact that these students showed no observed gain is presumably due to an unfortunate combination of errors of measurement.

(b) Similarly, the one student who showed an actual observed loss is nevertheless estimated to have a positive true gain.

(c) Students having identical observed gain do not have identical estimated true gain, as represented by the fact that the lines $\hat{G} = $ constant are not 45-degree lines and are thus not parallel to $g = 0$. This result reflects a regression effect. It reflects the fact that if no time had elapsed between first and second testings, the initially high-scoring students would tend to do less well on the final test, showing an apparent loss. This phenomenon occurs because the initially high-scoring students tend to include students having positive errors of measurement on the first test. When these students are retested, the expected error of measurement on the second test is no longer positive; it is zero. Thus these students tend to show a loss from first to second testing that does not reflect any true change in their ability. When other students show the same apparent loss, however, this may reflect a true decline in their ability. Hence students with the same observed change may not have the same estimated true change. All this is due to a regression effect acting on the errors of measurement; if there were no errors of measurement, this effect would disappear.

(d) Observed changes range from $g = -5$ score points to $g = +30$; estimated true changes range only from about $\hat{G} = +2$ to about $\hat{G} = +23$. The estimated values have a smaller range for two reasons: The observed g's contain errors of measurement that tend to inflate their range over what it would otherwise be. Estimated values obtained from a regression equation always show less variability than the values being estimated; this is an inconvenient property of such estimated values, arising from the regression effect, but this is the price we pay for having estimates that minimize the squared error of estimation.

If one looks at the observed gains in Figure 2.2, it seems that the initially good students are gaining about the same amount as the initially poor students. This is the erroneous conclusion likely to be drawn from the fact that the regression of eighth-grade on seventh-grade scores is roughly parallel to the line $g = 0$. A glance at the lines representing estimated true gains, however, shows that the good students are really gaining quite a bit more than the poor students.

If the good students had not learned more than the poor students, the observed gains would have seemed very strange, because regression effects would have caused many of the good students to show actual losses in score. Coffman suggests that the only reason such regression effects have not been forced on every teacher's attention long before now is that there is a very general tendency for good students to learn more than poor students, thus compensating for the regression effect that would otherwise appear.

BASIC RATIONALE

Any such comparison of gains for people at different parts of the score scale implies that the score scale is temporarily being treated as if it had "equal" units over the range involved. In the present case, each score unit is supposed to represent a tenth of a year of educational growth. Whether these or any other score units are to be treated as "equal" is sometimes made the subject of serious debate; however, the writer believes it is simply a question to be left to the momentary taste and convenience of each reader. Whether the units are called "equal" or not neither adds to nor subtracts from the meaning of the data (although the conclusions are somewhat awkward to state if one gives up the convention of treating the units as equal). What the data really tell us is that the initially good students on the average effectively covered the work of more grade-levels during the year (insofar as this work is measured by the test) than did the initially poor students. This is all the data can tell us, and any decision to consider the score units as "equal" may alter the statistical results, but it does not and cannot increase the information contained in the data.

The following question is frequently asked: "When one uses equation (3), the estimated value for the change of a particular individual depends in part upon certain group statistics required by this equation. If the same individual were considered as a member of some other group, the estimated value for his change would probably be different even though his test scores remain unchanged. How can one justify basing the estimate for a given individual on the totally irrelevant performance of other individuals with whom he happens to be considered?"

The answer to this query comes in two parts. In the first place, equation (3) is applicable only if the given individual actually is a member of some natural group under consideration. Such a group might be defined as "all current Princeton freshmen," or as "all patients who consulted Dr. _____ during 1962," or as "all Princeton freshmen who consulted Dr. _____ in 1962."

The second point is that knowledge that an individual belongs to a certain group constitutes genuine information about that individual. An efficient method of estimation can and should make use of this information. Furthermore, it is not to be expected or desired that an estimating procedure should yield the same estimate when the information available is altered, as is the case when we first consider an individual as a member of one group and then consider him as a member of another group.

If the individual belongs to several different groups, the group statistics for equation (3) should be derived from the subgroup consisting of those individuals who belong to all of these same groups. If the necessary group statistics are not available, then the information about group membership cannot be used efficiently. This is not a logical flaw of the estimating procedure, however.

Reliability of estimated change

It is well known that the difference between two fallible measures is frequently much more fallible than either. If the reliability $r_{xx'}$ is the correlation between experimentally independent replicate measurements, and similarly for $r_{yy'}$, then the reliability of the measured change is

$$(8) \qquad r_{gg'} = \frac{s_y^2 r_{yy'} - 2s_y s_x r_{xy} + s_x^2 r_{xx'}}{s_y^2 - 2s_y s_x r_{xy} + s_x^2} .$$

The formula

$$r_{gg'} = \frac{r_{yy'} + r_{xx'} - 2r_{xy}}{2(1 - r_{xy})} ,$$

given by Guilford (1954), Gulliksen (1950), and McNemar (1955), sometimes without sufficient explanation, is only for the rather exceptional case where $s_x = s_y$.

An estimate of the correlation between observed change and true change is

$$(9) \qquad r_{gG} = \sqrt{r_{gg'}}.$$

The correlation between estimated change and true change is necessarily the same as the multiple correlation $R_{G \cdot xy}$:

$$(10) \qquad r_{\hat{G}G} = \sqrt{\frac{r_{Gx}^2 + r_{Gy}^2 - 2r_{Gx} r_{Gy} r_{xy}}{1 - r_{xy}^2}} .$$

The necessary values for computing the right side of (10) may be estimated from the following equations which hold for sufficiently large samples of individuals.

$$(11) \qquad r_{Gx} = \frac{s_y r_{xy} - s_x r_{xx'}}{s_G} ,$$

$$(12) \qquad r_{Gy} = \frac{s_y r_{yy'} - s_x r_{xy}}{s_G} ,$$

$$(13) \qquad s_G^2 = r_{gg'}(s_y^2 - 2s_y s_x r_{xy} + s_x^2).$$

Since (10) is a multiple correlation, $r_{\hat{G}G}$ is necessarily as large as, and usually larger than, r_{gG}.

It is usually wise to compute r_{gG} or $r_{\hat{G}G}$ or both at the beginning of any study to be sure that the observed changes are not simply the result of random fluctuations, or so obscured by random fluctuations as to be not worthy of analysis. The test scores in Figure 2.2 are unusually reliable, each score shown being the median score obtained by an individual on the several tests in the battery, but even then the value of $r_{\hat{G}G}$ is only .813. The value of r_{gG} is .787. Higher values of $r_{\hat{G}G}$ and r_{gG} could be obtained by allowing two or three years, instead of only one year, to elapse between testings.

The effect of change on group heterogeneity

Since $Y = G + X$, we have

$$(14) \qquad\qquad s_Y^2 = s_G^2 + s_X^2 + 2s_{GX},$$

where s_{GX} is the covariance between true initial score and true gain. It is seen from (14) that the group will become more heterogeneous with the passage of time unless either (a) there is no true change at all, so that $s_G^2 = 0$ and $s_{GX} = 0$, or else (b) there is a negative correlation between true gain and true initial standing sizable enough so that $r_{GX} < -s_G/2s_X$. If $r_{GX} = -s_G/2s_X$, then $s_Y^2 = s_X^2$, we have a condition of dynamic equilibrium, and the value of r_{GX} is simply the value to be expected because of ordinary regression effects.

Correlations of other variables with change

When a correlation is computed between change and some other variable, it is not necessary to estimate the true change separately for each individual. Thus many of the problems considered in preceding sections will cause no trouble here. The types of difficulties most likely to be of concern are mentioned below under three separate headings. See Lord (1958).

SPURIOUS CORRELATIONS

The correlation of change with some other variable that is in part a function of x or y is in the case of fallible measures usually considered to be *spurious*, since the same errors of measurement are present in both quantities being correlated.

$$(15) \qquad r_{gx} = r_{(G+e_y-e_x)(X+e_x)} = \frac{s_G s_X r_{GX} - s_{e_x}^2}{s_g s_x}.$$

It is clear from (15) that r_{gx}, the correlation between observed gain and initial standing, need not even have the same sign as r_{GX}, the correlation between true gain and true initial standing, which is the only correlation that is ordinarily of any real interest. The latter correlation can be estimated from the formula

$$(16) \qquad r_{GX} = \frac{r_{gx} + \dfrac{s_x}{s_g}(1 - r_{xx'})}{\sqrt{r_{gg'}}\sqrt{r_{xx'}}},$$

derived by Zieve (1940) from an earlier formula of Thomson's (1924). Equation (16) makes it clear that if x is a fallible measure, r_{GX} will always be positive whenever $r_{gx} = 0$.

ATTENUATION

No spuriousness arises when the observed change is correlated with some other variable (c, say) that is not contaminated by the errors of measurement in x and y. Such a correlation, r_{gc}, can be dealt with in practice much as the correlation between c and any other fallible variable. In other words, r_{gc} is related to the coefficient of real interest, r_{Gc}, by the standard formula for correction for attenuation. See Guilford (1954, eq. 14.36) and Gulliksen (1950, Chapter 9).

$$(17) \qquad r_{Gc} = \frac{r_{gc}}{\sqrt{r_{gg'}}}.$$

Thus, r_{Gc} can be assumed to have the same sign as the observed value, r_{gc}, but to be somewhat closer to 1.00 (or -1.00). If the observed change has low reliability, as is frequently the case, then the discrepancy between r_{gc} and r_{Gc} may be quite marked.

The value of r_{gc} can be obtained without computing g at all by means of the formulas

$$(18) \qquad r_{gc} = \frac{s_y r_{yc} - s_x r_{xc}}{s_g},$$

$$(19) \qquad s_g^2 = s_y^2 + s_x^2 - 2s_x s_y r_{xy}.$$

PARTIAL CORRELATION

In the normal multivariate case, the partial correlation, $r_{ac \cdot x}$, between variables a and c with x "held constant" is the same as the zero-order correlation between a and c for any subgroup of individuals all having the same value of x. In the nonnormal case, the partial is a sort of weighted average of such zero-order correlations.

It is worth while to consider the partial correlation $r_{yc \cdot x}$, which by standard formulas is

$$(20) \qquad r_{yc \cdot x} = \frac{r_{yc} - r_{yx} r_{cx}}{\sqrt{1 - r_{yx}^2} \, \sqrt{1 - r_{cx}^2}},$$

and to compare it with r_{gc}. Suppose, for illustrative purposes, that $r_{gc} = 0$; then, by (18).

$$(21) \qquad r_{xc} = \frac{s_y}{s_x} r_{yc}.$$

If we substitute this value of r_{xc} into the numerator of (20), we have the result that when $r_{gc} = 0$, then

$$(22) \qquad r_{yc \cdot x} = \frac{r_{yc}(1 - b_{yx})}{\sqrt{1 - r_{yx}^2}\sqrt{1 - r_{cx}^2}},$$

where $b_{yx} = s_y r_{yc}/s_x$ is the ordinary regression coefficient of y on x. Since b_{yx} is usually less than 1, we see from (22) that when $r_{gc} = 0$, $r_{yc \cdot x}$ will *usually* be positive.

This conclusion assumes more meaning once it is pointed out that when x is constant $r_{cy} = r_{cg}$. For the normal multivariate case, the conclusion now reads:

If the correlation between observed change and some variable, c, is zero in the total group composed of all individuals, this same correlation will be found to be positive in every subgroup composed of all those individuals having the same initial value, x, except in the unusual case where the slope of the regression of final on initial measure is equal to or greater than 1.

Which r_{gc} does the researcher want? The r_{gc} for the total group, or the systematically different r_{gc} found in each homogeneous subgroup? In general, the more extraneous variables one can hold constant in a scientific study, the clearer the picture. For this reason, it is not the total-group correlation r_{gc} but rather the partial correlation $r_{gc \cdot x}$ ($= r_{yc \cdot x}$) that is usually of greatest interest.

A further complication arises at this point. It is really not $r_{gc \cdot x}$ that we want, but $r_{Gc \cdot X}$. Such a partial correlation involving true scores is obtained simply by correcting the zero-order correlations for attenuation before computing the partial:

$$(23) \qquad r_{Gc \cdot X} = r_{Yc \cdot X} = \frac{r_{Yc} - r_{YX} r_{cX}}{\sqrt{1 - r_{YX}^2}\sqrt{1 - r_{cX}^2}}.$$

We frequently can get along without correcting an ordinary correlation such as r_{gc} for attenuation because we know in advance the general effect of the correction—it will make the correlation a little larger in absolute magnitude. Unfortunately, we cannot usually know in advance the effect of correcting a partial correlation for attenuation; the correction may easily change even the sign of the partial. In view of this, we can hardly afford to neglect the correction for attenuation.

This poses somewhat of a dilemma, since, first, it is often hard to obtain the particular kind of reliability coefficients that are required for making the appropriate correction, and, further, the partial corrected for attenuation may be seriously affected by sampling errors. These obstacles can hardly justify the use of an uncorrected coefficient that may have the wrong sign, however.

Analysis of mean change

Consider the case where individuals are assigned *at random* to two or more "treatments." A before-treatment measure, x, and an after-treatment measure, y, are obtained for each individual. The problem is to estimate and compare the effects of the separate treatments.

The example discussed at the end of the first section of this paper has already shown that, because of regression effects, the natural procedure of comparing mean observed change for different treatments is likely to give a distorted view of the situation. Preferred procedures require either experimental or statistical control of pretreatment differences among the treatment groups arising from sampling fluctuations. If these differences cannot be effectively eliminated by experimental controls, the analysis of covariance may be used, provided its assumptions are met.

Reasons for controlling pretreatment differences rather than simply working with mean observed change are discussed with some care by Fisher (1951) in two sections, "56. Arbitrary Corrections" and "57. Calculation of the Adjustment," and by Cox (1958, sect. 4.4). A thorough treatment of the statistical properties of various possible procedures is given by Cox (1957). A statistical comparison between analysis of covariance, simple analysis of change scores, and a randomization procedure is given by Feldt (1958).

The fact that an analysis of change scores and an analysis of covariance are likely to yield different conclusions is shown with clarity by Figure 2.3. Here group A and group B are to be compared on the post-treatment measure, y, after making appropriate adjustments for initial differences in the pretreatment measure, x. All individuals were originally assigned at random to the two treatments, represented by A and B. (The fact that the two ellipses do not overlap is for graphic clarity—it does not indicate that the two groups are themselves nonoverlapping; the groups differ only because of sampling fluctuations and will be much alike unless the number of individuals is very small.) The group means on both variables lie on the dashed, 45-degree line, indicating that the mean change in group B, $\bar{g}_B = \bar{y}_B - \bar{x}_B$, is exactly equal to the mean change in group A. Thus an analysis of observed change will lead to the conclusion that treatment A appears to be no more effective and no less effective than treatment B.

An analysis of covariance, on the other hand, is essentially an analysis of "adjusted y-scores," which are simply deviations from the regression line of y on x. This regression line is shown for each group as a solid oblique line. The frequency distributions of the adjusted y-scores are ob-

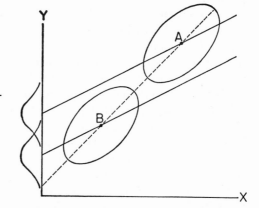

Fig. 2.3.—Scatterplots for hypothetical groups A and B.

tained by projecting the entire scatterplot onto the y-axis along lines parallel to the regression lines, as shown. The analysis of covariance is equivalent to a simple significance test between the means of the distributions of the adjusted y-scores. (This equivalence falls short of exact identity because the regression line itself is not known exactly and must be estimated from the data.) In the case illustrated, it is clear that these means do differ, unlike $\bar{g}_B$ and $\bar{g}_A$, and hence, given enough cases, that treatment A may be found to produce significantly more change than treatment B.

An obvious modification of Figure 2.3 would illustrate the fact that an analysis of observed gains might lead one to prefer treatment B to treatment A, when an analysis of covariance of the same data would lead to precisely the opposite conclusion. In general, the analysis of observed gains results in a built-in bias in favor of whatever treatments happen to be assigned to initially low-scoring groups. This bias is not likely to be large unless the number of individuals per group is small; thus analyses of observed gains will often not be seriously misleading. It would be preferable to avoid this bias altogether, however.

In view of the clear difference between the methods, it may puzzle readers to find Feldt (1958) and others saying simply that the analysis of difference scores has less "precision" than do the analysis of covariance and other methods. Actually, Feldt's statement is quite correct from a mathematical point of view, as would also be the following statement: "Ignoring initial group differences on the pretreatment measure altogether is less precise than taking these differences into account." Unless they are searching for computational short cuts, however, most researchers will not want to discard pretreatment measures altogether, nor to make a type of allowance for pretreatment differences that is not only arbitrary but is contraindicated by the data itself. See Fisher (1951, p. 168).

When treatments are assigned at random, it may be seen from sampling theory that the within-group regression line used in the analysis of covariance does provide the proper allowance. The reason is that under the null hypothesis the means of randomly chosen groups fall around the same regression line as do the individual cases.

It should be emphasized that all the discussion in this section up to this point has assumed that the individuals are assigned to the treatments at random. Such assignment is the logical (not merely the statistical) prerequisite to a controlled experiment. If the individuals are not assigned to the treatments at random, then it is not too helpful to demonstrate statistically that the groups after treatment show more difference than would have been expected from random assignment—unless, of course, the experimenter has special information showing that the nonrandom assignment was nevertheless random *in effect*. If, as often happens, randomized assignment is impossible, then there is often no way to determine what is the appropriate adjustment to be made for initial differences between groups, and hence often no way to show convincingly by statistical manipulations that one treatment is better than another.

An unfortunate complication must, finally, be pointed out. We frequently substitute a fallible measure for an infallible measure without giving the matter much thought. In the case of the "concomitant" variable in covariance analysis, however, such a substitution may change the entire character of the final result. Making allowances for initial differences among groups on a poor measure of some variable is not the same thing as making allowances for initial differences on the variable itself. If the variable in question cannot be reliably measured, it should be controlled experimentally (by randomization) if possible. Otherwise some special modification of the analysis of covariance is desirable (Lord, 1960).

The writer is indebted to Dr. Albert E. Myers for several stimulating discussions of this problem of analysis of mean change.

Three	The Reliability of Changes Measured by Mental Test Scores
	HAROLD WEBSTER AND CARL BEREITER

The measurement of change has always been a central problem of science, and the way in which change is defined, in diverse areas of research, has important consequences. It is hardly necessary to recall that some of the most fundamental and useful processes of analysis, including differential calculus, were inspired by efforts to understand change. A well-formulated dynamics is one of the proudest achievements of classical physics. In sharp contrast, only very rudimentary methods for measuring social and psychological change are known, at a time when much more of this kind of knowledge might easily be very useful.

The absence of reasonable methods for measuring and analyzing the kinds of change that interest social scientists seems partly due, historically, to the general reluctance to believe that man's own activities and institutions could properly be subjected to scientific scrutiny. But this reluctance has been slowly subsiding, and the technical problems of analyzing changes in persons and in social systems are now receiving an increasing amount of attention. Continuity conditions have been extended, in applied mathematics, to allow integration of functions of discrete observations, which are correlated over time because they are obtained from biological or social processes. Distribution functions for the occurrence of social phenomena are again being scrutinized seriously (Kendall, 1961). Concurrently, there has been increasing concern with "errors in the observations," or with the quality of data in general. Over a century ago the study of the reliability of observations became important in its own right, as for example, among astronomers. More recently, the effects of relatively large errors of measurement, such as those encountered in mental testing, have also been investigated.

The topic of this paper is fundamental to most other problems treated in this volume because social science data are practically always subject to large errors of measurement. This should be taken into account in any analysis, including the evaluation of changes by means of mental test scores.

Even though measurement experiments have provided a foundation for science, they are poorly understood. Measurement remains at best a kind of problem child of logic and of science. After stating a general condition for "fundamental" measurement, Hemple (1952) discards it in favor of other conditions that permit "derived" measurement. Derived measurement is rather vague; it might be described as consisting of any empirical activities, or "operations," that can be used to obtain numbers.

Anyone who supposes that modern statistics has greatly improved our understanding of measurement, or in particular of the analysis of measurement values, would do well to read Lubin's (1962) summary of recent "progress" in statistics. The picture presented is not very encouraging. On the other hand, mental test theory has certainly been strengthened by the intrusion of modern statistical methods. The attack on unreliability initiated by Spearman and by Kelley has been sustained, and some notable advances have been made recently, particularly by Lord (1955, 1959). Surely we can look forward confidently to a time when measurement in social science will be much more effective and useful.

The present writers became involved in measuring change in college students because of the need to understand large amounts of longitudinal data collected from students attending Vassar College, and from other institutions of higher learning that are now being studied at the Center for the Study of Higher Education in Berkeley. Many students' difference scores on mental tests, interview ratings, and the like, are available, and they require interpretation and tests of significance. This paper has therefore grown out of immediate research questions, and at this stage it is unlikely that we shall be able to present final answers. Much of what follows is necessarily in the nature of raising additional questions that seem important in order to encourage further progress.

Toward an arithmetic of test scores

Ideally we should be able to add or subtract test scores at will. When we attempt this, however, certain difficulties arise, some of which are due to the unreliability of the component scores (Lord, 1956, 1958). For example, extreme scores on a pretest tend to regress toward the mean on the post-test more than would be expected for reliable observations. In the absence of special precautions, a difference score will practically always be less reliable than its components; and persons will be ordered less precisely by a change score than they are by either of the component scores. But if allowance is made for unreliability, arithmetic operations on scores will lead to results that are reasonable.

Not all information in test scores is ordinal information in one dimension, and efforts to utilize all the metric information have been made by a few investigators in attacks on the "scaling" problem. If one dimension is assumed, the effects of distribution shape on functions of raw scores, such as difference scores, may be considerable. Nevertheless, the irregularities encountered in moving from single scores to difference scores are seldom so large that the same operations will fail to be meaningful for both. In other words, one can take the view that a difference score is enough like a single observation that it can be treated as such in most analyses, providing corrections can be made for unreliability.

Surely the most important information in a set of test scores is intrinsic to the (partial) ordering of the subjects on a single dimension. This suggests that reliability measures that are relatively insensitive to higher moments might be useful (Webster, 1962b). Obviously any transformations of raw scores to make them more tractable for analysis should be (at least) order-preserving for the subjects. But this is a very large class of transformations, and the search within it for "units" will therefore probably continue. For difference scores, the "units" defined by equation (8) below appear to have certain advantages. A similar approach for single scores, after centering by a true constant (a national norm, say, or else $k/2$, where k is the number of test items), might also be useful, but we have not fully investigated this.

The simplest transformations of raw scores should be used in preference to more complicated ones that unwittingly discard information. For example, in most studies the sample test mean and variance are *not* constants. They may have sizable sampling variances, and an uncritical use of deviation scores or standard scores will therefore seldom be advantageous, despite illusions to the contrary. We have explored some item-scoring methods that would stabilize item means, or item means and variances, in samples. The use of item deviation scores or item standard scores merely complicates the measurement problem, especially the problem of estimating total test reliability.

It now seems that the metric imposed on test scores by traditional item scoring is about as useful as any other for most purposes. If an item is scored with only two constants, however, its mean and variance will certainly not be independent, and the hypothesis that such items in a test come from the same population cannot be tested without first applying a transformation. The arcsin transformation, which is completely efficient, merits further study for this purpose.

Replication is necessary in a mental testing experiment

If a mental test is administered primarily for the purpose of ordering persons reliably on a single characteristic of some scientific interest, then this constitutes a measurement experiment; for each person the administration of a test item is a measurement trial. The response of one person to a single item is about as useless, taken alone, as a single observation would be in any other measurement situation; and this includes an item difference score obtained from one person on two occasions. In other words, there must be replications because the errors of measurement are large.

Replication of scores may take place in two ways, or by means of a combination of both: Persons can be replicated, or else item administrations with or without item sampling can be replicated. When there is random sampling for both, the combination has been referred to as "matrix sampling," because the obtained $k \times m$ matrix of responses of the m persons to the k items is a sample from a population represented by a very large, or infinite, matrix of such responses (Cornfield and Tukey, 1956; Lord, 1959). Statisticians are still questioning certain aspects of matrix sampling, and it may be some time before it can be employed with confidence in certain analysis of variance designs (Lubin, 1962; Plackett, 1960).

Sometimes one is asked to test for significance a difference between two test *item* means—one an initial mean, another a final mean—for the same persons. Usually the item will be identically or very similarly worded on the two occasions, because the difference would otherwise be difficult to interpret. Under the assumption of *person* random sampling, the hypothesis that this mean difference is zero is then examined, using a test of significance for correlated proportions or for correlated means. Such a test treats the difference scores for the m persons no differently from the way it would treat m single observations. And it is also interesting that the test itself is indifferent to the source of the observations; for example, they could as well be for m items responded to by *one* person on the two occasions (a case treated more realistically in the next section). This illustrates that in this situation that which is actually tested is a difference between sets of *measurement trial values*. Although we refer to "the same" persons, they may have "changed" during the interval. Even the item (or items, in the second case above) might be different on the retest, for example, in the context of the test format; or a parallel item might be used. Moreover, a person-item interaction could also differ on the two occasions.

Now an approach that avoids the attempt to decide exactly *what* has

changed between the occasions is to emphasize the measurement replications. To repeat, this test for correlated means is itself a simple one, and
it will not tell us whether it is the item(s), the person(s), or an interaction
that changes; we either have to decide this on other grounds, or else resort
to a more detailed design. So there is actually some choice here in how
we may think of the population: It is either a precisely defined but abstract population of measurement replications, or else it is a specific population of entities (persons or items or both). The usual choice is the latter
for this problem of testing correlated means; person sampling is assumed
simply because the experimenter decides that he has in fact administered
the same item twice to each of m persons, and that it is therefore only the
persons who *can* change. The more interesting problem is discussed in the
next section.

Significance of a change within one person

It will be necessary first to be more specific about test forms. *Identical
forms* are defined as forms in which identically worded items are presented
in the same order, and in the same format, in a pretest and a post-test,
which are administered to the same person (or group of persons) on the
two occasions. *Matched forms* may be either identical forms, or forms in
which items have been matched statistically, regardless of their content.
Unmatched forms refers to the case where items are not matched (or are
"randomly matched") between the two forms. Matched forms therefore
includes identical forms as a special case, the latter owing their effectiveness to statistical properties associated with content.

Next assume that k items are administered on each of the two occasions.
The two forms may be either matched or unmatched as defined above.
The pretest total score X for one person is $x_1 + \cdots + x_k = X$, where the
k item scores have been added with the intention that they will each contribute something useful to X. Beyond this, the assumptions are simply
that each x_i is one of a finite ordered set of scores, and that the k scores
are experimentally independent—that is, that the value of any score has
not been influenced by the person's responses to previous items. The
same assumptions apply for the final, or post-test, score $y_1 + \cdots + y_k$
$= Y$. This independence assumption means that here we choose to ignore
learning or other temporal effects, such as fatigue, that might depend upon
the order of the k item administrations.

Under these assumptions the difference score,

$$(1) \qquad\qquad Y - X = \sum_{i}^{k} (y_i - x_i) = D,$$

has the sampling variance,

$$(2) \qquad\qquad \text{Var } D = k(\overset{2}{\sigma_y} + \overset{2}{\sigma_x} - 2\sigma_{xy}),$$

where σ_x^2 and σ_y^2 are random sampling variances of the item scores, and σ_{xy} is their sampling covariance for the two occasions.

Note that in (2) it is the item *scores*, or measurement trial values, that are sampled. The items themselves may or may not be random samples from a population of items. The items are simply tools with which it is assumed that a series of independent measurement trials can be carried out. This sampling scheme, which might be called *measurement trial sampling*, is analogous to that used by an experimenter who measures a rod k times, by applying one or more tapes or rules in order to obtain a random sample of k values, each representing its length.

If matched forms are used, the matched items yield values that will not be independent between forms, the degree of relationship being represented by σ_{xy} in (2). An examination of the 204 cases on Form A (identical forms) of Table 3.1 showed that only 6 had small negative or zero values for $\hat{\sigma}_{xy}$, the remainder being positive.

The usual unbiased estimates of parameters in (2) for the person's item scores on the two occasions are

$$(3) \qquad\qquad \hat{\sigma}_y^2 = \left(\sum_i^k y_i^2 - k\bar{y}^2 \right) \Big/ (k-1),$$

$$(4) \qquad\qquad \hat{\sigma}_x^2 = \left(\sum_i^k x_i^2 - k\bar{x}^2 \right) \Big/ (k-1),$$

$$(5) \qquad\qquad \hat{\sigma}_{xy} = \left(\sum_i^k x_iy_i - k\bar{x}\bar{y} \right) \Big/ (k-1).$$

Substituting (3), (4), and (5) for the corresponding parameters in (2), an unbiased estimate of the sampling variance of the person's total difference score is obtained,

$$(6) \quad \hat{\text{Var}}\, D = k \left[\sum^k y^2 - k\bar{y}^2 + \sum^k x^2 - k\bar{x}^2 \right. $$
$$\left. - 2 \left(\sum^k xy - k\bar{x}\bar{y} \right) \right] \Big/ (k-1).$$

If each item is arbitrarily scored 0 or $+1$, (6) becomes

$$(7) \qquad \hat{\text{Var}}'\, D = [k(X+Y) - (X^2 + Y^2) - 2(kf - XY)]/(k-1),$$

where f is the number of items scored $+1$ on both occasions.

If forms are unmatched, the final covariance terms in (6) and (7) should not differ significantly from zero. In practice, k is nearly always sufficiently large that it is unnecessary to introduce special distribution theory for the item scores. Error variances such as (7), for use with the data of a single test administration, were first derived by Lord (1955), using item sampling assumptions. Again, the present derivation is compatible with, but does not require, the sampling of items *per se* (Webster, 1962a).

The square root of (6), or of (7), may therefore be used to test for significance an obtained "idiographic" change in an individual. Beck's (1953) discussion indicates a need for this kind of statistic, especially in personality research. The test ratio for the jth person,

$$(8) \qquad\qquad z(0, 1) = D_j/\sqrt{\text{Vâr } D_j},$$

can be treated as a normal deviate.

In this derivation, experimental independence of the k measurement trials is assumed in each of the two test administrations. This does not seem to be a hazardous assumption for most mental tests, but it deserves more thorough investigation. If the k trials are regarded as generating a Markoff process, then terms in (6) can be multiplied by a function of the serial correlations over the k trials, which will allow for infringement of the independence assumption. There may also be simpler alternatives, consisting of variations in the order in which the post-test items are presented. We are aware of no studies of this problem using mental test data.

The philosophy of measurement underlying the use of (8) is quite simple. It should be noted that the person is *not* treated as a member of a group or sample. By comparison with the theory of measurement long used in physical science, (6) is the estimated variance of a function that is a sum of difference scores with unit coefficients; the partial derivatives of the function with respect to its variable quantities are therefore also unity. Because of the person's temporal processes, we cannot administer a standard, identically worded item k times, in order to minimize the error variance within a single test administration. But we do administer k "similar" items, defined as items (a) which have small within-persons variance, and (b) which have joint validity or theoretical "import," as this term is used by Hemple (1952). The need for small within-persons variance makes it practical to score all test items, each in its direction of import, with an identical set of ordered constants, say 0, 1, or 1, 2, 3, 4, 5, rather than with sets that vary for different items. But these item similarity criteria are not *necessary* in the measurement theory leading to (8); they are, rather, empirical practicalities. The attitude in administering k items that satisfy (a) and (b) above is simply that a person scoring high (low) on some trials should score high (low) on most others. This is the traditional attitude toward a series of measurement trials.

At the same time, (6) leads naturally to expressions that are useful in comparing a number of persons simultaneously. In mental measurement, the discrimination of persons, each from the others, which is usually the primary objective, can be achieved in more than one way, and with varying degrees of success. A large number of discriminations of persons, each from another, is desired; but more important is the requirement that each person be discriminated, insofar as possible, from the *same* other persons in statistically inferred replications of the total test. In our opinion it is largely this last requirement that gives the reliability estimate of test scores, or of difference scores, its importance.

Significance of mean changes for groups

The mean of (6), for a fixed group of persons, happens to be important in estimating test reliability; but because of the assumptions in its derivation it cannot be used to test the group mean change for significance. The reason is that, when items (or measurement trials) are sampled, the (inferred) replications of the sets—each of size k—generate (sampling) correlations among the persons. In other words, the sampled sets would each have different means, and the m persons' scores D_j would rise and fall together over sets. Therefore, persons' scores are not independent in the *population* of measurements, and the mean of (6) is too small to serve as a sampling variance of their mean change. Under these assumptions (Lord, 1955, p. 13), an estimate of the sampling variance of the mean change scores will be

$$(9) \qquad \text{Vâr } \overline{D} = k^2 S_{\bar{d}}^2 / (k - 1) = k^2 S_W^2 / m^2 (k - 1).$$

Here $S_{\bar{d}}^2$ is the obtained variance of the item difference score means, and S_W^2 is the variance, over items, of the difference between total item scores (or "counts") for the two occasions.

Assume, on the contrary, that persons comprise the random sample, and that the items are fixed. Then

$$(10) \qquad \text{Vâr}' \overline{D} = \text{Vâr} \left(\sum^m D/m \right) = (m \text{ Vâr } D)/m^2 = S_D^2/(m - 1),$$

where S_D^2 is the variance of the persons' total difference scores, D, as in (1). This expression can hardly be regarded as a *measurement* error variance, and only (9) will reduce to the previous case where change is measured in one person. If we choose to disregard the lack of independence among the k trials, implicit in (10), then it can be used to set confidence limits for a difference parameter in a population of persons. In other cases (9) would seem to be appropriate.

The failure of independence, either among items or among persons, is not avoided by matrix sampling; in matrix sampling, however, a lack of independence induced in one factor, or "effect," by the other would have to be statistical (not experimental). Using the approach due to Lord (1955, pp. 18–20), an approximate sampling variance for a mean difference, under his joint item and person sampling assumptions, will be

$$(11) \qquad \text{Vâr}'' \ \overline{D} \doteq k^2 S_W^2 / m^2 (k-1) + S_D^2 / (m-1).$$

This result uses all the degrees of freedom available from the two test administrations, in a way such that increasing the size of the sample of persons decreases the sampling variance of their mean change.

Reliability estimates for change scores

Of several requirements for the reliability coefficient, two will probably continue to be most important: (*a*) a reliability measure should provide an easily computed estimate of the proportion of true variance in the obtained scores; and (*b*) it should be a regression coefficient for predicting true from obtained scores. In both cases it is the *persons'* scores, not the scores associated with the items (or comparable measures), that are referred to; for the latter, the "dual" of the reliability coefficient, obtained by interchanging item and person parameters, has been shown to serve as one kind of "profile similarity" measure (Webster, 1957; Webster and Asprey, 1958). Two related properties are also useful: (*c*) the reliability estimate serves as a measure of the consistency of the items with respect to the persons (its dual—which is of some interest in Guttman scaling— is a measure of the consistency of the persons with respect to the items); and (*d*) it is the estimated average (intraclass) correlation among measurement replications of the subjects' set of total scores, of which only one set is available in the data at hand. Some consequences of these properties are very important. For example, the reliability of a test is one measure of its precision, for tests of low reliability yield relatively large numbers of erroneous inversions in the ordering of subjects. Also a reliability measure that is not estimable from a single set of observations (which might be a single set of difference scores) is of very limited value.

The theory of the reliability of measures of change that will be considered below also utilizes these four requirements. A consequence of (*d*) above, sometimes overlooked, is that change scores for individuals are meaningful in relation to changes that do or do not occur for other members of the group or sample. Even though the mean change might be meaningful, reliability of the change scores would be meaningless if each subject made the same obtained gain (or loss) over the test-retest interval. In effect, then, it is differential, or relative, change among individuals (or in some situations among subgroups) that will be assessed by the reliability estimate. The estimate is not available when only a single total change score is considered.

As remarked earlier, the mean of (6) for the group of m persons is useful in reliability theory (whether it is computed for single or for difference scores). This average happens to be the error variance term of either of two reliability estimates that satisfy, either exactly or to a close approximation, each of the four requirements given above. We will first write this error variance for total scores X_j, obtained for the m persons on a single testing occasion, with the understanding that the single score statistics will later be replaced by those for difference scores:

$$(12) \quad \frac{1}{m} \sum \text{Vâr } X_j = \frac{1}{k-1}\left[k \sum_{}^{k} S_i^2 + k^2 S_p^2 - S_X^2 \right]$$

$$\equiv \left[S_X^2 + \frac{k^2 S_p^2}{k-1} \right] - \frac{k}{k-1}\left[S_X^2 - \sum_{}^{k} S_i^2 \right]$$

$$\equiv S_X^2 - \frac{k}{k-1}\left[S_X^2 - \sum_{}^{k} S_i^2 - k S_p^2 \right].$$

Here S_i^2, S_p^2, and S_X^2 are obtained variances for scores on the ith item, for the item means, and for the total scores of the persons, respectively.

The error variance (12) has been partitioned into obtained and true variance in two ways, and this requires discussion. First note, however, an expression frequently occurring in test theory,

$$(13) \quad k \sum_{}^{k} S_i^2 + k^2 S_p^2 \equiv k\overline{X} - \overline{X}^2, \quad (0, 1) \textit{ item scores.}$$

This identity is true if each item score consists of one of the two constants, 0 or $+1$. The procedure for relaxing item scoring restrictions, by moving from the right to the left side of (13), is easily verified by an analysis of variance of the persons' scores on the items.

The ratio of the second to the first term in the second partitioning of (12) is, aside from two relatively minor corrections for bias, a reliability estimate that was described as "generalized KR 21" in a previous article (Webster, 1960a):

$$(14) \qquad \hat{\rho} = \frac{k}{k-1}\left[1 - \frac{\sum\limits_{}^{k} S_i^2 + kS_p^2}{S_X^2}\right].$$

In the development leading to (14) it was assumed that the person effect was the only effect worth isolating. The Cornfield-Tukey (1956) two-way model can be reduced to a one-way model (with one tied error) by restricting the general mean to equal the single effect mean; and in this case (14) may be obtained from it (Webster, 1960b). It is a fact, however, that the usual analysis of variance models I and II can be viewed, for balanced one-way designs, as formally indistinguishable. In other words, whether persons, in addition to measurement trials, are also regarded as random samples is of questionable importance for (14).

For this reason we were pleased to find, after applying (13), that Lord's (1959, formula 47) regression coefficient for predicting true from obtained scores had the error variance (12), for Lord's derivation requires *no* assumptions beyond those needed when random samples of trials of size k are used in conjunction with a least-squares model. When Lord's formula 47 is modified by substituting the left side of (13), it is found to be the ratio of terms in the first partitioning of (12),

$$(15) \qquad \hat{B}' = \frac{k}{k-1}\left[\frac{S_X^2 - \sum\limits_{}^{k} S_i^2}{S_X^2 + k^2 S_p^2/(k-1)}\right].$$

Here the prime indicates that the item-scoring restrictions have been relaxed.

This result is obviously slightly larger than (14), since either estimate ranges between zero and one; but for practical purposes (14) and (15) are about the same, and a choice between them must be made on theoretical grounds. Theory seems now to favor (15) because it makes allowance for the fact that the obtained total scores from any set of k item administrations are likely, on the average, to be either too high or too low; and this warrants the addition of the estimated sampling variance of the mean, $k^2 S_p^2/(k-1)$, to the usual obtained variance term S_X^2 (and the absence of an identical term from the "true" variance).

We will therefore write (15) for the reliability of difference scores,

$$(16) \quad \hat{B}_D' = \frac{k}{k-1}\left[\frac{S_D^2 - \sum\limits_{}^{k} S_{d_i}^2}{S_D^2 + k^2 S_d^2/(k-1)}\right] = 1 - \frac{\frac{1}{m}\sum\limits_{}^{m} \text{Vâr } D_j}{S_D^2 + k^2 S_w^2/m^2(k-1)},$$

where (12), rewritten for difference scores, and (9) have been used. When the numerator in the final part of (16) is expanded, using (1) and (6), we obtain

$$(17) \quad \frac{1}{m} \sum_{}^{m} \text{Vâr } D_j$$

$$= [k(\overline{\Sigma y^2} + \overline{\Sigma x^2}) - (\overline{Y}^2 + \overline{X}^2) - S_D^2 - 2(k\overline{\Sigma xy} - \overline{X}\overline{Y})]/(k-1),$$

in which the summations are over k squares or cross products of item scores for one person, and the bars indicate means of these values for the m persons. In case the items are each scored either 0 or $+1$, (17) simplifies to

$$(18) \quad \frac{1}{m} \sum_{}^{m} \text{Vâr}' D_j$$

$$= [k(\overline{Y} + \overline{X}) - (\overline{X}^2 + \overline{Y}^2) - S_D^2 - 2(k\overline{f} - \overline{X}\overline{Y})]/(k-1),$$

where $\overline{f}$ is the mean number of items, for the m persons, that are scored $+1$ on both occasions.

Substituting (17) in (16), the reliability estimate of the difference scores is

$$(19) \quad \hat{B}'_D = \frac{k}{k-1}\left[1 - \frac{k(\overline{\Sigma y^2} + \overline{\Sigma x^2}) - (\overline{X}^2 + \overline{Y}^2) - 2(k\overline{\Sigma xy} - \overline{X}\overline{Y}) + P}{k(S_D^2 + P)}\right],$$

with $P = k^2 S_d^2/(k-1) = k^2 S_W^2/m^2(k-1)$. And if the item scores are restricted to 0 and $+1$, (19) will reduce to

$$(20) \quad \hat{B}''_D = \frac{k}{k-1}\left[1 - \frac{k(\overline{Y} + \overline{X}) - (\overline{X}^2 + \overline{Y}^2) - 2(k\overline{f} - \overline{X}\overline{Y}) + P}{k(S_D^2 + P)}\right],$$

which can be checked by substituting (18) in (16). Except for the term P, (20) is equivalent to the KR 21 formula for the case where the test scores are difference scores. The mean number of items $\overline{f}$ scored $+1$ on both tests for the m persons is the statistic in (20) that is most difficult to obtain without relying on large computers.

A traditional formula for the reliability of differences, which may be derived by a method due to Mosier (1943), is

$$(21) \quad r_{DD} = \frac{r_{XX}S_X^2 + r_{YY}S_Y^2 - 2r_{XY}S_X S_Y}{S_D^2}.$$

A persistent question has been how to calculate the reliability estimates for pretests and post-tests, r_{XX} and r_{YY}, in this formula. If the usual

KR 21 expressions are substituted for these values in (21), we can write

$$(22) \quad r_{DD} = \frac{k}{k-1}\left[1 - \frac{k(\overline{Y} + \overline{X}) - (\overline{X}^2 + \overline{Y}^2) - 2r_{XY}S_XS_Y}{kS_D^2}\right].$$

Comparing this with (20), the two expressions differ in the term P and in their correlation terms. The presence of P in (20) was explained in the discussion following (15), and ignoring P in any of the formulas in the present paper is merely the same as preferring (14) to (15) as a reliability estimate. But the difference between $2r_{XY}S_XS_Y$ in (22) and $2(k\bar{f} - \overline{X}\overline{Y})$ in (20) requires further discussion.

It is known that (21) assumes that the correlation between the error components of the total scores X and Y is zero (Gulliksen, 1950, p. 352), but if the test forms are matched, as defined above, then this is an unrealistic assumption. If the error components are correlated between forms, then the true and error components of the difference score are also likely to be correlated. Consider first the item-person data matrix in the test-retest case. This is a matrix of m double columns, each corresponding to a person, and each having the two score totals X and Y at the bottom. For simplicity, suppose the items are scored 0 or $+1$. Then each jth double column will contain a number f_j of $(1, 1)$ score pairs. By analogy with analysis of variance, which could be applied to single columns, analysis of covariance of the double-column matrix relates covariance within and between persons to the total covariance.

In fact, the total covariance, say $r_{ij}S_iS_j$, over all the score pairs in the matrix, is in this case

$$(23) \quad r_{ij}S_iS_j \equiv [(k\bar{f} - \overline{X}\overline{Y}) + r_{XY}S_XS_Y]/k^2$$
$$= (k\bar{f} - \overline{X}\overline{Y} + \overline{X}\overline{Y} - \overline{X}\overline{Y})/k^2$$
$$= (k\bar{f} - \overline{X}\overline{Y})/k^2.$$

The quantity required in (20) is therefore k^2 times the total covariance of the matrix, and not the between-persons covariance term $r_{XY}S_XS_Y$ that appears in the numerators of (21) and (22). The latter assume that the within-persons covariance is negligible, but this is obviously not realistic in the case of matched forms, which require that (20) be used.

In case matched forms are employed, (20) will exceed (21) by a significant amount, as seen from the data at the bottom of Table 3.1. This increase in reliability is subject to other interpretations, but the one that we now prefer, in the case of attitude tests, is that matching the forms has made them more uniform, with the result that the precision of the measurement has been improved by comparison with that which could be achieved with unmatched or randomly matched forms.

Before this section is concluded, it may be noted that substitution of difference scores (1) in the KR 20 formula gives

$$(24) \qquad r_{20} = \frac{k}{k-1} \left[1 - \frac{\overline{X} + \overline{Y} - \sum\limits^{k} (\bar{x}^2 + \bar{y}^2 - 2\bar{x}\bar{y}) - 2\bar{f}}{S_D^2} \right],$$

where $\bar{x}$ and $\bar{y}$ are item means for the m persons, and as before $\bar{f}$ is the mean number of items scored $+1$ on the two occasions. As for the other estimates, this version of KR 20 requires data at the item-score level.

Correlated score components and mental test theory

We have stated that if matched forms are used, the reliability of difference scores will be higher than for unmatched forms. If matched forms are used, the usual assumption that the obtained score components (of the difference scores) are uncorrelated need not hold. Test theory can be extended to include the case where these components are correlated.

For example, in the case of difference scores, we first write

$$(25) \qquad X = t + e,$$
$$Y = u + f,$$
$$D = Y - X = (u - t) + (f - e) = v + g,$$

where t, u, and v are true score components and e, f, and g are the error components. Traditionally, the reliability of the scores D would be

$$(26) \qquad r = 1 - S_g^2/S_D^2 = 1 - r_{gD}S_gS_D/S_D^2 = 1 - r_{gD}^2,$$

which may be obtained directly from the condition that the covariance between v and g is zero:

$$(27) \qquad C(g, v) = C(g, D - g) = C(g, D) - S_g^2 = 0;$$

or $\qquad S_g^2 = r_{gD}S_gS_D, \qquad S_g^2/S_D^2 = r_{gD}^2.$

A more general approach, however, does not depend upon setting (27) equal to zero:

$$(28) \qquad C(g, v) = C(g, D) - S_g^2;$$

or $\qquad S_g^2 = r_{gD}S_gS_D - r_{gv}S_gS_v, \quad$ and

$$r = 1 - S_g^2/S_D^2 = 1 - (r_{gD}S_gS_D - r_{gv}S_gS_v)/S_D^2.$$

In the theory underlying (19) or (20), the term $r_{gv}S_gS_v$ need not be zero, as it is in (26). This result provides a defensible extension of the definition of reliability, at least in the case of difference scores.

Reliability of other functions

The reliability of raw score differences has been discussed above. In general, however, the reliabilities of other functions of scores are not readily available. Procedures to obtain them, in specific cases, should differ little from methods employed in other kinds of investigations where sampling variances of functions of random variables must be estimated.

In some situations, inexact solutions are helpful. For example, a measure of change may be needed that is practically independent of variations in the initial scores. For this purpose we may agree to define the obtained change as

$$(29) \qquad G = Y - bX,$$

such that X, the pretest scores, and G are uncorrelated in the sample for the m persons. Ideally, b would also be treated as a random variable, and the true scores corresponding to X and Y would be entirely independent; but *if m is large*, and exact comparisons with other samples are unnecessary, it is reasonable (and much more convenient) to regard b as constant. If the sample covariance of G with X is zero, then b must be $r_{YX}S_Y/S_X$. After substitution of this value in (29), Mosier's approach leads to a reliability formula for G,

$$(30) \qquad r_G = [r_{YY} - r_{XY}(2 - r_{XX})]/(1 - r_{XY}^2),$$

where the reliabilities, r_{YY} and r_{XX}, may be calculated as in (15). But this result is useful only for test forms known to be unmatched at the item level.

If forms are matched (or identical) then the appropriate estimate, analogous to (19), is

$$(31) \qquad r_G' = \frac{k}{k-1}$$
$$\cdot \left[1 - \frac{k(\Sigma y^2 + b^2\,\overline{\Sigma x^2}) - (\overline{Y}^2 + b^2\overline{X}^2) - 2b(k\overline{\Sigma xy} - \overline{X}\,\overline{Y}) + P}{k(S_Y^2 + b^2 S_X^2 - 2br_{XY}S_XS_Y + P)}\right],$$

where $b = r_{YX}S_Y/S_X$, $P = k^2 S_{(y-bx)}^2/m^2(k-1)$. If items are scored 0 or $+1$, (31) will simplify, as in (20).

Considered apart from any group, the best estimate of an individual's true difference score, say T, is his obtained difference score D; confidence limits for T may be set up by using (6) or (7). If the individual is to be treated as a group member, however, then the mean and reliability provide additional information, and a better estimate of his true score is

$$(32) \qquad \hat{T} = \hat{B}'_D D + (1 - \hat{B}'_D)\overline{D} = \overline{D} + \hat{B}'_D(D - \overline{D}),$$

where $\hat{B}'_D$ is obtained from (19). In this regression equation, the difference scores are treated as single observations; if partial regressions of true gain on initial, and on final, scores are employed in place of $\hat{B}'_D$, then a different result is obtained.

In fact, the difference between the partial and the total regression equations can be used to help answer the question whether it is appropriate to treat difference scores as single observations. If one estimated partial regression equals the negative of the other, then they both equal the estimated total regression $\hat{B}'_D$ for the raw score difference D. And this orthogonality of the partials implies that $\hat{B}'_D S_D$ will equal the standard deviation of the difference $(\hat{b}_{TY \cdot X} Y - \hat{b}_{TX \cdot Y} X)$ between (partially) regressed raw scores. Then it can be argued that, if a test of significance showed that one partial did not differ significantly from the negative of the other, we should treat the difference scores as single observations; but that otherwise the partial regression equation would be significantly more precise than (32) for predicting true change. In (32), $\hat{B}'_D$ is the reliability estimate, but for the partial regression equation it is the squared multiple correlation estimate (of true change on pretest and post-test scores) that is the best *single* reliability estimate of the change.

The usual variance "error of estimate" for (32) is

$$(33) \qquad S^2_{T \cdot D} = S^2_T(1 - \hat{B}'_D) = (S^2_D + P)(\hat{B}'_D - \hat{B}'^2_D).$$

This is an estimate of the variance of true scores *for a constant individual obtained score* selected at random. An estimate in which $\hat{B}'_D$ and D were both free to vary would be more realistic for some testing problems. If $\hat{B}'_D$ is already known, or if m is quite large, a suitable approximate sampling variance of (32) is

$$(34) \qquad \text{Vâr } \hat{T} = \hat{B}'^2_D \text{ Vâr } D + (1 - \hat{B}'_D)^2 \text{ Vâr } \overline{D},$$

in which the estimates on the right side are calculated by using (6) and (9). In (34) m should be large, because $\hat{B}'_D$ is treated as a constant, and because the covariance between D and $\overline{D}$ is ignored.

Kelley (1948) derived (32) for scores from a single test administration, and noted its useful properties. He ignored a term equivalent here to the second term of (34), which is indeed small for typical values of m. Equation (32) is not a typical regression equation, because the problem posed would not exist for perfectly reliable observations; in the latter case, B'_D would equal one, and (32) would be trivial. A more precise version of (34) would be useful when the "individual" is one of a *small* number of groups, for example, one of m student bodies with a total mean score $\overline{D}$.

Kelley's recommendation that regressed scores be used in place of obtained scores deserves a more thorough investigation than it has received in the past. In particular, regressed difference scores are the same as the difference between (totally) regressed scores only if the regressions are equal; the kinds of relations existing for departures from equality should suggest methods for improving the arithmetic of scores and of functions of scores.

Programming to study change

We have spent much time exploring approximations for the estimates f in (7) and $\bar{f}$ in (20) and (24). In studying large numbers of change scores for individuals, considered entirely apart from their groups, it has been found convenient to use $(k/2)$ as a working approximation for (7). The problem of approximating $\bar{f}$ will reduce to approximating a sum-of-products term for the interaction of persons and items, a term that cannot be determined from the marginal data alone of the change scores matrix. It is of course important not to overestimate the parameter for which $\bar{f}$ is an estimate, because this would inflate the reliability. A conservative approximation using only marginal data is

$$(35) \qquad \bar{\bar{f}} = \frac{1}{m}\left(\frac{\sum\limits_{}^{m} X_j Y_j}{k} + \frac{\sum\limits_{}^{k} V_i W_i}{m} - \frac{\sum\limits_{}^{m} X_j \sum\limits_{}^{m} Y_j}{km} \right).$$

That is, (35) may underestimate, but it will not overestimate, the parameter. Here V_i and W_i are, respectively, the sum of scores (over m persons) for the ith item in the pretest, and the corresponding sum of scores in the post-test.

Obviously, in any large-scale study of changes in persons, a general computer program is needed that will utilize all the data in the $k \times m$ difference scores matrix. The required operations are easy to write out, but the computer capacity should be large. Ideally, the program will obtain sums of scores and squares for both the rows and the columns of a pretest item score matrix $[x_{ij}]$, and a post-test matrix $[y_{ij}]$, and then compute a variety of statistics for both. The program should next form the difference matrix $[y_{ij} - x_{ij}]$ and repeat these operations a third time, after which any of the formulas of the present paper can easily be evaluated and printed. An initial technical problem now under study at the Center for the Study of Higher Education, University of California, Berkeley, is the taping of hundreds of item responses in a way that will permit recovery of any k of them needed for a particular test.

Some applications

It is true that the reliability of change scores on mental tests is often discouragingly low and that one cannot, therefore, place much confidence in the precision with which persons are ordered by their difference scores. As can be seen from (32), this does not rule out the use of scores from tests of low reliability for testing hypotheses concerning mean changes in groups of persons. The data of Table 3.1 illustrate this.

A 144-item personality scale, for which reliability had exceeded .92 in several large, heterogeneous college samples, was split into two halves, A and B, containing 72 items each. The latter were scored for a new and relatively homogeneous sample of 204 college freshmen; a year later the same subjects took forms A and B again, with the results set forth in Table 3.1.

First we note that there is an apparent increase in the characteristic measured by A and B over the year, whether measured using the same, or the differently worded, post-test. The average gain for the identical forms is, from Table 3.1, $(5.36 + 4.81)/2 = 5.085$; for the unmatched forms this average is $(6.04 + 4.14)/2 = 5.090$. Individual gains of these magnitudes are not significant, but they are easily significant for a group this large.

The reliability estimates described in footnotes "b" and "c" of Table 3.1 are larger than their respective symmetric elements in the lower part of the matrix, a difference that we have attributed to the increased precision with which change can be measured using identical (or matched) test forms in place of unmatched (or randomly matched) forms.

Change scores of higher reliability than those of Table 3.1 can be obtained, given special conditions. For example, if items that are known to be specially sensitive to change have been selected for inclusion in the test, and if the test administrations are separated by a relatively long period of time, then results such as those in Table 3.2 may be obtained.

The data of Table 3.2 are for a 60-item personality scale very similar in content to the two scales of Table 3.1. The test administrations were four years rather than one year apart, and the scale had been developed so as to increase reliability, in three successive independent samples, as measured by (24). The obtained gain in Table 3.2 is 7.02. The scale comes very close to providing change scores of sufficient reliability for general

TABLE 3.1

Pretest and Post-test Statistics for Test Forms A and B, Unmatched at the Item Level, Administered to 204 College Freshmen

		Freshmen		Sophomores	
		A	B	A	B
Means		44.79	44.12	50.16	48.93
Sample Variances		85.68	83 74	74.21	74.07
S.D.'s		9.26	9.15	8.62	8.61
$KR\ 21$[a]		.82	.81	.81	.80
Correlations					
Freshmen	A	1.00			
	B	.86	1.00		
Sophomores	A	.73	.67	1.00	
	B	.67	.69	.83	1.00
Mean differences					
Freshmen	A	—			
	B	−.68	—		
Sophomores	A	5.36	6.04	—	
	B	4.14	4.81	−1.23	—
Reliability estimates, formula (22) except as indicated					
Freshmen	A	—	−.32	.55[b]	.42
	B	−.32	—	.41	.57[c]
Sophomores	A	.31	.41	—	−.13
	B	.42	.37	−.13	—

[a] Calculated using 203 degrees of freedom in the denominator.

[b] Formula (20) with $P = 0$. The mean number of items scored $+1$ on both occasions is $\bar{f} = 37.21$.

[c] Formula (20) with $P = 0$. The mean number of items scored $+1$ on both occasions is $\bar{f} = 35.68$.

use in detecting true gains *of average magnitude* for individuals.

Table 3.2 also contains the value of $\bar{f}$ approximated by (35), and the corresponding reliability values. In order to study (35) more closely, the $\bar{f}$ values of Table 3.1 were also approximated by (35). The resulting values, 33.38 and 31.41, reduced the exact reliabilities from .55 to .38, and from .57 to .40, respectively. These decreases are large, and for this reason exact values for $\bar{f}$ should be used whenever this is possible.

E 3.2

...lity Statistics for a 60-Item Test Administered to 100 College Women in the Freshman Year, and Readministered in the Senior Year

Statistic	Freshman	Senior	Change
Mean	25.61	32.63	7.02
Variance	73.92	73.29	64.26
S.D.	8.60	8.56	8.02
KR 20, (24)[a]	.84	.84	.70
KR 21, or $\hat{B}_D''$ with $P = 0$, (20)	.82	.81	.69
r_{DD}, (22)	—	—	.57
$\bar{j}$	—	—	18.36
$\bar{\bar{j}}$, (35)	—	—	16.18
KR 20, (24, 35)[b]	—	—	.64
KR 21, (20, 35)[b]	—	—	.62

[a] Numbers in parentheses refer to formulas in the present article that were used to obtain the statistics for the change scores.

[b] Uses $\bar{\bar{j}}$ obtained from formula (35).

Summary

Some problems of measuring change using mental test data have been discussed. A current problem is the specification of the relative advantages and disadvantages in treating a difference score as though it were a single observation. A test of significance, formula (8), was derived for change within a person who is not regarded as a member of a known sample or group. Tests of significance for mean changes for groups of persons were also discussed. The theory of the reliability of change scores was considered from two similar viewpoints; it was concluded that the estimate derived by Lord, which leads to formula (15), was the more reasonable model. A relaxation of item-scoring restrictions extended the results to a wider variety of mental tests; this also suggests applications to other kinds of social science data for which measures of change are much needed. Another modification of mental test theory was suggested—namely, its extension to admit correlated obtained score components. It appeared that the measurement of change was enhanced by using identical forms, even though in this case true and error score components are not likely to be independent.

The reliability of some functions of scores other than raw score differences was briefly considered. A regression equation for predicting true from obtained change scores expresses rather well the fact that at least two parameters (the *mean* change and the *reliability* of the change scores) are required in order to understand changes within groups. Three applications of reliability formulas to change scores on personality scales were discussed, along with some practical problems encountered in attempts to analyze large numbers of such scores.

The need for a measurement dynamics in social science is urgent, but it must depend upon a coherent theory of measurement. If social science is to have an adequate empirical foundation, then the measures employed must be routinely assessed for precision. In particular, the majority of personality tests now employed in psychological and educational research are seriously lacking in the precision with which they are able to order persons. It seems unlikely that multivariate analyses can lead to useful knowledge about the comparative development of persons unless the reliabilities of the individual measures employed are known and utilized in the equations. Any general model for understanding changes in persons or in institutions will certainly have to allow for large errors of measurement.

We wish to thank Frederic M. Lord and Lee J. Cronbach for some helpful criticisms of an earlier version of this paper.

Four

Univariate Analysis of Variance Procedures in the Measurement of Change

JOHN GAITO
AND DAVID E. WILEY

Univariate procedures and univariate approximations to multivariate procedures have been used extensively and effectively in behavioral research. These procedures involve the partitioning of the variation within an experiment into a number of independent components, each with specified degrees of freedom (df). Hypotheses relative to one or more of these components are then evaluated by F-tests. The univariate hypotheses specify that the experimental data represent random samples drawn *independently* from the same *normal* population which obviously must have a *single variance*. Thus the assumptions of zero covariance, normality of distribution, and homogeneity of variance follow from the hypotheses and are important assumptions to justify the use of univariant procedures.

A variance-covariance matrix of responses for an analysis in which there are k such responses would be

$$(1) \qquad \begin{bmatrix} \sigma_1^2 & \sigma_{12} & \cdots & \sigma_{1k} \\ \sigma_{21} & \sigma_2^2 & \cdots & \sigma_{2k} \\ \cdot & & & \\ \cdot & & \cdots & \\ \cdot & & & \\ \sigma_{k1} & \sigma_{k2} & \cdots & \sigma_k^2 \end{bmatrix},$$

where σ_{ij} is the covariance of response i with response j. The assumptions of zero covariance and homogeneity of variance require that the matrix become

$$(2) \qquad \begin{bmatrix} \sigma^2 & 0 & \cdots & 0 \\ 0 & \sigma^2 & \cdots & 0 \\ \cdot & & & \\ \cdot & & \cdots & \\ 0 & & \cdots & \sigma^2 \end{bmatrix} = I\sigma^2,$$

where I is the identity matrix of order k, $\sigma_i^2 = \sigma^2$, and $\sigma_{ij} = 0$ when $i \neq j$.

On the other hand, exact multivariate analysis procedures are concerned with sampling from a number of normal distributions which need not have the zero covariance and equality of variance assumptions for testing the hypothesis of equality of means (T. W. Anderson, 1958). The response covariance matrix for exact multivariate procedures would be as matrix (1) above in which none of the nondiagonal entries needs to be equal to zero nor do the diagonal entries need to be equal to each other.

A case intermediate between the orthodox univariate analysis with equal variance–zero covariance assumptions and the multivariate analysis with unequal variance–unequal covariance allowances is that of equal variance–constant covariance. The variance-covariance matrix would be

$$(3) \qquad \begin{bmatrix} \sigma^2 & \rho\sigma^2 & \cdots & \rho\sigma^2 \\ \rho\sigma^2 & \sigma^2 & \cdots & \\ \cdot & & \cdots & \\ \cdot & & & \\ \rho\sigma^2 & \cdot & \cdots & \sigma^2 \end{bmatrix},$$

where ρ is the correlation between observations.

As is obvious, univariate analysis is a special case of multivariate analysis. Similarly, the equal variance–constant covariance possibility is a special case of multivariate analysis. If conditions for either of these are met, the univariate analysis with F-tests is theoretically correct. However, if (2) or (3) above does not hold and the variance-covariance matrix is not known, multivariate analysis is appropriate. Fortunately, in many cases (2) or (3) may not be met completely, but univariate analysis can still provide a reasonable approximation. This problem will be discussed later.

In certain cases univariate analysis can be considered as a regression problem (Scheffé, 1959). To show this, let us write a linear regression equation,

$$y = B_1 x_1 + B_2 x_2 + \cdots + B_n x_n + e,$$

where y is the observed score which depends on the B's, x's, and e. The B's are parameters or *effects* and e is experimental error. B_1 is usually the general mean and x_1 is 1. Then: (*a*) If all independent variables are of a qualitative nature, the x's are either 1 or 0, indicating presence or absence of the effects, the B's. This is the situation in which anova has most frequently been used. (*b*) If all the dimensions are of a quantitative nature, the x's vary continuously and we have a case of the usual regression analysis. (*c*) In some situations we have x's of both kinds, some continuous and some either 1 or 0. An example is the usual analysis of covariance in which the regression of one variable on another is used to adjust the second variable (i.e., remove the effects of the first) and then an analysis of variance is performed on the adjusted scores.

Trend analyses are examples of the second and third possibilities and require that at least one variable be of a quantitative nature. These procedures appear to be useful techniques for the measurement of change and will be the main concern of this paper.

In the analysis of variance procedures, mathematical models with associated expectations of mean squares $[E(MS)]$ have been used to great advantage by mathematical statisticians (Anderson and Bancroft, 1952; Cornfield and Tukey, 1956; Eisenhart, 1947; Green and Tukey, 1960; Harter and Lum, 1955; Kempthorne, 1952; Mood, 1950; Scheffé, 1959; Snedecor, 1946; Tukey, 1949; Wilk and Kempthorne, 1955). It is only within the last few years that this information has begun to permeate the general behavioral science area (Edwards, 1960; Ferguson, 1959; Gaito, 1958a, 1958b, 1958c, 1960; Haggard, 1958; Lindquist, 1953; Stanley, 1956a, 1956b).

The $E(MS)$'s follow from the mathematical model which is involved. From the $E(MS)$ one can understand clearly what components of variation are expected (on a probability basis) in each mean square, determine the appropriate error term for evaluation of each hypothesis, and estimate parameters of interest. The general $E(MS)$ model for use with various designs involving a number of fixed and/or random effects has been provided by Cornfield and Tukey (1956) and by Wilk and Kempthorne (1955). Paradigms for Latin square designs have been presented by Gaito (1958c) and by Wilk and Kempthorne (1957). "Nesting" or "partially hierarchical" paradigms (the "mixed" designs of Lindquist) have been provided by Brownlee (1960) and Harter and Lum (1955). These latter designs are important in some repeated-measurements types of trend analyses.

Now let us consider trend analyses as a possibility for measuring changes over time and look at the $E(MS)$'s involved in each mathematical model. We will consider the equal variance–zero covariance, equal variance–constant covariance, and equal or unequal variance–unequal covariance cases, in that order.

Equal variance–zero covariance

The analysis of variance procedures for a trend analysis are essentially the same as with qualitative dimensions but with an added step; one must determine the trend of the quantitative variable over the other variables. Alexander (1946) was one of the first to describe the procedure whereby the trends of treatments and of individual subjects could be evaluated within the analysis of variance framework. Grant (1956) further extended the procedure within a repeated-measurements factorial design so as to provide for more orthogonal components using orthogonal polynomials. Other individuals have considered trend analyses (Edwards, 1960; Lewis, 1960; Lindquist, 1947, 1953; Snedecor, 1946). Our concern will be mainly with the orthogonal polynomial approach to trend analysis. We will consider both hypothesis testing and estimation problems.

ONE-FACTOR DESIGN

Let us begin with the simplest type of design and work up to the more complex ones. We will make use of the general rules for $E(MS)$. Assume that we are concerned with the change of educational goals over college years. Let us specifically concentrate on a single goal, Vocational Preparation. We have a sample composed of freshmen, sophomores, juniors, and seniors. Each individual indicates by a number varying from 1 to 7 the strength of the goal, Vocational Preparation, for him. We wish to determine the shape of the curve relating strength of the goal to the year in college.

There are four points on the curve; thus the curve can be completely described by an equation of the third degree. The equation for a single variable experiment, of cubic degree, is

$$y = B_0 + B_1 x + B_2 x^2 + B_3 x^3 + e,$$

where B_0 is the general mean and B_1, B_2, and B_3 refer to the regression coefficients for the linear, quadratic, and cubic components, respectively. We then partition the expressions in this model equation into orthogonal components by the use of orthogonal polynomials.

The sum of squares for each of the orthogonal components is obtained by the following formula:

$$SS = \frac{1}{n_i \sum k^2} \left[\sum (k Y_j) \right]^2,$$

where the k's are orthogonal coefficients, Y's are the sums for each of the treatments, and n_i is the number in each group. The k coefficients can be derived (Lewis, 1960) or obtained from available tables (Edwards, 1960; Fisher and Yates, 1957). In estimating the regression coefficients (B's), the same formula is used without the squaring operation for the components within the parentheses. A simple, but excellent, discussion is given by Edwards (1960).

The $E(MS)$'s for this example are shown in Table 4.1. In this table we

TABLE 4.1

Anova Table for One-Factor Design

Source	df	$E(MS)$
Years	3	$\sigma_e^2 + n\sigma_y^2$
Linear	1	$\sigma_e^2 + n\sigma_{y(l)}^2$
Quadratic	1	$\sigma_e^2 + n\sigma_{y(q)}^2$
Cubic	1	$\sigma_e^2 + n\sigma_{y(c)}^2$
Within years	$4(n-1)$	σ_e^2

denote the constant components of the $E(MS)$, which are due to the fixed effects, by the usual pseudo-variance notation,

$$\sigma_f^2 = \frac{1}{f-1}\left(\sum_{i=1}^h \alpha_i^2\right),$$

following the practice of Scheffé (1959) and others. A similar procedure will be followed in the remaining tables, with respect to both the fixed effects and their interactions.

The test of each of the orthogonal components is by an F-ratio with the mean square for within years as the denominator. If the F-test for a component is not significant, we then remove that component from our equation which is describing the experimental results. For example, if the test for both quadratic and cubic components showed nonsignificance, $\sigma_{y(q)}^2$ and $\sigma_{y(c)}^2$ would disappear and the equation becomes

$$y = \alpha_0 + \alpha_1 x + e.$$

This is an equation of the first degree, indicating that the trend over years can be described by a straight line with a slope not equal to zero.

TWO-FACTOR DESIGN

If both variables are qualitative, a trend analysis would not be attempted because of an inability to order the levels of each qualitative dimension in a meaningful manner. If both variables are quantitative in nature we have a straightforward regression problem. The general equation would be

$$y = B_0 + B_{1100}x_1 + B_{2100}x_2 + B_{1200}x_1^2 + B_{2200}x_2^2 + \cdots + B_{1n00}x_1^n$$
$$+ B_{2n00}x_2^n + B_{1121}x_1x_2 + B_{1221}x_1^2x_2 + \cdots + B_{1n2n}x_1^nx_2^n + e,$$

where B_0 is t e general mean and the first subscript (in each pair) of the remaining parameters refers to the particular independent variable of concern and the second subscript (in each pair), to the power of these variables. A zero indicates that the variable is absent.

Again we can partition the experimental data into expressions corresponding to those in the model via the orthogonal polynomial procedure. The sum of squares for each component and each variable would be obtained as in the one-factor design. The $E(MS)$ for this example would depend upon whether the variables are random or fixed effects. However, quantitative variables which are random would be unusual (except for

TABLE 4.2

Matrix of Interaction Terms

		A		
		L	*Q*	*C*
	L			
B	Q_1			
	C			
	Q_2			

Note: Q_1 refers to quadratic; Q_2, to quartic. Each cell is based on an SS with 1 df.

special cases, one of which will be discussed later) and thus, only fixed effects or Model I would be meaningful to consider.

Let us assume that one of our dimensions (A) has four levels whereas the other (B) has five. The sum of squares with 3 df for A can be partitioned into linear, quadratic, and cubic components; B with 4 df, into linear, quadratic, cubic, and quartic portions. The AB interaction matrix would consist of 12 cells, each with 1 df as in Table 4.2. Each cell shows an interaction between A and B components, i.e., $AB_{(ll)}$, $AB_{(lq_1)}$, $\cdots$, $AB_{(cq_2)}$. The anova table is indicated in Table 4.3. The appropriate error term for all F-tests is the within-groups mean square. An informative codification of this approach is given by Myers (1959). He describes a rationale for the interpretation of these interactions and presents a straightforward procedure for their computation.

Let us now look at the situation wherein one dimension (A) is quantitative and the other (B) is qualitative. The quantitative variable would be a fixed effect but the qualitative dimension could be of either fixed or

TABLE 4.3

Anova Table for Fixed Effects Design, Both Factors Quantitative

Source	df	$E(MS)$
A	3	$\sigma_e^2 + nb\sigma_a^2$
Linear	1	$\sigma_e^2 + nb\sigma_{a(l)}^2$
Quadratic	1	$\sigma_e^2 + nb\sigma_{a(q)}^2$
Cubic	1	$\sigma_e^2 + nb\sigma_{a(c)}^2$
B	4	$\sigma_e^2 + na\sigma_b^2$
Linear	1	$\sigma_e^2 + na\sigma_{b(l)}^2$
Quadratic	1	$\sigma_e^2 + na\sigma_{b(q_1)}^2$
Cubic	1	$\sigma_e^2 + na\sigma_{b(c)}^2$
Quartic	1	$\sigma_e^2 + na\sigma_{b(q_2)}^2$
$A \times B$	12	$\sigma_e^2 + n\sigma_{ab}^2$
$L \times L$	1	$\sigma_e^2 + n\sigma_{ab(ll)}^2$
$L \times Q_1$	1	$\sigma_e^2 + n\sigma_{ab(lq_1)}^2$
$L \times C$	1	$\sigma_e^2 + n\sigma_{ab(lc)}^2$
$L \times Q_2$	1	$\sigma_e^2 + n\sigma_{ab(lq_2)}^2$
$Q \times L$	1	$\sigma_e^2 + n\sigma_{ab(ql)}^2$
$Q \times Q_1$	1	$\sigma_e^2 + n\sigma_{ab(qq_1)}^2$
$Q \times C$	1	$\sigma_e^2 + n\sigma_{ab(qc)}^2$
$Q \times Q_2$	1	$\sigma_e^2 + n\sigma_{ab(qq_2)}^2$
$C \times L$	1	$\sigma_e^2 + n\sigma_{ab(cl)}^2$
$C \times Q_1$	1	$\sigma_e^2 + n\sigma_{ab(cq_1)}^2$
$C \times C$	1	$\sigma_e^2 + n\sigma_{ab(cc)}^2$
$C \times Q_2$	1	$\sigma_e^2 + n\sigma_{ab(cq_2)}^2$
Within group	$20(n-1)$	σ_e^2

random nature. Table 4.4 shows the interaction matrix. Now we cannot partition the interaction into 12 meaningful orthogonal components. If the qualitative dimension is fixed, the anova table is as shown in Table 4.5, Model I again. The anova table now contains fewer components than in the previous case.

The AB linear component refers to the variation between linear trends for the different levels of B; the quadratic component, the variation between quadratic trends of the different levels of B; etc. If the F-ratio of the AB linear component to the within-groups mean square is significant, this indicates that the straight-line portions of each B level over A do not

TABLE 4.4

Interaction Matrix; A Quantitative, B Qualitative

have the same slope. If this F-test is not significant, this result indicates that the null hypothesis that all trends have the same slope is not rejected. Similar statements would be made relative to the quadratic and cubic components of AB.

If now we look at the situation in which the quantitative effect is fixed whereas the qualitative dimension is random, we have an important design within the Mixed Model. An example is the Treatments $\times$ S's design which is used frequently in educational and psychological studies. The repeated-measurements extension of this design is the one with which

TABLE 4.5

Anova Table for Two Factors: One Quantitative, One Qualitative, Both Fixed Effects

Source	df	$E(MS)$
A	3	$\sigma_e^2 + nb\sigma_a^2$
Linear	1	$\sigma_e^2 + nb\sigma_{a(l)}^2$
Quadratic	1	$\sigma_e^2 + nb\sigma_{a(q)}^2$
Cubic	1	$\sigma_e^2 + nb\sigma_{a(c)}^2$
B	4	$\sigma_e^2 + na\sigma_b^2$
AB	12	$\sigma_e^2 + n\sigma_{ab}^2$
Linear	4	$\sigma_e^2 + n\sigma_{ab(l)}^2$
Quadratic	4	$\sigma_e^2 + n\sigma_{ab(q)}^2$
Cubic	4	$\sigma_e^2 + n\sigma_{ab(c)}^2$
Within groups	$20(n-1)$	σ_e^2

Alexander and Grant were concerned. With the introduction of a random variable the $E(MS)$'s change somewhat. See Table 4.6.

Each of the AB interaction components consists of a single column from Table 4.4. Each of the components of A has in its mean square the corresponding portion of interaction, not the σ^2 representing the total interaction. For example, linear has the linear portions of σ_a^2 and σ_{ab}^2. The $E(MS)$ components can be determined intuitively by using the interaction matrix of Table 4.4 and the usual rules. Thus the appropriate F-test of

TABLE 4.6

Anova Table for Two-Factor Design: One, Quantitative and Fixed; Second, Qualitative and Random

Source	df	$E(MS)$
A	3	$\sigma_e^2 + n\sigma_{ab}^2 + nb\sigma_a^2$
Linear	1	$\sigma_e^2 + n\sigma_{ab(l)}^2 + nb\sigma_{a(l)}^2$
Quadratic	1	$\sigma_e^2 + n\sigma_{ab(q)}^2 + nb\sigma_{a(q)}^2$
Cubic	1	$\sigma_e^2 + n\sigma_{ab(c)}^2 + nb\sigma_{a(c)}^2$
B[a]	4	$\sigma_e^2 + na\sigma_b^2$
AB	12	$\sigma_e^2 + n\sigma_{ab}^2$
Linear	4	$\sigma_e^2 + n\sigma_{ab(l)}^2$
Quadratic	4	$\sigma_e^2 + n\sigma_{ab(q)}^2$
Cubic	4	$\sigma_e^2 + n\sigma_{ab(c)}^2$
Within groups	$20(n-1)$	σ_e^2

[a] If B represents S's, σ_e^2 consists of errors of measurement; whereas if independent groups are used, σ_e^2 contains errors of measurement plus sampling variability (σ_s^2).

A-linear, quadratic, and cubic would be the corresponding portion of AB, i.e., A-linear is tested by AB-linear; A-quadratic, by AB-quadratic; etc. An excellent discussion of this procedure is given in the article by Grant (1956).

If the random qualitative dimension is subjects, we have the repeated-measurements design. Each subject has an observation on a number of occasions or trials. This design has been a favorite for many people. However, there are certain difficulties involved in its use. These will be discussed below.

MORE COMPLEX DESIGNS

We could continue in the present manner and indicate the model for many complex designs, but the user should be able to work these out for himself from the rules above. However, there is a complex design used frequently in research which we should discuss. This is a "partially hierarchical" design (Brownlee, 1960), known in educational and psychological statistics as the Type 1 "mixed" design of Lindquist (1953). This design involves two or more groups of different subjects with each subject having a measurement on two or more occasions. The simplest example is the situation in which a control group and an experimental group are run in a learning experiment. The model for this design is

$$y = B_0 + \sum_{i,j} B_{ij} x_{ij} + e,$$

where B_0 is the general mean and the $\sum_{i,j} B_{ij} x_{ij}$ refer to the Between Groups, Between Subjects Within Groups, Trials, Trials $\times$ Groups, and Trials $\times$ Subjects Within Groups effects, respectively, and e is error. Each of these effects is indicated by a different value of j and the X_{ij}'s are indicator variables determined by the levels. This model can be written as

$$y = \alpha + g_i + s_{j(i)} + t_k + (gt)_{ik} + (st)_{jk(i)} + e,$$

where the effects are consecutively as in the above equation.

Let us assume that we have an experiment with four trials for the control and experimental groups, each with five S's. The $E(MS)$ for this trend analysis is given in Table 4.7, assuming that subjects is the only random variable and n observations are present within each cell. If there is only one observation per cell, the term $(st)_{jk(i)}$ drops out because subjects $\times$ trials is confounded with e. The within-cells portion of Table 4.7 is deleted, and no estimate of σ_e^2 is available. However, if for example one is willing to assume that $\sigma_{ts(c)}^2$ is zero, the cubic portion of trials $\times$ S's within groups could be used as error estimate.

In the design of Table 4.7 there are three different sources of variation for which trends can be obtained. The trials $\times$ S's within groups source of variation is concerned with differences between S's in linear trend, differences between S's in quadratic trend, and differences between S's in cubic trend. Each of these trends is tested against the within-cells mean square. The trials (or overall trend) and the trials $\times$ groups (between-groups trend) sources of variation are each partitioned into linear, quadratic, and cubic components. Each of these is tested by the corresponding component of the trials $\times$ S's within-groups portion.

In discussing trend analysis we have restricted ourselves to commonly tabulated orthogonal polynomials which require that the quantitative dimension of concern have equal differences between its various levels (e.g., trials) and that an equal number of subjects are within each group.

If these two conditions are not met, the orthogonal polynomial procedure can still be used but the existing tabled orthogonal coefficients are not applicable. In this situation one must solve a series of simultaneous equations to obtain the orthogonal coefficients. These procedures are discussed by Acton (1959), Robson (1959), Steel and Torrie (1960), and Wishart and Metakides (1953).

Trend analysis can be performed within an analysis of variance frame-

TABLE 4.7

Type 1—Mixed Design: Subjects a Random Factor

Source	df		$E(MS)$
Between S's			
Groups	1		$\sigma_e^2 + nt\sigma_s^2 + nst\sigma_g^2$
Between S's within groups	8		$\sigma_e^2 + nt\sigma_s^2$
Within S's			
Trials	3		$\sigma_e^2 + n\sigma_{ts}^2 + gsn\sigma_t^2$
Linear		1	$\sigma_e^2 + n\sigma_{ts(l)}^2 + gsn\sigma_{t(l)}^2$
Quadratic		1	$\sigma_e^2 + n\sigma_{ts(q)}^2 + gsn\sigma_{t(q)}^2$
Cubic		1	$\sigma_e^2 + n\sigma_{ts(c)}^2 + gsn\sigma_{t(c)}^2$
Trials $\times$ groups	3		$\sigma_e^2 + n\sigma_{ts}^2 + ns\sigma_{tg}^2$
Linear		1	$\sigma_e^2 + n\sigma_{tsl}^2 + ns\sigma_{tg(l)}^2$
Quadratic		1	$\sigma_e^2 + n\sigma_{tsq}^2 + ns\sigma_{tg(q)}^2$
Cubic		1	$\sigma_e^2 + n\sigma_{sc}^2 + ns\sigma_{tg(c)}^2$
Trials $\times$ S's within groups	24		$\sigma_e^2 + n\sigma_{ts}^2$
Linear		8	$\sigma_e^2 + n\sigma_{ts(l)}^2$
Quadratic		8	$\sigma_e^2 + n\sigma_{ts(q)}^2$
Cubic		8	$\sigma_e^2 + n\sigma_{ts(c)}^2$
Within cells	$40(n-1)$		σ_e^2

work even though the orthogonal polynomial procedure is not used. The sum of squares for each regression component is obtained and F-tests are performed in the usual manner. Details of these procedures are well known and can be found in Brownlee (1960), Lewis (1960), or Snedecor (1946).

In this section we have emphasized hypothesis testing. The investigator may wish only to test whether an effect is present or absent so as to determine gross aspects of the curve, i.e., whether the function is of first degree, second degree, etc. However, in most cases he is interested in ascertaining the equation of the curve by estimating the regression coefficients as was discussed above. Occasionally he may also be concerned with estimating the σ^2 terms. This can be effected by setting each obtained mean square equal to the components in the $E(MS)$ column and solving these equations (Gaito, 1960; Scheffé, 1959). Confidence limits for these variance components can then be established (Lindquist, 1953; Scheffé, 1959).

In an interesting article, Grant (1962) has argued that traditional hypothesis testing may be inappropriate to the intentions of the experimenter if he is concerned with comparing experimental outcomes with predictions from a theoretical model. He maintains that the theorist should not be concerned with accepting or rejecting a finished theory (as might be implied by hypothesis testing) but should attempt to construct better versions of the theory. This latter strategy would be facilitated by statistical estimation.

He suggested a method involving point and interval estimation. The variance of the discrepancies between the estimated curve and the theoretical curve was to provide an index of the adequacy of the fit of the theoretical model; the smaller this variance, the better the model, and vice versa. This variance estimate could be obtained by setting up equations in which each of the obtained mean squares is equal to the components of the corresponding $E(MS)$ and solving. He also provided a procedure for estimating the confidence interval for this variance estimate, and suggested the possibility of comparing each data point to the corresponding point on the theoretical curve and setting up confidence intervals for each theoretical point. Such procedures would appear to be valuable ones for the investigator in trend analyses or curve-fitting situations where one has some theoretical basis for an expected type of change over time.

Equal variance–constant covariance

The previous section was concerned with hypothesis testing and estimation procedures when equal variance and zero covariance assumptions hold. If the measurement of change involves the use of independent groups, the assumption of zero covariance should be met. The assumptions of homogeneity of variance and normality of distribution do not provide real problems. Investigation has shown that failure to meet these assumptions usually has minimal effects on F-tests (N. H. Anderson, 1961; Boneau, 1960; Box, 1954; Gaito, 1959; Lindquist, 1953). If a treatments × subjects design, Type 1 design, or other repeated measurement procedures are used, there is usually some correlation between treatments which could negate the use of univariate procedures. However, if the covariance is constant from one treatment to the next (and equal variances are present) as indicated by matrix (3), then univariate analysis procedures are appropriate even though the $E(MS)$'s change slightly.

For a treatments $\times$ subjects design such as represented by Table 4.6, the $E(MS)$'s are given in Table 4.8. Because of the correlation, all sources of variation involving subjects (B) contain terms involving the coefficient ρ. Even though portions of the $E(MS)$ are modified by terms involving ρ, the F-tests are the same as in the equal variance–zero covariance situation. Estimation of regression coefficients and variance components can still be accomplished.

The $E(MS)$'s for similar repeated-measurements designs have been

TABLE 4.8

Anova Table for Treatments (A) $\times$ S's Design: Constant Covariance Present

Source	df		$E(MS)$
A	3		$\sigma_e^2 + (1 - \rho)n\sigma_{ab}^2 + nb\sigma_a^2$
Linear		1	$\sigma_e^2 + (1 - \rho)n\sigma_{ab(l)}^2 + nb\sigma_{a(l)}^2$
Quadratic		1	$\sigma_e^2 + (1 - \rho)n\sigma_{ab(q)}^2 + nb\sigma_{a(q)}^2$
Cubic		1	$\sigma_e^2 + (1 - \rho)n\sigma_{ab(c)}^2 + nb\sigma_{a(c)}^2$
B	4		$\sigma_e^2 + [1 + (a - 1)\rho]na\sigma_b^2$
AB	12		$\sigma_e^2 + (1 - \rho)n\sigma_{ab}^2$
Linear		4	$\sigma_e^2 + (1 - \rho)n\sigma_{ab(l)}^2$
Quadratic		4	$\sigma_e^2 + (1 - \rho)n\sigma_{ab(q)}^2$
Cubic		4	$\sigma_e^2 + (1 - \rho)n\sigma_{ab(c)}^2$
Replication	$20(n - 1)$		σ_e^2

considered by Danford, Hughes, and McNee (1960), and Hughes and Danford (1958). These authors do not have a replication source of variation, and thus σ_e^2 and $(1 - \rho)\sigma_{ab}^2$ (treatment $\times$ subjects interaction variance component) are confounded to give a σ^2. They also have another treatment variable superimposed on S's, and a between S's source is confounded with σ_e^2 to give a test for these treatments.

Unequal variance–unequal covariance

Unequal variances and unequal covariances constitute the most general of the three cases with which we have been concerned. As has been stated above, a serious problem can occur with the repeated-measurements designs. For univariate analysis procedures to be correct, the covariance matrix should have equal variances in the principal diagonal and zero or constant covariance elsewhere, thus showing homogeneity of variance and zero or constant correlation between treatments. Of these two requirements, the zero or constant correlation one appears to be more critical. It has been assumed by many individuals that partitioning a source of variation attributable to subjects handles the problem of correlation. That this assumption is not true has been indicated by a number of people (Box, 1954; Danford and Hughes, 1957; Danford, Hughes, and McNee, 1960; Gaito, 1961; Geisser and Greenhouse, 1958; Greenhouse and Geisser, 1959; Lubin, 1957, 1958, 1961; Scheffé, 1959).

Box (1954) indicated that when there is moderate correlation within rows (in educational and psychological experiments the row variable would represent S's or S's nested within treatments), a great distortion occurs in the probability levels for between-rows comparisons but little distortion is introduced for between-columns comparisons. The maximum correlation that Box studied was $\pm.40$ (serial correlation of lag one). In the case of the negative correlation, the per cent probability for the test of columns (treatments) was 5.90 rather than 5.00 (which would result when correlation is zero); for positive correlation the per cent probability was 6.68. Box made use of an approximate technique in which the degrees of freedom are reduced by multiplying each df by a fraction (ϵ) which depends on the correlation within rows. The upper limit of ϵ is 1, which will occur only if the variances are equal and the correlation is constant among the treatments. In this case the F-ratio with the usual df can be used. In the event that just two treatments are involved, ϵ equals 1 if the variances are equal. However, in many designs using three or more treatments, ϵ will be less than 1; thus if the usual df's are employed (without reduction by ϵ), an increase in Type 1 errors will occur.

Geisser and Greenhouse (1958) extended Box's result to develop a conservative F-test of treatments. They showed that $\epsilon \geq (k-1)^{-1}$ and thereby determined the lower limit for the df to be 1 and $n-1$, where k refers to the number of treatments and n is the number of S's. This result can be obtained by multiplying the df for treatments $(k-1)$ and for treatments $\times$ subjects $[(k-1)(n-1)]$ each by $(k-1)^{-1}$. Thus the F-test with df of 1 and $n-1$ can be employed when unequal covariation occurs with one group of S's. They also developed a conservative test when more than one group is involved. In this case the df for the approximate F-test of treatments is 1 and $N-g$, where N is the total number of S's and g is the number of groups. However, the authors maintain that the use of the lower limit may be too conservative.

In a later article Greenhouse and Geisser (1959) indicated that the univariate analysis can be used if the df's are reduced by a constant (ϵ) which can be estimated from the sample variances and covariances. However, they suggest the conservative test and show an example in which the results of the two are essentially the same. They recommend that in the use of univariate analysis the investigator proceed as follows: (*a*) Use the regular df for *F*-tests. If the result is insignificant, the analysis is completed. (*b*) If the result of (*a*) is significant, the conservative test with reduction of df is attempted. If the *F*-test is significant, the analysis stops. (*c*) If (*b*) shows lack of significance, the approximate test requiring estimation of ϵ from the sample variance–covariance matrix is utilized. Scheffé (1959) has also called attention to the problems inherent in repeated measurements. McGregor (1960) gives an approximate test for the existence of serial correlation.

Lubin (1957, 1958, 1961) has considered the repeated-measurements designs, not only considering the effects of correlated observations but also treatment × order interactions, and other learning or "carry-over" effects. Because of these contaminating effects, he recommended the use of a modification of Hotelling's T^2 test, or a nonparametric rank-order test if one is interested in the relative efficacy of several treatments (unless a treatment × order interaction is present). If this interaction is present, he advocated a matched *S*'s design in which each *S* receives only one treatment.

On the other hand, Danford and Hughes (1957) argued for the use of the usual analysis of variance design, maintaining that the equal covariance assumption (constant correlation) is approximated for certain experimental situations. They stated that some experimental data have shown comparable correlation coefficients (*r*'s of .70 to .90). They indicated that if the equal covariance assumption is correct, the power of the usual *F*-test is greater (in some cases, much greater) than is the power of Hotelling's test. Danford, Hughes, and McNee (1960) later showed that essentially the same results were obtained in an example using both univariate and multivariate analyses. They stated that as *N* becomes large, the univariate and multivariate tests approach identical results.

The $E(MS)$'s for the general case would be complex and difficult to derive and are not available in the literature at the present time.

In summary, with repeated-measurement designs *F*-tests of hypotheses are exact if the covariance matrix is as (2) or (3) above. If (1) holds and univariate analysis is employed, the df must be reduced by ϵ or the conservative test of Geisser and Greenhouse made to provide approximate tests. However, if treatment by order or other "carry-over" effects are present, these approximate tests may be less suitable.

Even though univariate analysis can provide approximations in testing hypotheses when unequal variances and covariances prevail, under these conditions the estimation of regression coefficients and of variance components is in error. Thus for maximum benefit in such trend analyses, techniques are required which can completely or partially eliminate the contaminating effects.

Special procedures for the elimination of contaminating effects

A possible method of eliminating a trend which contaminates the treatments effect is by covariance analysis. This method is effective only if the investigator is able to get an estimate of this trend. An example of such an analysis is given by the work of Noble, Gruender, and Meyer (1959). These individuals were interested in determining the optimal conditioned stimulus–unconditioned stimulus interval for classical conditioning procedures with various animals. In their experiments the duration of the UCS was fixed (e.g., at 1.0 seconds). The CS began before the UCS but both terminated at the same time. The CS–UCS interval was the difference in duration between the CS and UCS. They found that a two-second interval is optimal for fish and that this interval is optimal for several other species also (Noble, private communication). Noble has indicated that the presentation of the CS alone at different durations corresponding to the various CS–UCS intervals has an effect on the percentage of CR's obtained, with the curve for CS alone being an increasing monotonic function (up to a point). Therefore, he maintained that the curve for CS–UCS should be corrected to consider the nonzero slope of the CS curve. This correction could be easily effected by covariance analysis. In some cases, this procedure might be used with a repeated-measurements design.

There are two procedures developed by Box which offer promise. Box (1950) suggested that the assumption of constant correlation will be more nearly approximated if a differencing technique is employed, i.e., the difference between the score on time j and the score on time $j+1$ is used rather than the actual scores. This tends to reduce the carry-over effect from one time period to the next. The second procedure (Box, 1952; Box and Hay, 1953) has provided some interesting possibilities for the elimination of time effects with the selection of treatments by an orthogonal polynomial procedure such that the treatments will be orthogonal to the time variable. Before looking at the implications of this approach for trend analysis, let us consider certain aspects of linear models. Linear models are those which can be put in the form:

$$(4) \qquad E(y_u) = \sum_{i=0}^{k} \theta_i x_{iu},$$

where $u = 1, \cdots, N$. In this representation, the y_u represent the measurements obtained from the uth experimental unit or a transformation thereof. It is significant to note that the model is linear in the θ_i and not in the x's. That is to say, each x_i could represent some nonlinear function of a set of original variables. For example, suppose it is hypothesized that the relationship between some measurable response and a set of manipulable variables is of the following form:

$$(5) \qquad E[h] = A^{az-w[\ln(z)]} B^{b[\sin(w)]+\cos(z)},$$

where z and w are manipulable variables and the other symbols are constants. If we make the transformation $E[y] = \log[E(h)]$ and define $\theta_1 = b[\log(A)]$, $\theta_2 = -[\log(A)]$, $\theta_3 = b[\log(B)]$, $\theta_4 = \log(B)$, $x_1 = z$, $x_2 = w[\ln(z)]$, $x_3 = \sin(w)$, and $x_4 = \cos(z)$, we have the following linear model:

$$(6) \qquad E[y] = \theta_1 x_1 + \theta_2 x_2 + \theta_3 x_3 + \theta_4 x_4,$$

where all of the θ's are estimable (if $N \geq 4$), and the x's are known.

In the light of these observations, it can be seen that if a model can be put in linear form, then all of the parameters of interest can be estimated. The question then arises: What actions must the experimenter take in order to impart desirable properties to these estimates? This is the basic problem of experimental design. In order to deal with this problem in our context, we must consider a few definitions. The first of these is a direct consequence of (4). In matrix form equation (4) can be expressed in the form:

$$(7) \qquad E = X\theta,$$

where E is the N by 1 vector of expected values of the y's, X is an N by k matrix which is the transpose of (x_{iu}), and θ is the k by 1 vector of the θ_i's. X is called the *matrix of independent variables*. θ is called the *effect* or *parameter matrix*. As we can see from the example which gave us equations (5) and (6), the matrix X is entirely determined by the original variables, w and z, of which X is a function. The matrix of values which these variables take on is an N by p matrix, where p is the number of original variables. This matrix, D, is called the *design matrix*.

Since the least squares and normal theory assumptions yield the following results:

$$(8) \qquad \hat{\theta} = (X'X)^{-1}X'y,$$

$$(9) \qquad \text{var-cov}(\hat{\theta}) = (X'X)^{-1}\sigma^2,$$

it is obvious that the properties of our estimates of θ are highly dependent on X, which is in turn completely dependent on D, the design matrix. It remains, then, to decide what are desirable properties for our estimates of θ and then to deduce what the structure of the matrix D must be to assure these properties. Two desirable properties which have been considered are the unbiasedness of our estimates of θ and the absence of any covariance between these estimates. In order for these criteria to be met, we must first assume that the model is correct and that the original observations are independent. Once these assumptions are met, the first implies that the estimates are unbiased and both imply that the form of the variance–covariance matrix is that given in equation (9). We can now see that the estimates will be uncorrelated only if the matrix $(X'X)^{-1}$ is diagonal. This will occur only if the matrix X is an orthogonal matrix. Therefore, it seems that the basic problem of experimental design reduces to the problem of choosing the elements of the design matrix, D, so that the matrix of independent variables, X, is orthogonal or a maximal portion of it is orthogonal.

Box and Hay make this clear in their 1953 *Biometrics* article (p. 304):

It has long been appreciated that it is the *orthogonal* property of designs which produces efficiency. The factorial method . . . is often a convenient way of obtaining orthogonality but it is, of course, by no means the only way. Designs which may be used to determine the effects of a number of factors but which are not necessarily factorial designs or parts of factorial designs may conveniently be called *multi-factor* designs.

These multifactor designs and their application to trend analysis in the behavioral sciences will be covered later. It should, however, be recognized that one of the most important aspects of any design is its orthogonality characteristics.

One of the many important consequences of orthogonality is independence of the sums of squares. Scheffé (1959, p. 127) proves that orthogonality yields, along with the usual normality assumptions, the property that the results of the partitioning are independent, noncentral, chi-square statistics. Needless to say, the independence result is a consequence of orthogonality.

A useful outcome of this partitioning theorem is that if the particular model which the experimenter uses is correct, the residual sum of squares, which remains after the regression sum of squares due to the model is removed, is really due to error. In many psychological experiments which purport to measure change, this is often the only kind of error available. These results stress the great value of proper experimental design. It is readily apparent that if the experiment is not designed with all of the hypotheses of interest in mind, it will probably not be the case that orthogonality and therefore independence of the sums of squares will result.

Now let us investigate a simplified version of a typical factorial design used in the evaluation of time trends to see why this design is orthogonal. Suppose we have one treatment variable, x, which has two levels of interest, say -1 and $+1$. Also suppose that we assume that the time trend has at most a quadratic effect in our experiment. The usual design for this experiment would consist of a factorial experiment with time as one factor and the treatment variable as the other. Also each level of the treatment variable would be replicated by the use of a group of subjects whose responses would be observed at each point in time. Let us assume that each treatment group consists of only one subject.

Suppose, in addition, that we assume the following model:

$$(10) \qquad E(y_u) = b_0 + b_1 x_u + c_1 t_{1u} + c_2 t_{2u} + c_{11} x_u t_{1u},$$

where t_{iu} is the orthogonal polynomial of order i. In other words, we are assuming that the time trend interacts in a linear manner with the treatment, in addition to the assumptions listed above. We then know that the design matrix is

$$(11) \qquad D = \begin{array}{c} \\ 1 \\ 2 \\ 3 \\ 4 \\ 5 \\ 6 \end{array} \begin{array}{cc} x & t \\ \left[\begin{array}{cc} -1 & -1 \\ 1 & -1 \\ -1 & 0 \\ 1 & 0 \\ -1 & 1 \\ 1 & 1 \end{array}\right], \end{array}$$

where t consists of the levels of the first-order orthogonal polynomial.

The matrix of independent variables will then be

$$(12) \qquad X = \begin{array}{c} \\ 1 \\ 2 \\ 3 \\ 4 \\ 5 \\ 6 \end{array} \begin{array}{ccccc} x_0 & x & t_1 & t_2 & xt_1 \\ \left[\begin{array}{ccccc} 1 & -1 & -1 & 1 & 1 \\ 1 & 1 & -1 & 1 & -1 \\ 1 & -1 & 0 & -2 & 0 \\ 1 & 1 & 0 & -2 & 0 \\ 1 & -1 & 1 & 1 & -1 \\ 1 & 1 & 1 & 1 & 1 \end{array}\right], \end{array}$$

which directly implies that

$$
(13) \qquad X'X = \begin{bmatrix} 6 & 0 & 0 & 0 & 0 \\ 0 & 6 & 0 & 0 & 0 \\ 0 & 0 & 4 & 0 & 0 \\ 0 & 0 & 0 & 12 & 0 \\ 0 & 0 & 0 & 0 & 4 \end{bmatrix},
$$

and we obtain, by inversion, the variance-covariance matrix of effects:

$$
(14) \qquad (X'X)^{-1}\sigma^2 = \begin{bmatrix} 1/6 & 0 & 0 & 0 & 0 \\ 0 & 1/6 & 0 & 0 & 0 \\ 0 & 0 & 1/4 & 0 & 0 \\ 0 & 0 & 0 & 1/12 & 0 \\ 0 & 0 & 0 & 0 & 1/4 \end{bmatrix}\sigma^2.
$$

In this case the matrix X is orthogonal (but not orthonormal) and the effects are completely independent. The crux of the matter is the source of the orthogonality which exists between the x and the t vectors. Upon examination of the matrix of independent variables, we see that both levels of the treatment, x, are repeated at each level of the orthogonal polynomial for time. This is the characteristic which induces the orthogonality. We can then see that *as long as a complete factorial experiment is run at each point in time, the matrix X will always be orthogonal, since the factorial design is orthogonal to constant effects*. The time effect is constant for fixed time.

One interesting thing to note about this design, and others like it, is that subjects were used as replicates. Because of this, the error terms which would be used to test various hypotheses embodied in the model would necessarily be composed of between-subject variability. What kind of design could be constructed to investigate within-subject variability and the effects of treatments, time, and their interactions within a given subject?

There exists a general class of designs, due to Box, which attack this problem. These designs do not seem to have been used in the behavioral sciences. The idea is based on the concept of orthogonal polynomials. It was reasoned that if one could use orthogonal polynomials to make the various orders of the time trend orthogonal to one another, they could be used to make the various treatment variables orthogonal also.

Suppose we look at an example which is based on the model and assumptions of the previous example. In this example, however, let us use only one subject. Obviously in this case our time variable will take on six values instead of three, if we take six observations. The x vector in the design matrix will be the same, but the t vector will take on six levels:

(15)
$$D = \begin{array}{c} \\ 1 \\ 2 \\ 3 \\ 4 \\ 5 \\ 6 \end{array} \begin{array}{cc} x & t \\ \left[\begin{array}{cc} -1 & -5 \\ 1 & -3 \\ -1 & -1 \\ 1 & 1 \\ -1 & 3 \\ 1 & 5 \end{array}\right]. \end{array}$$

Now in this case the inner product of the two vectors, $x't$, is equal to 6 instead of 0, and the vectors are not orthogonal.

Let us look back at our original model for a solution. This model can be expressed in the following manner:

(16)
$$E(y) = b_0 z_0 + b_1 z_1 + c_1 z_2 + c_2 z_3 + c_{11} z_4,$$

where z_0 is a column vector of 1's and the other substitutions are obvious. A necessary and sufficient condition for the orthogonality of the design is that the following inner products be zero: $z_0' z_1$, $z_0' z_2$, $z_0' z_3$, $z_0' z_4$, $z_1' z_2$, $z_1' z_3$, $z_1' z_4$, $z_2' z_3$, $z_2' z_4$, $z_3' z_4$. Box's solution to the problem of making these orthogonal would be to construct z_1, which is our new designation for the x vector, out of a linear combination of orthogonal polynomials of higher order than those already used to take care of the time trend. If this were done in this example, all of the above cited inner products would be zero except those involving z_4 (which is the interaction vector). One could then solve for the proper coefficients in the linear combination, subject to the restraint that these inner products be zero. However, we can see from this procedure that in order for the levels of a treatment variable to be selected in this way, the variable must be scaled or quantitative. This handicap can be avoided (Box and Hay, 1953) but these methods will not be covered in this paper.

Suppose we go on to a model of a little greater generality.

(17)
$$E(y) = \sum_{i=0}^{k} b_i x_i + \sum_{j=1}^{p} c_j t_j + \sum_{i=1}^{k} \sum_{h=1}^{i} b_{ih} x_i x_h + \sum_{i=1}^{k} \sum_{j=1}^{p} c_{ij} x_i t_j,$$

where x_0 is again an N by 1 column vector of 1's.

Inner product equations corresponding to those given above hold in this case and one can make fairly general statements about the equations to be solved and the solutions which will be found. The number of parameters to be estimated in this design is

$$1 + k + p + (k/2)(k + 1) + kp,$$

which is equal to $(1/2)(k + 1)[k + 2(p + 1)]$. Now if the total number of observations, N, is greater than or equal to this number, then all of the parameters are estimable and the number of degrees of freedom left for error is

$$N - (1/2)(k + 1)[k + 2(p + 1)].$$

Now if we define:

(18)
$$x_i = \sum_{n=p+1}^{N} a_{ni} t_n,$$

then the x's are linear combinations of orthogonal polynomials of higher order than those postulated to represent the time trend. In this case, the linear effects of our treatment variables are automatically orthogonal to the orthogonal polynomials representing the time trend of all *specified* orders. Now we must specify the x's completely in such a manner as to make the other effects in the experiment orthogonal. To do this, we subject equation (18) to the following constraints and solve for the a_{ni}'s:

(19)

1. $\sum_{u=1}^{N} (x_{iu} x_{hu}) x_{gu} = 0,$

2. $\sum_{u=1}^{N} (x_{iu} x_{hu}) t_{ju} = 0,$

3. $\sum_{u=1}^{N} (x_{iu} x_{hu})(x_{gu} t_{ju}) = 0,$

4. $\sum_{u=1}^{N} x_{iu}(x_{gu} t_{ju}) = 0,$

5. $\sum_{u=1}^{N} (x_{iu} t_{ju}) t_{fu} = 0,$

6. $\sum_{u=1}^{N} x_{iu} x_{hu} = 0, \qquad i \neq j,$

$$7. \quad \sum_{u=1}^{N} (x_{iu}x_{hu})(x_{gu}x_{vu}) = 0, \qquad (i, h) \neq (g, v),$$

$$8. \quad \sum_{u=1}^{N} (x_{iu}t_{ju})(x_{hu}t_{fu}) = 0, \qquad (i, j) \neq (h, f).$$

In these equations, x is indexed by i, h, g, and v; t is indexed by j and f.

This procedure can be simplified by taking the x's to be linear combinations of different orthogonal polynomials. Another simplification occurs because of a property of orthogonal polynomials. This property is that the sum of a product of orthogonal polynomials is zero if there are an odd number of odd-order polynomials in the product. Still another occurs because of a reduction in the number of constraints. An example of this is the fact that the second equation is formally equivalent to the fourth. This is true since, if t_j is orthogonal to $x_i x_h$, then it is automatically true that x_i is orthogonal to $x_h t_j$.

This procedure is simple conceptually, but it involves some rather tedious algebraic manipulation in practice. The computational problem is related to the algebraic group structure of the orthogonal polynomials (Box, personal communication) and will probably yield to simplification from this approach. However, even at the present time, a specification of the model and enough algebraic effort will yield a workable solution.

The analysis of variance when applied to this design is the standard regression analysis. Another interesting property of designs of this type may be noted. It can be seen that when we partition the sum of squares into components due to the model and the residual, we have the above cited number of degrees of freedom left for error. This number of degrees of freedom in the residual component is a measure of the freedom which we have in selecting coefficients (the a_{ni}'s) which determine the levels of our treatment variables. This is true since the more orthogonality restrictions we impose on the treatments, the smaller becomes the number of sets of coefficients which satisfy these restrictions. The converse of this relation is true also, so that the fewer the restrictions, the larger the number of solution sets. Box has shown that if we select from a table of random normal deviates the maximal number of coefficients which are free to vary, this imparts unusual properties to the testing procedure. Box (1952) notes that " . . . the t and F criteria are functions of the angles between the vector of observations y and the x vectors. To ensure the validity of the usual tests of significance involving these criteria, it is sufficient that on the null hypothesis the relative orientation of the y and the x vectors is spherically random. Angular randomization thus ensures that these tests are exact *whatever* the nature of the residual variation in *y*." Since the procedure above is an angular randomization procedure, this implies that the test is valid whether the model is correct or not.

It can be seen that designs with the properties detailed above have many desirable properties in a psychological context. For one thing, they allow the experimenter to study treatment effects, time-trend effects, and their interactions, *within* individuals. This is a major accomplishment, since designs have heretofore been constructed using individuals as replicates. This practice gives no information about effects which may vary differentially from individual to individual. Secondly, they allow for exact testing of effects, even when the model is incorrect.

An obvious extension of this design is its replication using many subjects. In this manner one could obtain information about effects, both within and across subjects.

Some cautions with trend analyses

Our main purpose in this paper has been to present various anova models for trend analyses so that the investigator interested in measuring changes in performance over time may choose an appropriate model. However, there are two important problems in trend analyses.

(*a*) Even though we have proceeded to test each of the linear and higher components in each design, the investigator should have some *a priori* basis for making certain *F*-tests rather than all. The components which contribute significantly (according to *F*-tests) should be accepted only if there are good *a priori* reasons for expecting them or plausible *ad hoc* reasons for not discounting them (Lewis, 1960). Whenever the investigator is doing preliminary work with no definitive *a priori* notions about the problem, he obviously must rely completely on statistical tests.

(*b*) In Mixed Model experiments there has been some disagreement between statisticians as to whether the partitioned or unpartitioned interaction term should be employed in testing the linear, quadratic, and higher components of the quantitative fixed effect.

Snedecor (1946) maintained that the proper error for each of the various components of the treatments effect was the corresponding component of the interaction of treatments with the random effect (as discussed above). However, he used the overall interaction term when the various components were homogeneous. Grant (1956) suggested that the linear component of the fixed effect be tested against the linear portion of the *S*'s by fixed effect interaction; the quadratic, by quadratic; cubic, by cubic; etc. Others favor testing each of these components by the overall or unpartitioned interaction source of variation. Among those suggesting or implying this procedure are Lindquist (1947, 1953), Lewis (1960), and Edwards (1960); however, they state that the various components should be homogeneous.

Even though the assumption of homogeneity of interaction components appears plausible as a justification for the pooling of these components so as to use the unpartitioned interaction as the error term, such assumptions are realistic only if all treatments $\times$ S's interactions are absent, and are apt to lead to biased F-tests when some components are present and others absent. This assumption becomes even more unrealistic as the number of points on the curve increases. For example, if the curve is based on ten points, the probability is great that some of these components for the interaction will be present. Frequently only the first or the first and second components are existent.

Let us take a treatment $\times$ subjects design with a curve based on four points. Let us suppose an unusual event occurs, i.e., $\sigma^2_{ts(l)} = \sigma^2_{ts(q)} > 0$ and $\sigma^2_{ts(c)} = 0$. The F-tests of the treatments components using the unpartitioned interaction as error would be, deleting coefficients for simplicity and denoting by σ^2_{ts}, the appropriate linear combination of $\sigma^2_{ts(l)}$ and $\sigma^2_{ts(q)}$:

$$\text{Ratio of } E(MS) \text{ for linear effect } = \frac{\sigma^2_e + \sigma^2_{ts(l)} + \sigma^2_{t(l)}}{\sigma^2_e + \sigma^2_{ts}},$$

$$\text{Ratio of } E(MS) \text{ for quadratic effect } = \frac{\sigma^2_e + \sigma^2_{ts(q)} + \sigma^2_{t(q)}}{\sigma^2_e + \sigma^2_{ts}},$$

$$\text{Ratio of } E(MS) \text{ for cubic effect } = \frac{\sigma^2_e + \sigma^2_{ts(c)} + \sigma^2_{t(c)}}{\sigma^2_e + \sigma^2_{ts}}.$$

Since σ^2_{ts} is an averaging of the interaction components, $\sigma^2_{ts} = (2/3)\sigma^2_{ts(l)} = (2/3)\sigma^2_{ts(q)}$ and $\sigma^2_{ts} > \sigma^2_{ts(c)} = 0$. Thus F-tests of linear and quadratic components would be positively biased whereas the test of the cubic portion would be negatively biased. Because of these possible biased tests, the partitioned interaction terms, suggested by Grant (1956) and utilized in the present paper, are recommended.

In conclusion, even though some problems may be encountered, the use of trend analyses within the univariate analysis framework provides a relatively flexible procedure in determining the form of the curve indicating the change of performance over a specified quantitative fixed effect. The anova models and procedures discussed should be of value to the investigator when faced with the problem of choosing an appropriate model of analysis.

Five | Multivariate Analysis of
Variance of
Repeated Measurements

R. DARRELL BOCK

Preparation of this paper was supported by the National Science Foundation, Grant NSF-G5824.

Data for the study of growth and change by the longitudinal method often take the form of measurements, similar in metric, repeated on each subject at fixed intervals. In many cases the subjects are also classified into groups according to an experimental or sampling design, and the purpose of the study is to demonstrate differences between the mean "time-curves" (plots of the group means vs. time) of these groups. Interest in the mean time-curves implies, of course, that the group means have a substantive interpretation—for example, as in studies of productivity vs. time-in-training, when the dollar value of the group product is proportional to the group mean productivity.

The statistical analysis appropriate for estimation of differences between the mean time-curves, and for related tests of hypothesis and confidence bounds, can be formulated in terms of a random sampling model in which subjects within groups are the sampling unit. Under this model measurements on different subjects are statistically independent, but in general the measurements repeated on each subject must be assumed to have correlated sampling variation. It follows, therefore, that any rigorous procedures for statistical inference from repeated-measurements data must be developed from a general multivariate sampling model.

This does not necessarily mean, however, that procedures derived from the general model will be multivariate in every case. We find rather that when the sampling covariance matrix has certain favorable patterns, useful univariate analyses are available on the usual normal assumptions. These analyses lead to tests of the hypothesis that the mean "time-

86   *R. Darrell Bock*

curves" (plots of the experimental population means vs. time) are *parallel* for all experimental groups. Where parallelism is not rejected, we may also test the subhypothesis that the curves are *coincident*. In addition, we obtain efficient estimates of various contrasts between the time-curves of different groups and their standard errors.

The most widely used method of this type is the conventional Mixed Model analysis which was developed originally for agricultural field trials conducted in the so-called "split-plot" design. In field trials there appear to be good physical, or biological, reasons for believing that the variation due to sampling plots will be of a form amenable to univariate analysis of variance. But we should not freely assume that a similar form will hold for repeated measurements in behavioral studies. On the contrary, in studies of growth and change it is more plausible to assume that the variation of subjects about their true time-curves follows a stationary Gaussian stochastic process. It is well known that the autoregressive effect in the process will then give rise to a sampling covariance matrix of the so-called "simplex" form; i.e., the covariance will decrease in successive diagonals away from the main diagonal (T. W. Anderson, 1960). No useful exact univariate analysis for the repeated-measurements design appears feasible in the presence of this type of error.

Nevertheless, in particular cases we may wish to leave open the possibility that a univariate analysis is appropriate. Taking this approach, we first test the hypothesis that the expected covariance pattern is favorable by methods referred to in this paper. If so, we proceed with a univariate analysis; if not, we have available a general multivariate analysis along lines which will be suggested. The calculations required contain those of the univariate analysis, and when appropriate, a univariate solution is immediately obtained.

The problem of correlated sampling error also arises when the conventional Mixed Model analysis is used with scores from standardized test batteries to test the hypothesis of parallel group "profiles." Greenhouse and Geisser (1959) have presented an example of this kind where the sampling covariance pattern is unsuited to a conventional univariate analysis. They propose both an approximate test due to Box (1954), based on an adjustment of the degrees of freedom of the conventional F-test, and exact tests based on multivariate statistics. Both of these approaches are potentially useful for the analysis of repeated-measurements designs. However, in one respect their treatment of the problem is somewhat lacking. The multivariate analysis which they propose does not account for the nonindependence of the mean square for groups and groups × tests interaction (in their terminology), nor for the nonindependence of the mean squares for individuals within groups and individual $\times$ tests within groups. The treatment in the present paper indicates that this nonindependence can be taken account of by methods of multivariate analysis of variance.

A multivariate model and analysis for the repeated-measurement design

In the multivariate formulation of a repeated-measurements experiment we consider the measurements obtained from each subject on r fixed occasions to be an $r \times 1$ random vector. Using a boldface lower-case letter to designate a column vector, we write the assumed composition of the observation for the ith subject in the jth experimental group as

$$\underset{r \times 1}{\boldsymbol{y}_{ij}} = \boldsymbol{\tau} + \boldsymbol{\theta}_j + \boldsymbol{\varepsilon}_{ij},$$

where $\boldsymbol{\tau}$ is the vector of general means for the r occasions, $\underset{r \times 1}{\boldsymbol{\theta}_j}$ is the vector of effects for the jth group, subject to the restriction $\Sigma_j \boldsymbol{\theta}_j = 0$, and $\underset{r \times 1}{\boldsymbol{\varepsilon}_{ij}}$ is a

vector of sampling errors assumed distributed in multivariate normal form with zero mean and covariance matrix $\boldsymbol{\Sigma}$.

This model is very general, but may be specialized for particular applications by assigning suitable linear forms to $\boldsymbol{\tau}$, $\boldsymbol{\theta}_j$, and $\boldsymbol{\varepsilon}_{ij}$. For purposes of estimation and tests of hypotheses with any of these specializations, the necessary sample statistics can be obtained from a multivariate analysis of variance as follows:

Let t be the number of experimental groups and n_j, the number of subjects in the jth group. Represent the mean of the jth group by $\boldsymbol{y}._j = \Sigma_i^{n_j} \boldsymbol{y}_{ij}/n_j$ and the general mean by $\boldsymbol{y}.. = \Sigma_j^t \Sigma_i^{n_j} \boldsymbol{y}_{ij}/N$, where $N = \Sigma_j^t n_j$.

Then the partition of sum of squares and products (briefly, sum of products) for the multivariate analysis of variance takes the form of Table 5.1.

The role of the partition of sums of products in tests of hypothesis under various specifications of the model can be described in terms of the expected sums of products shown in Table 5.2.

Under the model the general occasion effect, $\boldsymbol{\tau}$, is not estimable and hypotheses on it are not testable in the presence of group effects, Θ. This is of little consequence in most studies of growth and change, since primary interest is in demonstrating and describing differences in the mean time-curves of the experimental populations. If the group effects are negligible, so that general occasion effects are testable, the procedures for

TABLE 5.1

Multivariate Analysis of Variance of r Repeated Measurements

Source of dispersion	Degrees of freedom	Sums of products
Occasion means	1	$\underset{r \times r}{C} = N \mathbf{y}..\mathbf{y}..'$
Experimental groups	$n_B = t - 1$	$\underset{r \times r}{S_B} = \Sigma_j^t n_j \mathbf{y}_{\cdot j} \mathbf{y}_{\cdot j}' - C$
Subjects within groups	$n_W = N - t$	$\underset{r \times r}{S_W} = S_T - S_B - C$
Total	N	$\underset{r \times r}{S_T} = \Sigma_j^t \Sigma_i^{n_j} y_{ij} y_{ij}'$

testing group effects making use of S_B can then be applied to C for tests of corresponding hypotheses on τ. It will therefore be sufficient to consider only differences in the population mean time-curves parameterized by Θ. For this purpose we may introduce the following linear specification for Θ.

We assume that the time-curves are continuous functions of the time parameter, and have continuous derivatives in the relevant range, and so their representation by a polynomial of degree at most $r - 1$ is possible. Differences between time-curves are then polynomials of the same degree and provide a useful model for θ_j, say,

$$\theta_j^* = \beta_{0j}1 + \beta_{1j}\mathbf{x} + \beta_{2j}\mathbf{x}^2 + \cdots + \beta_{kj}\mathbf{x}^k, \quad k \leq r - 1,$$
$$= X\boldsymbol{\beta}_j, \quad \text{say,}$$

TABLE 5.2

Expected Sums of Products

$$\mathcal{E}(C) = N\boldsymbol{\tau}\boldsymbol{\tau}' + \Theta D \frac{11'}{N} D\Theta' + \Sigma$$

$$\mathcal{E}(S_B) = \Theta \left(D - D \frac{11'}{N} D \right) \Theta' + n_B \Sigma$$

$$\mathcal{E}(S_W) = n_W \Sigma$$

$$\underset{t \times 1}{1} = [1, 1, \cdots, 1]'; \quad \underset{t \times t}{D} = \text{diag}\,[n_1, n_2, \cdots, n_t]; \quad \underset{r \times t}{\Theta} = [\theta_1, \theta_2, \cdots, \theta_t]$$

where x is the $r \times 1$ vector of fixed time points, x^2 is the vector of squared time points, etc.

Investigating the degree of the polynomial compatible with the data is considerably facilitated if the time points are equally spaced. We can then use orthogonal polynomials of degree $r - 1$ in a simpler, but equivalent, regression analysis. In the example to follow, the procedure is illustrated using the polynomials of degree three (Fisher and Yates, 1957):

$$
\underset{4 \times 4}{P^{(3)}} = [p_0^{(3)}, p_1^{(3)}, p_2^{(3)}, p_3^{(3)}]
$$

$$
= \begin{bmatrix} 1/2 & (\ 1 & 1 & 1 & 1) \\ 1/\sqrt{20} & (-3 & -1 & 1 & 3) \\ 1/2 & (\ 1 & -1 & -1 & 1) \\ 1/\sqrt{20} & (-1 & 3 & -3 & 1) \end{bmatrix}'.
$$

Note that matrices of orthogonal polynomials are orthonormal: $PP' = P'P = I$. They are obtained by a Gram-Schmidt orthogonalization by columns of the Vandermonde matrix

$$
X = [1, x, x^2, \cdots, x^{r-1}].
$$

This process is equivalent to the post-transformation of X by an *upper triangular* matrix $(T^{-1})'$, say, which is the inverse Cholesky (or Crout, or square-root) factorization of the matrix $X'X$. That is $P = X(T^{-1})'$ where $X'X) = TT'$, $(T^{-1})T = (T^{-1})'T' = I$, and $(T^{-1})'T^{-1} = (X'X)^{-1}$. In other words, T^{-1} is the Cholesky factorization of the inverse of $X'X$. See Bock (1961) for a convenient machine method for constructing T^{-1}.

We may then write the polynomial specification as

$$
\theta_j^* = X(T^{-1})'T'\beta_j
$$

$$
= X(T^{-1})'\gamma_j
$$

$$
= P\gamma_j, \quad \text{say.}
$$

Since T' is upper triangular, the kth row of γ is a function only of the coefficients of the kth and higher degree terms in the original polynomial. Thus the hypothesis that $\gamma_{jk}, \gamma_{j,k+1}, \cdots, \gamma_{j,r-1}$ are null simultaneously is equivalent to the same hypothesis on $\beta_{jk}, \beta_{j,k+1}, \cdots, \beta_{j,r-1}$. The convenience of the orthogonal polynomials in the present context is that estimates of γ_j can be obtained from estimates of θ_j^* by simple transformation

TABLE 5.3

Transformation of the Between-Group and Within-Group Sums of Products

Source of dispersion	Degrees of freedom	Transformed sums of products
Experimental groups	$n_B = t - 1$	$\underset{r \times r}{V_B} = P'S_B P$
Subjects within groups	$n_W = N - t$	$\underset{r \times r}{V_W} = P'S_W P$

$$\gamma_j = P'\theta_j^*.$$

The estimates of the regression coefficients β_j can be recovered by

$$\beta_j = (T^{-1})'\gamma_j.$$

Since we consider only linear estimators of θ_j^*, the analysis in terms of orthogonal polynomials could be obtained by transforming the original vector observations before the multivariate analysis of variance is carried out. Let P be the $r \times r$ matrix, the columns of which are the orthogonal polynomials of $0, 1, 2, \cdots, r - 1$ degree. Then the transformed vector variate

$$v_{ij} = P'y_{ij}$$

has multivariate normal distribution $N(0, P'\Sigma P)$. It is on these vectors that we will perform the multivariate analysis. However, in actual calculation it is not necessary to perform this transformation directly on observed measurements. Its effect in the multivariate analysis of variance is obtained by pre- and post-multiplying the original sums of products by P. The result is shown in Table 5.3.

To use the transformed sums of products for tests of hypotheses on the polynomial representation of group differences, we have three courses open depending on our assumptions about the structure of Σ:

Assumption I.

$$\Sigma = \mathcal{E}(\nu_{ij}1 + \zeta_{ij})(\nu_{ij}1 + \zeta_{ij})' = \sigma_\nu^2 11' + \sigma^2 I,$$

where ν_{ij} is a random component due to subject i in the jth population and is distributed as $N(0, \sigma_\nu^2)$. ζ_{ij} is an $r \times 1$ random vector of independent errors with multivariate distribution $N(0, \sigma^2 I)$.

Assumption I states that the expected form of S_W is the so-called compound symmetry pattern (i.e., equal variances and equal covariances).

The likelihood ratio test for this pattern is illustrated by Greenhouse and Geisser (1959). If S_W is compatible with Assumption I, the analysis proceeds along the lines of a conventional Mixed Model solution: That is, we use variance ratio

$$n_W \sum_{i=1}^{r-1} \boldsymbol{p}_i' S_B \boldsymbol{p}_i / n_B \sum_{i=1}^{r-1} \boldsymbol{p}_i' S_W \boldsymbol{p}_i,$$

which is distributed in the null case as F on $(r-1)n_B$ and $(r-1)n_W$ degrees of freedom, to test the hypothesis that the mean time-curves of the t experimental populations are parallel. Assuming parallelism, we may use the variance ratio

$$n_W \boldsymbol{p}_0' S_B \boldsymbol{p}_0 / n_B \boldsymbol{p}_0' S_W \boldsymbol{p}_0,$$

which is distributed in the null case as F on n_B and n_W degrees of freedom, to test the hypothesis that the mean time-curves are *coincident*.

If parallelism is rejected, the degree of the polynomial representation of the group differences should be investigated. Variance ratios for an isolated effect, say

$$(r-1)n_W \boldsymbol{p}_k' S_B \boldsymbol{p}_k / n_B \sum_{i=1}^{r-1} \boldsymbol{p}_i' S_W \boldsymbol{p}_i, \qquad 0 < k < r,$$

are, of course, distributed as F on n_B and $(r-1)n_W$ degrees of freedom in the null case. But tests of hypotheses employing two or more such ratios will not be independent because the respective variance ratios have the same denominator. Recently, however, T. W. Anderson (1962) has proposed a decision theoretic approach to ascertaining the degree polynomial compatible with the data, starting from $k = r - 1$ and working down, which appears to be a satisfactory solution to this problem.

Assumption II: $P' \Sigma P$ is diagonal.

This is weaker than Assumption I. To test Assumption II statistically, we may use the likelihood ratio criterion for no association in the correlation matrix of $P' \Sigma P$, say,

$$\Lambda = \left| \text{corr } (P' \Sigma P) \right|.$$

Percentage points for the distribution of this criterion under independence are well approximated by the χ^2 statistic,

$$\chi^2 = - \left[n_W - \left(\frac{2r + 5}{6} \right) \right] \log_e \Lambda,$$

on $r(r-1)/2$ degrees of freedom.

Under Assumption II, the variance ratios

$$n_W \boldsymbol{p}_i' S_B \boldsymbol{p}_i / n_B \boldsymbol{p}_i' S_W \boldsymbol{p}_i, \qquad i = 0,\, 1,\, 2,\, \cdots,\, r-1,$$

are *independently* distributed as F on n_B and n_W degrees of freedom in the null case. Thus, if none of the ratios for $i = 1,\, 2,\, \cdots,\, r-1$ reaches significance at the α level, say, we accept the hypothesis of parallelism at level $1 - (1-\alpha)^{r-1}$. The degree of departures from parallelism may be established by starting with $i = r-1$ and working down until a significant ratio is encountered (adjusting the α level appropriately at each stage).

If the hypothesis of parallelism is accepted, the hypothesis of coincidence may be tested as under Assumption I. (See also the comment at the end of this section.)

Assumption III: General $P'\Sigma P$.

This is the case considered by Greenhouse and Geisser (1959). However, in their treatment they ignore possible correlations of the subject effect and the subject $\times$ occasion interactions. In terms of the orthogonal polynomial reduction of the error covariance matrix these correlations are

$$\rho_{0,i} = \boldsymbol{p}_0' \Sigma \boldsymbol{p}_i / \sqrt{\boldsymbol{p}_0' \Sigma \boldsymbol{p}_0 \boldsymbol{p}_i' \Sigma \boldsymbol{p}_i},$$

and are estimated by similar forms with S_W replacing Σ. Their interpretation may be exemplified by $\rho_{0,1}$, which is the common correlation of general level vs. linear trend in the time-curves of the subjects. Positive values of $\rho_{0,1}$ indicate a tendency for subjects with higher average levels to have steeper curves.

If a general, unknown Σ is assumed, no direct method of investigating the degree of the polynomial representation is apparent. Exact multivariate tests of the general hypothesis of no group differences are available, however. See Potthoff and Roy (1962). The variance ratio corresponding to the kth degree term, say,

$$n_W \boldsymbol{p}_k' S_B \boldsymbol{p}_k / n_B \boldsymbol{p}_k' S_W \boldsymbol{p}_k, \qquad 0 < k < r,$$

is still distributed in the null case as F on n_B and n_W degrees of freedom, but two or more such ratios are not independent. The only obvious way out of this difficulty is to state the null hypothesis in conditional form: That is, replace the hypothesis that γ_k is null unconditionally with the hypothesis that it is null given $\gamma_{k-1}, \gamma_{k-2}, \cdots, \gamma_0$. This means that if the linear trend in the groups is proportional to the general level, for example, the analysis will lead us to accept the hypothesis of no difference in linear trend if the groups were adjusted to the same general level. Provided the origin of the original data is well defined, such a conclusion is of genuine interest. It means that a simple logarithmic transformation of the original data will make the time-curves of the groups parallel and, therefore, make the general levels of the groups estimable.

Similar reasoning can be applied to higher degree terms. If the kth degree term $(1 < k < r)$ is significant in isolation, it will be of interest to determine whether it has a significant partial effect, given all effects of lower degree. For this purpose we may use the Roy-Bargmann (1958) step-down procedure (which is just a step-wise analysis of covariance applied to multiple variates) to test the contribution of the linear term, holding fixed the constant term, or indeed any higher degree term, holding fixed all lower degree terms. See also J. Roy (1958). The general procedure is as follows:

Consider the problem of testing the partial contribution of the kth term in the representation of the orthogonal polynomial. First let $V_T = P'(S_B + S_W)P$ be the transformed total sum of products, and partition the first $k + 1$ rows and columns of V_W and V_T as follows:

$$\begin{bmatrix} V_W^{(k-1)} & v_W^{(k)} \\ v_W^{(k)'} & v_W^{(k)} \end{bmatrix}$$

and

$$\begin{bmatrix} V_T^{(k-1)} & v_T^{(k)} \\ v_T^{(k)'} & v_T^{(k)} \end{bmatrix}.$$

Then form the "step-down coefficient"

$$\beta^{(k)} = \frac{v_W^{(k)} - v_W^{(k)'}\left[V_W^{(k-1)}\right]^{-1}v_W^{(k)}}{v_T^{(k)} - v_T^{(k)'}\left[V_T^{(k-1)}\right]^{-1}v_T^{(k)}} = \frac{d_W^{(k)}}{d_T^{(k)}}, \qquad \text{say.}$$

Note that the $d_W^{(k)}$ and $d_T^{(k)}$ are just the "pivotal" elements (row divisors) which appear in the inversion of the matrices V_W and V_T by Gauss-Doolittle elimination, or in the enlargement (simple bordering) method (Faddeeva, 1959).

When there are no group differences in the conditional distribution of the kth degree effect, holding fixed the $0, 1, 2, \cdots, k - 1$ degree effects, the step-down coefficients follow the beta distribution, the percentage points of which can be obtained from the F-distribution by the relation

$$\beta_\alpha^{(k)} = \frac{1}{\left[n_B F_\alpha^{(k)}/(n_W - k + 1)\right] + 1},$$

where the $F_\alpha^{(k)}$ is on n_B and $n_W - k + 1$ degrees of freedom. It has been shown by Roy and Bargmann (1958) that these beta-statistics are independent in the null case. Hence, the corresponding F-statistics may be interpreted in the same way as under Assumption II, but with the understanding that significant effects have only a conditional meaning. The interpretation of the step-down analysis is further clarified in the numerical example that follows.

The preceding analysis can also be formulated as an analysis of hypothetical discriminant functions in the manner of Bartlett (1951). Consider the zero[th] degree orthogonal polynomial a hypothetical discriminant function to be used in classifying subjects into the experimental groups. We can then ask whether all association between the classification of the subjects and their scores on the original variates can be explained by the single score for each subject on this hypothetical function. A likelihood ratio criterion for this purpose can be expressed in terms of the step-down coefficients,

$$\Lambda^{(0)} = \prod_{i=1}^{r-1} \beta^{(i)}.$$

Percentage points for the null distribution of this statistic are well approximated by those of the χ^2 statistic

$$\chi^2 = -\left[n_B + n_W - 1 - \left(\frac{r - 1 + n_B + 1}{2} \right) \right] \log_e \Lambda^{(0)}$$

on $(r - 1)n_B$ degrees of freedom. If this hypothesis is accepted, only the average of the measures observed on a subject can be considered useful for classifying him into one of the experimental groups.

The test generalizes to k hypothetical functions in terms of the criterion

$$\Lambda^{(0,1,\cdots,k)} = \prod_{i=k+1}^{r-1} \beta^{(i)}, \qquad 1 < k < r - 1.$$

The corresponding χ^2 statistic is

$$\chi^2 = -\left[n_W + n_B - k - \left(\frac{r - k + n_B + 1}{2} \right) \right] \log_e \Lambda^{(0,1,\cdots,k)},$$

on $(r - k)n_B$ degrees of freedom.

Note that if we wish to classify subjects according to their general level, linear trend, etc., in repeated measurements, the preceding analysis remains pertinent regardless of our assumptions about Σ. We may therefore elect to use it even when Assumption I or II is satisfied.

A substantive example

Data for this example are taken from E. A. Haggard's long-term study of gifted children in the University of Chicago Laboratory School. In the course of that study a marked difference in the arithmetic achievement of pre-adolescent boys and girls was noted. The boys were consistently superior to girls in fourth, fifth, sixth and seventh grade arithmetic, although they were not uniformly superior in other areas of achievement (Haggard, 1957).

TABLE 5.4

Sample, Class, and Subclass Numbers

Year-groups	Sex		Total
	Boys	Girls	
1	18	20	38
2	25	20	45
3	20	19	39
Totals	63	59	122

An obvious further question is whether the disparity in arithmetic achievement is increasing, decreasing, or constant over the period of the study. Let us attempt to answer it by the methods of this paper. At the time of Haggard's study, data suitable for this purpose were available for 122 children who attended the University of Chicago Laboratory School from the fourth grade through the seventh grade. The children comprised three successive year-groups completing the seventh grade in 1955, 1956, and 1957, respectively. Since the program of the school was not completely constant for each year-group, we will retain the classification by year-group as well as sex in the analysis. The number of subjects in each class and subclass of the sample is shown in Table 5.4. As is usually the case in educational research, the subclass numbers are disproportionate and an orthogonal multivariate analysis of variance is not possible. Since the sex-effect is clearly first in priority of interest, however, a useful *non*-orthogonal analysis is possible. It requires computation of a sum of products for the sex-effect, eliminating the year-group effect, and, as a

TABLE 5.5

Test Schedule

	Test form for each year-group and grade[a]											
	A				B				C			
Test	4	5	6	7	4	5	6	7	4	5	6	7
Arithmetic												
Iowa Every Pupil Test D: Basic Arithmetic Skills	L	M	P[b]		M	O	O[b]		O	L	O[b]	
Functional Evaluation in Mathematics				A				A				
Snader General Mathematics Test								(AM)				AM[c]
Reading												
Chicago Reading Test D	2	3			2	3			2	3		
Cooperative English Test C1: Reading Comprehension			R	Y			Y	R			R	Y

[a] Number and letter designations of the test forms are those of the test publisher.

[b] Advanced form.

[c] Scores on this test were equated to those of the Functional Evaluation in Mathematics on the basis of the joint administration of these tests to Group *B*.

test of an additive model, the sum of squares for interaction, eliminating the main effects. Discussion of the arithmetic of the nonorthogonal multivariate analysis of variance is not necessary here since it is available elsewhere (Roy and Gnanadesikan, 1959; Bock, 1962). Indeed the computer programs which are available for this purpose (Bock, 1962) make a detailed knowledge of the arithmetic unnecessary in applied work.

The schedule of achievement tests from which the data were obtained is presented in Table 5.5. These tests are administered yearly by qualified personnel of the Records Office of the University of Chicago Laboratory School. I am indebted to Mr. Francis Hicklin, Director of the Records Office, for making the data available. The tests in each subject area are closely comparable in content from year to year, but they are not necessarily in the same scale. They can be considered parallel for practical purposes, but only *up to a linear transformation*. To put the scores in the similar metric required for repeated-measurements analysis, the location and scale of the tests for each grade level must be set to common values. For location, it is sufficient to set the mean for each grade to zero. This is

TABLE 5.6

Nonorthogonal Analysis of Variance of Arithmetic Scores

Source of dispersion	Degrees of freedom	Mean products,[a] grade			
		4	5	6	7
Occasion means	1	(Identically zero)			
Year-groups, ignoring sex and interaction	2	17.7424			
		−2.2294	3.8108		
		−4.0068	.3389	.9125	
		−.4808	.9775	.0658	.2512
Sex, eliminating year-groups and ignoring interaction	1	5.5680			
		5.2679	4.9838		
		8.3960	7.9433	12.6602	
		8.4596	7.9988	12.7485	12.8375
Year-groups × sex, eliminating sex and year-group main effects	2	.1688			
		.2176	.4817		
		−.2582	−.0746	.7269	
		−.3597	−.5878	.3912	.8431
Subjects within groups	116	1.0000			
		.5142	1.0000		
		.6567	.5271	1.0000	
		.7343	.4975	.7967	1.0000

[a] Symmetrical elements omitted.

equivalent to removing the occasion-mean sum of products. For scale, on the other hand, it is not desirable simply to standardize over all subjects for each year. This practice makes the within-group variance depend upon possible between-group variation, and is clearly not desirable in connection with analysis of variance. A better practice is to standardize the within-group variance. (Strictly speaking a large independent sample should be used for this purpose.) This has been done in computing the mean products (sums of products divided by their degrees of freedom) in Table 5.6. All computations were performed on the General Precision LGP-30 computer of the Psychometric Laboratory, University of North Carolina.

The within-group covariance matrix of Table 5.6 does not show the simplex pattern, suggesting that differences in the reliability or factorial structure of the tests are dominating any possible autoregressive effect.

Neither is the sample covariance pattern entirely favorable for transformation to independence by the 4×4 orthogonal polynomial matrix. Table 5.7 shows that the mean, linear, and quadratic effects are virtually uncorrelated, but their correlations with the cubic effect are appreciable. The likelihood ratio test contradicts the assumption of independence, indicating that an analysis under Assumption III is required. The results of the step-down analysis for this purpose, as performed with the multivariate analysis of variance program of the Psychometric Laboratory, are shown in Table 5.8.

TABLE 5.7

Variances and Correlations of the Transformed Within-Group
Mean Product for Arithmetic Scores

	Degree			
	0	1	2	3
Variances	2.8633	.3334	.3981	.4051
Correlations[a]	1.0000			
	.0928	1.0000		
	.0971	.0220	1.0000	
	−.1248	−.3398	−.40313	1.0000

Determinant $= .7119280$

$$\chi^2 = \left[116 - \frac{2 \times 4 + 5}{6} \right] \log_e .7119280; \text{ d.f.} = 6$$

$$= 39.02; \ p < .0005$$

[a] Symmetrical elements omitted.

Both the conventional F-statistics and step-down F-statistics computed from the corresponding beta-statistic are shown. Note that the usual tabular values for the α per cent level apply when an isolated F-statistic is interpreted. When several independent F-statistics are interpreted jointly, however, the percentage points must be chosen so that the intersection of the acceptance regions is some prescribed value. In the present example an unbiased critical region of about size 4 per cent results if the acceptance region of each separate test is set at 99 per cent. A 10 per cent region is obtained by a 97.5 per cent acceptance region for the separate tests. The appropriate critical F-statistics for an isolated test and for four joint tests are shown at the bottom of Table 5.8.

For the sex–year-group interaction we have no prior interest in particu-

TABLE 5.8

Test of Significance for the Orthogonal Polynomial Regression
of Arithmetic Scores

Source of variation	Effect, degrees of freedom	Degree of effect			
		0	1	2	3
Year-groups, ignoring sex and interaction	2				
Simple F		1.05	26.97	20.60	6.19
Step-down F		1.05	27.44	14.36	4.90
Sex, ignoring interaction and eliminating year-groups	1				
Simple F		12.02	3.74	<1	<1
Step-down F		12.02	2.36	<1	<1
Sex $\times$ year-group interaction, eliminating sex and year-group main effects	2				
Simple F		<1	3.84	1.15	<1
Step-down F		<1	3.80	1.14	<1
Step-down degrees of freedom for error		116	115	114	113

Critical Points:

Single F-test	$F_{.05}^{(1,116)} = 3.93$	$F_{.10}^{(1,116)} = 2.75$
	$F_{.05}^{(2,116)} = 3.08$	$F_{.10}^{(2,116)} = 2.36$
Four joint F-tests	$F_{.04}^{(1,116)} = 6.86$	$F_{.10}^{(1,116)} = 5.14$
	$F_{.04}^{(2,116)} = 4.77$	$F_{.10}^{(2,116)} = 3.81$

lar effects, and so the critical F-statistics for the joint tests apply. (Note
that because the degrees of freedom for error decrease by one for each
step-down F-statistic, the critical values for each should differ slightly. In
the present example the degrees of freedom for error are so numerous that
change of critical point is negligible.) We find that none of the F's reaches
the 10 per cent level, and we accept the null hypothesis. Note that the
simple F (conventional F) for the linear interactive effect exceeds the 5
per cent level.

For the sex-effect, the significance of the between-sex difference in mean
level of arithmetic achievement has already been established and is of
no interest here. Chief interest is in the linear trend in sex-effect as a
measure of increasing or decreasing disparity between sexes. We may

therefore consider the linear effect in an isolated test. On this basis the conventional F falls between the 5 and 10 per cent points, but the step-down F is considerably lower. This indicates a marginally significant linear effect which, however, depends to some extent on the general levels of the groups. When the general level is eliminated, the effect is reduced to insignificance.

The general year-group effect is, of course, confounded with the significant general sex-effect and is not interpretable. Since the sex trend-effects are not significant, the year-group trend-effects are not confounded and may be tested, this time against the critical points for three joint tests. All trend-effects—linear, quadratic, and cubic—are obviously sig-

TABLE 5.9

Arithmetic Contrasts

| Grade | Sex Boys–Girls S.E. = .1816 | Year-groups | |
		1–3 S.E. = .2281	2–3 S.E. = .2189
4	.4285	1.3562	.4593
5	.4054	−.2518	−.6182
6	.6461	−.2726	−.1103
7	.6506	−.0367	−.1813

nificant. The source of these effects will be apparent when we examine the estimated contrasts shown in Table 5.9.

These contrasts are estimated on the assumption of no interactive effect; i.e., a rank four additive model is fitted to the data and selected contrasts of the main effects are estimated. We see that the difference between the largest and the smallest sex-contrast is less than twice the standard errors of these contrasts, again suggesting only a general sex-effect. (The sampling covariance matrix of the estimated contrasts depends on the subclass numbers and is generated in the course of the machine solution.) For the year-group effects the two degrees of freedom available are allotted to contrasts of the first group vs. third and the second vs. third. It is apparent that the significant "trends" in the year-group differences are due chiefly to a large, isolated difference between the first and third year-groups in the fourth grade. Such an effect cannot be considered functionally dependent on time, and its orthogonal polynomial representation is quite artificial. In this case the orthogonal polynomials provide only one of many possible sets of contrasts which would detect the effect, and not necessarily the best set from the point of view of the power of the resulting tests of significance. This peculiar year-group effect could perhaps be explained in terms of the history of the first year-group prior to or during the fourth grade if it were known. Or perhaps it could be attributed to a blunder somewhere in the collection, reporting, or transcribing of the data before it came to analysis. Since much of the data is now nearly ten years old, no attempt has been made to settle this point.

Regarding the general sex-effect, we could argue that it may reflect only a general superiority of the boys in the Laboratory School. To investigate this contention, we can use the step-down analysis in its role of analysis of covariance in order to test whether the sex-effect in arithmetic is significant when some other measure of achievement is held fixed. This has been done using as a controlling variable the general reading level

TABLE 5.10

Variance of the General Reading Effect and Correlation with Arithmetic Effects

	Degree of arithmetic effect			
	0	1	2	3
Correlations	.5243	.1686	.2398	− .2538

Variance of general reading effect 3.3876.

measured by the tests listed in Table 5.5. The within-group variance of the mean reading score and its correlation with the arithmetic effects is shown in Table 5.10. We observe substantial correlation between reading and mean arithmetic scores. However, when mean reading level is held fixed, the partial sex-effect in arithmetic achievement remains significant, as shown in Table 5.11. The group trend-effects also remain significant. Thus, the effects observed in the arithmetic scores cannot be attributed to general factors of achievement which are also measured by the reading test.

Remarks on applications to "profile" analysis

The methods proposed here for the analysis of growth and change make particular use of the orthogonal polynomial representation of between-group differences. The choice of this transformation is based on the ordered metric properties of the time dimension. The step-down analysis depends in an essential way on this transformation and would not necessarily be the same if some other were used. In the case of profile analysis, we cannot ordinarily assume an ordering of the tests (unless the tests have a known simplex structure) and the orthogonal polynomial trans-

TABLE 5.11

Test of Significance of the Orthogonal Polynomial Regression of
Arithmetic Scores, Eliminating General Reading Effect

Source of variation	Effect, degrees of freedom	Degree of arithmetic effect			
		0	1	2	3
Year-groups, ignoring sex and interaction	2				
Step-down F		<1	28.46	14.01	5.41
Sex, ignoring interaction and eliminating year-groups	1				
Step-down F		9.82	2.56	<1	<1
Sex × year-group interaction, eliminating sex and year-group main effects	2				
Step-down F		<1	4.02	1.19	<1
Step-down degrees of freedom for error		115	114	113	112

formation has nothing to recommend it. Nevertheless, when the tests can
be constructed in such a way that their expected covariance structure is
specified *a priori*, an analysis along these lines is possible. Bock (1960)
has shown an example in which the covariance-variance structure of a 2^2
factorial arrangement of content in standardized, equally reliable tests
can be assumed to satisfy the (positive-definite) equipredictability form
(Bargmann, 1957), say,

$$\begin{bmatrix} v & a & b & c \\ a & v & c & b \\ b & c & v & a \\ c & b & a & v \end{bmatrix}.$$

This form yields to analysis under Assumption II on transformation by
the 2^2 Hadamard matrix

$$\frac{1}{2}\begin{bmatrix} 1 & 1 & 1 & 1 \\ 1 & 1 & -1 & -1 \\ 1 & -1 & 1 & -1 \\ 1 & -1 & -1 & 1 \end{bmatrix}.$$

Other arrangements of test content with expected covariance patterns which are favorable for multivariate analysis of variance also appear possible.

Another possible approach is to abandon the simple mean as a measure of general effect. This would eliminate the requirement that one of the rows of the transformation matrix be $1/\sqrt{n}$. Then the proper vectors of the *sample* covariance matrix could be used as a diagonalizing transformation. If the proper values were determined in a sufficiently large sample, the transformed scores computed from them would be virtually uncorrelated in the population. Then if a suitable interpretation of the proper vectors as functions of the effects, Θ, were found, an analysis could proceed under Assumption II.

I am indebted to Lyle V. Jones for comments on this paper.

| Six | Multivariate Models for |
| | Evaluating Change |

PAUL HORST

This study was supported in part by Office of Naval Research Contract Nonr-477(33) and Public Health Research Grant M-743(C7). Reproduction in whole or in part is permitted for any purpose of the United States Government.

We shall base our discussion of multivariate models for evaluating change on a very general type of model from which specific models may be developed. First, we introduce some fundamental concepts essential for the development of the general model. Let us begin with the familiar concept of a data matrix in which we have measures on each of a number of attributes for each of a number of entities. We may assume that changes in these measures take place over a period of time. Let us assume, therefore, that the same measures on each of the same attributes for each of the same entities are taken on a number of different occasions. Let us also assume that the measures are taken under several different conditions.

For the purpose of discussion, suppose we have a questionnaire with a set of 64 items to which 18 individuals will respond. Let us assume that these entities or individuals are requested to give responses under a number of different sets or instructions. For example, they may be asked to respond to the items as they apply to themselves, to the average person, to the ideal person, to the respondent as he would like to be, etc. One may have as many different conditions as he can invent. However, let us assume there are eight of these conditions. Assume the respondents are a group of psychiatric residents in a mental hospital. It may be expected that these residents are undergoing training and experience which will

104

modify their responses to the items over a period of time for the varying conditions. Suppose, then, that these individuals are requested to repeat the eight sets of responses to each of the 64 items on four different occasions—at six-month intervals, perhaps.

Let us now review the basic essentials of the model. First, we have sets of matrices involving 18 entities and 64 attributes or variables. For each condition on each occasion we have such a matrix. For example, if we have eight conditions and four occasions, this means that we have 32 matrices of order 18 by 64.

One may conceive of an additional categorical set which would consist of a set of instruments or evaluators. This would involve a number of different ways of evaluating or measuring each attribute for each entity under each condition and on each occasion. It is interesting to note that the instrument and the occasion categories are the basic concepts involved in the theory of reliability. The instruments correspond to comparable form or comparable measure reliability, and the occasions correspond to consistency or stability over time.

In most of the measurement models, comparable form reliability usually involves only two instruments. These instruments may be sets of persons, test booklets, hardware, or what not. For example, we may have a number of different raters evaluating the same individual on the same attribute for a given occasion. In the case of differing occasions, we have the special case of retest reliability which ordinarily involves only two occasions. The problem of evaluating change becomes sufficiently complicated from the model point of view even if we have only the four categories of entities, attributes, conditions, and occasions. Intriguing as it may be, we shall, therefore, not include in our detailed discussion the additional category of instruments.

Let us briefly discuss the relationship of the reliability concept and the evaluation of change in the multidimensional matrix model. It is probable that the traditional concepts and constructs of reliability theory will become assimilated as part of the general multidimensional data matrix model in which two of the dimensions are instruments and occasions, respectively. It appears that the natures of the instrument and the occasion categories in this model are essentially different, and a clear recognition of this difference may well lead to a thorough and drastic remodeling and restructuring of current reliability theory. For example, in the case of retest reliability, we are basically dealing with the predictable variance which occurs with respect to sets of entities over a number of occasions. To illustrate, let us consider a three or more dimensional category matrix in which one of the dimensions is occasions. If from such a matrix we can remove the systematic effect of time, then presumably the residual variance would be the unreliable variance of the system.

Viewing the problem in this way, it is interesting to see how the temporal or occasion dimension of such a multicategory data matrix differs essentially from the other categories. In general, the entities and the attribute dimensions are not ordered on any *a priori* or rational basis. It does not matter if we permute either the entities or the attributes as far as a basic structure, least square, or other traditional type of analysis is concerned. Such permutations do not affect least square, maximum likelihood, or other optimal types of solution involving reduced-rank matrix approximations. For the condition dimension of a multidimensional matrix, also, there is no *a priori* rational ordering of the conditions. However, for the occasion or temporal dimension, the ordering is dictated by the passage of time.

Let us now consider what parameters may be involved in examining systematic change over time for the temporal dimension. Obviously, the simplest case we can have is that of only two occasions. If we have only two occasions, then it is impossible to indicate a trend for each entity since more than two points are required to overdetermine even a linear trend. Three occasions will overdetermine a linear trend for each individual. In general, if we assume that a trend can be represented by a polynomial of appropriate degree, then, of course, a polynomial of lesser degree than the number of occasions will be required in order to avoid overfitting for each individual.

We may also consider a vector of the multicategory matrix for one condition and one variable for a given individual over a period of time. Such a vector may be supplemented with a temporal vector of numbers ranging from one to the number of occasions to yield a data matrix amenable to various kinds of multivariate analysis. One can generate additional vectors from the temporal vector by taking successive powers to yield additional attribute vectors. It should be noted, however, that by generating additional vectors for the computation of polynomial parameters we have greatly complicated the model.

Another variation of a predictive structure from the occasion dimension of the multidimensional data matrix involves the serial correlation type of approach. Consider, for example, a single vector of observations for an entity over a number of occasions for a given attribute and a given condition. From such a vector one may generate a matrix such that each successive vector of the matrix is obtained from the previous one by displacing each of the elements from the previous vector by one occasion. Such a matrix implies estimation of the measure for a given occasion from the same measure on previous occasions. The matrix would have triangular empty spaces in the upper left and lower right corners. It may, therefore, be called the trapezoidal model. Very little seems to have been done with this particular type of model for the estimation of change or prediction of future occasions. The model presents interesting challenges from the point of view of the triangular empty spaces. Here the problem is one of optimal estimation of the elements in empty spaces. This particular model might be called the multivariate serial model. It appears to be essentially different from the multivariate polynomial model discussed previously.

We have mentioned the rather obvious proliferations of the occasion dimensions not only to indicate possibilities for further elaboration and refinement of a more general model appropriate to the measurement of change, but also to indicate the great complexity of designs which readily suggest themselves in connection with the problems of reliability and measurement of change. We shall have little further to say about these extensions of the occasion category, since the problems involved even without them will appear to be sufficiently complex to challenge the current status of our multivariate analysis technology.

Next, let us observe that if we have a number of different attributes, one of the first questions to be raised is whether or not these are statistically independent measures. In other words, is there a smaller set of measures which may adequately represent the larger *a priori* or experimental set? The same question may also be appropriately raised in connection with the number of conditions or treatments. For example, it is not difficult to invent ten, twelve, or even more conditions with respect to personality, attitude, and other inventory type items. In the case of different kinds of treatments, it is not difficult to formulate a sizable number of *a priori* treatments with which it seems feasible to experiment. The question is, then, are these really different conditions or treatments or may they be regarded as linear combinations of some more basic or fundamental kind of condition or treatment? The same question may be asked with regard to the successive occasions. Are these essentially different occasions in the sense that the individuals are unpredictably different from one time to the next, are they essentially the same, or do they exhibit some systematic trend over time?

Obviously, then, the general rank-reduction model implied by factor analysis procedures suggests itself. We shall therefore proceed with a structuring of the general model, after which we shall suggest several specific approaches which might be fruitful.

Suppose we have measures for each of n_e entities on each of n_a attributes under each of n_c conditions for each of n_o occasions. We let x_{ij} be the n_e by n_a matrix of measures under the ith condition for the jth occasion. We let I_a be an identity matrix of order n_a and I_e be an identity matrix of order n_e. As a basis for further analysis, we shall define a series of supermatrices involving the x_{ij} and identity matrices.

First, let us consider the series of definitions given by equations (1) through (9) below.

$$(1) \qquad D_{x_{ij}} = \begin{bmatrix} x_{1j} & \cdots & 0 \\ \cdot & \cdot \cdot \cdot \cdot & \cdot \\ 0 & \cdots & x_{n_c j} \end{bmatrix};$$

$$(2) \qquad V_{x_{ij}} = \begin{bmatrix} x_{1j} \\ \vdots \\ x_{n_c j} \end{bmatrix};$$

$$(3) \qquad V'_{P_{ij}} = [x_{1j} \cdots x_{n_c j}];$$

$$(4) \qquad D_{D_{x_{ij}}} = \begin{bmatrix} D_{x_{i1}} & \cdots & 0 \\ \cdot & \cdot \cdot \cdot \cdot & \cdot \\ 0 & \cdots & D_{x_{in_o}} \end{bmatrix};$$

$$(5) \qquad V_{D_{x_{ij}}} = \begin{bmatrix} D_{x_{i1}} \\ \vdots \\ D_{x_{in_o}} \end{bmatrix};$$

$$(6) \qquad D_{V_{x_{ij}}} = \begin{bmatrix} V_{x_{i1}} & \cdots & 0 \\ \cdot & \cdot \cdot \cdot \cdot & \cdot \\ 0 & \cdots & V_{x_{in_o}} \end{bmatrix};$$

$$(7) \qquad V_{V_{x_{ij}}} = \begin{bmatrix} V_{x_{i1}} \\ \vdots \\ V_{x_{in_o}} \end{bmatrix};$$

$$(8) \qquad V'_{V_{x_{ij}}} = [V_{x_{i1}} \cdots V_{x_{in_o}}];$$

$$(9) \qquad V'_{V_{x_{ij}}} = \begin{bmatrix} V'_{x_{i1}} \\ \vdots \\ V'_{x_{in_o}} \end{bmatrix}.$$

Equation (1) indicates a diagonal matrix in which the diagonal elements are themselves matrices. The first element is the entity-attribute matrix of observations for the first condition and the jth occasion. The last element is the entity-attribute matrix for the condition n_c and occasion j.

Equation (2) is a column supervector in which each of the elements is an entity-attribute matrix. The first element is the entity-attribute matrix for the first condition and the jth occasion, while the last element is the entity-attribute matrix for the last condition, n_c, and the jth occasion. This supervector has the same elements as those in equation (1). The difference between the two is that one is a diagonal matrix and the other is a column vector.

Equation (3) is a row supervector in which the elements are the same as for equations (1) and (2). However, now the elements are arranged in row form rather than in diagonal or in column form. It must be noted that equation (3) is not the transpose of equation (2). If it were, then the elements in the right of equation (3) would also be transposed.

It will be noted that equations (1), (2), and (3) consist of supermatrices, the elements of which are matrices with scalar elements. Beginning with equation (4), we have a series of matrices whose elements are themselves supermatrices made up from the supermatrices defined in equations (1), (2), and (3).

In further discussion it will be convenient to refer to the hierarchy of a matrix. A matrix whose elements are matrices with scalar elements will be called a first hierarchy supermatrix, one whose elements are first hierarchy supermatrices will be called a second hierarchy supermatrix, etc.

In equation (4) we have a supermatrix whose elements are, in turn, the supermatrices defined in equation (1) for values of j, the occasion index, which range from 1 to n_o. This matrix is a second hierarchy diagonal supermatrix of diagonal supermatrices of the entity-attribute matrices.

Equation (5) is a column supervector of diagonal supermatrices. These diagonal supermatrices are again those defined in equation (1) for the occasion index ranging from 1 to n_o. It will be seen that the supermatric elements of (5) are the same as those in equation (4). The essential difference between the two matrices is that the supermatric elements are arranged in diagonal order in (4) and in column order in (5).

Equation (6) is a diagonal supermatrix whose diagonal elements are the column vectors of matric elements defined in equation (2), where the range is from 1 to n_o occasions. Each vector of equation (6) consists of the entity-attribute matrices for the n_c conditions with respect to a given occasion.

Equation (7) is a column supervector whose elements are themselves column supervectors. This equation is obtained by arranging the elements of equation (6) in column form.

Let us now review the notation on the left-hand side of equations (4) through (7) so that we may understand the meaning of the symbols from left to right. The notation on the left of equation (4) means the diagonal matrix of diagonal matrices of the x_{ij} simple matrices; of equation (5), a column vector of the diagonal matrices of simple matrices; of equation (6), a diagonal matrix of column vectors of simple matrices; and of equation (7), a column vector of column vectors of simple matrices. In general, then, the uppermost left-hand symbol indicates whether the second hierarchy supermatrix is in diagonal or in vector form. The next symbol to the right indicates whether the supermatric elements are diagonal supermatrices or column vectors of supermatrices. The final symbol, x_{ij}, refers to the entity-attribute matrix for the ith condition and the jth occasion.

In equations (8) and (9) we have still other arrangements of the entity-attribute matrices. Equation (8) indicates a second hierarchy row super-vector whose elements are column supervectors of the entity-attribute matrices x_{ij}. The first column is a vector of matrices for each condition under the first occasion, and the last is a column vector of matrices under each condition for the last or n_o occasion.

Equation (9), on the other hand, is a column supervector of super-matrices. However, the elements of this second hierarchy supermatrix are row supervectors whose elements are the x_{ij} values ranging from the first to the n_c condition. Each row represents a different occasion. It is important to note that equations (8) and (9) are not mutual transposes. If they were mutual transposes, then the x_{ij}'s in equation (9) would also have the prime after them to show that they are transposed. This distinction between the second hierarchy supermatrices in equations (8) and (9) is important in considering factor resolutions of the two supermatrices. If one were the transpose of the other, then the factor resolution would be the same except for the commutation and transposition of the factors.

Next we shall consider the series of definitions indicated by equations (10) through (15). In each of these equations the subscript external to the brackets indicates the superorder of the matrices, whether they be first or second hierarchy supermatrices. The symbol I indicates an identity matrix. The subscript a means that the identity matrix is of the same order as the number of attributes.

$$(10) \qquad D_{I_a} = \begin{bmatrix} I_a & \cdots & 0 \\ \cdot & \cdot & \cdot & \cdot \\ 0 & \cdots & I_a \end{bmatrix}_{n_c} ;$$

$$(11) \qquad V_{I_a} = \begin{bmatrix} I_a \\ \cdot \\ \cdot \\ \cdot \\ I_a \end{bmatrix}_{n_c} ;$$

$$(12) \qquad D_{D_{I_a}} = \begin{bmatrix} D_{I_a} \cdots 0 \\ \cdot \cdot \cdot \cdot \cdot \cdot \\ 0 \cdots D_{I_a} \end{bmatrix}_{n_o} ;$$

$$(13) \qquad V_{D_{I_a}} = \begin{bmatrix} D_{I_a} \\ \cdot \\ \cdot \\ D_{I_a} \end{bmatrix}_{n_o} ;$$

$$(14) \qquad D_{V_{I_a}} = \begin{bmatrix} V_{I_a} \cdots 0 \\ \cdot \cdot \cdot \cdot \cdot \cdot \\ 0 \cdots V_{I_a} \end{bmatrix}_{n_o} ;$$

$$(15) \qquad V_{V_{I_a}} = \begin{bmatrix} V_{I_a} \\ \cdot \\ \cdot \\ V_{I_a} \end{bmatrix}_{n_o} .$$

Equation (10) is a diagonal supermatrix of identity matrices where the number of identity matrices is equal to the number of conditions n_c. Equation (11) is a column vector of identity matrices where again the number of identity matrices is equal to the number of conditions n_c. The two matrices in equations (10) and (11) are used to construct second hierarchy supermatrices, as indicated in equations (12) through (15).

These supermatrices have in general the same meanings, respectively, as those from equations (4) to (7), which have been previously defined. An exception is that the matric elements are all identity matrices. Equation (12) indicates a second hierarchy superdiagonal matrix with n_o super-diagonal matrices, each of which is a diagonal of n_c identity matrices. Similarly, equation (13) is a column vector of diagonal matrices of identity matrices. Equation (14) is a diagonal matrix of column vectors of identity matrices. Equation (15) is a column of column vectors of identity matrices where the second hierarchy superorder is equal to the number of occasions n_o and the first hierarchy superorder is equal to the number of conditions n_c.

Analogous to equations (10) through (15), we define another set in equations (16) through (21).

$$(16) \qquad D_{I_e} = \begin{bmatrix} I_e & \cdots & 0 \\ \cdot & \cdot & \cdot \\ 0 & \cdots & I_e \end{bmatrix}_{n_c} ;$$

$$(17) \qquad V_{I_e} = \begin{bmatrix} I_e \\ \vdots \\ I_e \end{bmatrix}_{n_c} ;$$

$$(18) \qquad D_{D_{I_e}} = \begin{bmatrix} D_{I_e} & \cdots & 0 \\ \cdot & \cdot & \cdot \\ 0 & \cdots & D_{I_e} \end{bmatrix}_{n_o} ;$$

$$(19) \qquad V_{D_{I_e}} = \begin{bmatrix} D_{I_e} \\ \vdots \\ D_{I_e} \end{bmatrix}_{n_o} ;$$

$$(20) \qquad D_{V_{I_e}} = \begin{bmatrix} V_{I_e} & \cdots & 0 \\ \cdot & \cdot & \cdot \\ 0 & \cdots & V_{I_e} \end{bmatrix}_{n_o} ;$$

$$(21) \qquad V_{V_{I_e}} = \begin{bmatrix} V_{I_e} \\ \vdots \\ V_{I_e} \end{bmatrix}_{n_o} .$$

The first hierarchy supermatrices given by equations (16) and (17) are the same as those given by (10) and (11), respectively, except that the order of the identity simple matrices is equal to the number of entities. This is indicated by the subscript e.

Equations (18) through (21) are analogous to equations (12) through (15), respectively. Again, the only difference is that the order of the simple identity matrices is equal to the number of entities, rather than the number of attributes.

A consideration of the three sets of second hierarchy supermatrices given, respectively, by equations (1) through (7), (10) through (15), and (16) through (21) suggests at once the typical structure of a factorial experimental design. However, here the elements of the submatrices within a design matrix are matrices themselves rather than scalar quantities.

We shall now use these definitions to consider the various ways in which the elements of a four-category data matrix may be ordered for purposes of further analysis. Equation (22) provides a basis for exhibiting systematically the various types of ordering of the entity-attribute matrices, which may suggest some rational bases for further analysis.

$$
(22) \quad
\begin{bmatrix} D_{D_{I_e}} \\ V'_{D_{I_e}} \\ D_{V'_{I_e}} \\ V'_{V'_{I_e}} \end{bmatrix} \cdot [D_{D_{x_{ij}}}] \cdot [D_{D_{I_a}}, V_{D_{I_a}}, D_{V_{I_a}}, V_{V_{I_a}}]
$$

$$
= \begin{bmatrix} M_{11} & M_{12} & M_{13} & M_{14} \\ M_{21} & M_{22} & M_{23} & M_{24} \\ M_{31} & M_{32} & M_{33} & M_{34} \\ M_{41} & M_{42} & M_{43} & M_{44} \end{bmatrix} = M.
$$

If we examine the left-hand side of this expression, we see that the left-hand factor is a third hierarchy column supervector whose elements consist, respectively, of the transposes of the second hierarchy supermatrices defined in equations (18) through (20). The middle term is simply the second hierarchy superdiagonal matrix defined in equation (4). The right-hand factor is a third hierarchy row supervector whose elements are, respectively, the second hierarchy supermatrices defined in equations (12) through (15), respectively. The right-hand side of this equation provides the element designations of the third hierarchy supermatrix.

Equations (23) through (38) indicate specifically the composition of the matric elements M in equation (22) in terms of their second-order supermatric elements. Each of these will now involve in some form all of the entity-attribute matrices for all occasions and all conditions.

$$
(23) \quad D_{D_{x_{ij}}} = \begin{bmatrix} D_{x_{i1}} & \cdots & 0 \\ \cdots & \cdots & \cdots \\ 0 & \cdots & D_{x_{in_o}} \end{bmatrix} = M_{11};
$$

$$
(24) \quad V'_{D_{x_{ij}}} = [D_{x_{i1}} \cdots D_{x_{in_o}}] = M_{21};
$$

$$
(25) \quad D_{V'_{x_{ij}}} = \begin{bmatrix} V'_{x_{i1}} & \cdots & 0 \\ \cdots & \cdots & \cdots \\ 0 & \cdots & V'_{x_{in_o}} \end{bmatrix} = M_{31};
$$

$$
(26) \quad V'_{V'_{x_{ij}}} = [V_{x_{i1}} \cdots V_{x_{in_o}}] = M_{41};
$$

$$
(27) \quad V_{D_{x_{ij}}} = \begin{bmatrix} D_{x_{i1}} \\ \vdots \\ D_{x_{in_o}} \end{bmatrix} = M_{12};
$$

$$(28) \qquad V'_{D_{I_e}} V_{D_{x_{\cdot j}}} = \sum_{j=1}^{n_o} D_{x_{ij}} = M_{22};$$

$$(29) \qquad D_{V'_{I_e}} V_{D_{x_{ij}}} = V_{V'_{x_{ij}}} = \begin{bmatrix} V'_{x_{i1}} \\ \vdots \\ V'_{x_{in_o}} \end{bmatrix} = M_{32};$$

$$(30) \qquad V'_{V'_{I_e}} V_{D_{x_{ij}}} = \sum_{j=1}^{n_o} V'_{x_{ij}} = M_{42};$$

$$(31) \qquad D_{V_{x_{ij}}} = \begin{bmatrix} V_{x_{i1}} & \cdots & 0 \\ \cdot & \cdots & \cdot \\ 0 & \cdots & V_{x_{in_o}} \end{bmatrix} = M_{13};$$

$$(32) \qquad V'_{D_{I_e}} D_{V_{x_{ij}}} = V'_{V_{x_{ij}}} = [V_{x_{i1}} \cdots V_{x_{in_o}}] = M_{23};$$

$$(33) \qquad D_{V'_{I_e}} D_{V_{x_{ij}}} = \begin{bmatrix} \sum_{i=1}^{n_c} x_{i1} & \cdots & 0 \\ \cdot & \cdots & \cdot \\ 0 & \cdots & \sum_{i=1}^{n_c} x_{in_o} \end{bmatrix} = M_{33};$$

$$(34) \qquad V'_{V'_{I_e}} D_{V_{x_{ij}}} = \left[\sum_{i=1}^{n_c} x_{i1} \cdots \sum_{i=1}^{n_c} x_{in_o} \right] = M_{43};$$

$$(35) \qquad V_{V_{x_{ij}}} = \begin{bmatrix} V_{x_{i1}} \\ \vdots \\ V_{x_{in_o}} \end{bmatrix} = M_{14};$$

$$(36) \qquad V'_{D_{I_e}} V_{V_{x_{ij}}} = \sum_{j=1}^{n_o} V_{x_{ij}} = M_{24};$$

$$(37) \qquad D_{V'_{I_e}} V_{V_{x_{ij}}} = \begin{bmatrix} \sum_{i=1}^{n_c} x_{i1} \\ \vdots \\ \sum_{i=1}^{n_c} x_{in_o} \end{bmatrix} = M_{34};$$

$$(38) \qquad V'_{V'_{I_e}} V_{V_{x_{ij}}} = \sum_{j=1}^{n_o} \sum_{i=1}^{n_c} x_{ij} = M_{44}.$$

For convenience in further analysis, equations (23) through (38) have been assembled into matrix form in equation (39).

$$(39) \quad
\begin{bmatrix}
\begin{bmatrix} D_{x_{i1}} \cdots 0 \\ \vdots \quad \ddots \quad \vdots \\ 0 \cdots D_{x_{in_o}} \end{bmatrix} &
\begin{bmatrix} D_{x_{i1}} \\ \vdots \\ D_{x_{in_o}} \end{bmatrix} &
\begin{bmatrix} V_{x_{i1}} \cdots 0 \\ \vdots \quad \ddots \quad \vdots \\ 0 \cdots V_{x_{in_o}} \end{bmatrix} &
\begin{bmatrix} V_{x_{i1}} \\ \vdots \\ V_{x_{in_o}} \end{bmatrix} \\[2em]
\begin{bmatrix} D_{x_i} \cdots D_{x_{in_o}} \end{bmatrix} &
\begin{bmatrix} \sum_{j=1}^{n_o} D_{x_{ij}} \end{bmatrix} &
\begin{bmatrix} V_{x_{i1}} \cdots V_{x_{in_o}} \end{bmatrix} &
\begin{bmatrix} \sum_{j=1}^{n_o} V_{x_{ij}} \end{bmatrix} \\[2em]
\begin{bmatrix} V'_{x_{i1}} \cdots 0 \\ \vdots \quad \ddots \quad \vdots \\ 0 \cdots V'_{x_{in_o}} \end{bmatrix} &
\begin{bmatrix} V'_{x_{i1}} \\ \vdots \\ V'_{x_{in_o}} \end{bmatrix} &
\begin{bmatrix} \sum_{i=1}^{n_c} x_{i1} \cdots 0 \\ \vdots \quad \ddots \quad \vdots \\ 0 \cdots \sum_{i=1}^{n_c} x_{in_o} \end{bmatrix} &
\begin{bmatrix} \sum_{i=1}^{n_c} x_{i1} \\ \vdots \\ \sum_{i=1}^{n_c} x_{in_o} \end{bmatrix} \\[2em]
\begin{bmatrix} V'_{x_i} \cdots V'_{x_{in_o}} \end{bmatrix} &
\begin{bmatrix} \sum_{j=1}^{n_c} V'_{x_{ij}} \end{bmatrix} &
\begin{bmatrix} \sum_{i=1}^{n_c} x_{i1} \cdots \sum_{i=1}^{n_c} x_{in_o} \end{bmatrix} &
\begin{bmatrix} \sum_{j=1}^{n_o} \sum_{i=1}^{n_c} x_{ij} \end{bmatrix}
\end{bmatrix}
= \begin{bmatrix}
M_{11} & M_{12} & M_{13} & M_{14} \\
M_{21} & M_{22} & M_{23} & M_{24} \\
M_{31} & M_{32} & M_{33} & M_{34} \\
M_{41} & M_{42} & M_{43} & M_{44}
\end{bmatrix}.$$

Equations (23) through (26) provide the elements for the first column of equation (39), those from (27) through (30) the elements of the second column, those from (31) through (34) the elements of the third column, and those from (35) through (38) the elements of the fourth column.

Let us now consider the elements of equation (39) in somewhat more detail. The submatrices in M vary with respect to the unique condition and occasion information preserved in the rows and columns for each of the entity-attribute matrices. The amount of information uniquely preserved is greater for the first row than for the last row, and for the first column than for the last column. The first row of M in equation (39) preserves information uniquely by entities, conditions, and occasions; the second row by entities and conditions; the third row by entities and occasions; and the fourth row only by entities. The first column preserves information uniquely by attributes, conditions, and occasions. The second column preserves information uniquely by attributes and conditions, the third column by attributes and occasions, and the fourth column only by attributes.

We may combine these two analyses to consider the type of unique information preserved by rows and columns for any particular matrix M_{ij}. For example, the M_{11} matric elements preserve column information by attributes, conditions, and occasions. On the other hand, the M_{44} matrix collapses all of the condition and occasion information and preserves only the entity-attribute information.

It is of interest to distinguish the matrices which collapse information through the addition of entity-attribute matrices from those which may confound information because of the particular row and column placement of the entity-attribute matrices. For example, all but the first diagonal matric elements collapse information through the addition of entity-attribute matrices. So do the M_{42}, M_{43}, M_{24}, and M_{34} matrices.

It is of particular interest to compare the M_{41} matrix with the M_{14} matrix, and the M_{32} matrix with the M_{23} matrix. In each of these four matrices all of the individual measures are preserved, but the ordering of the matrices is radically different. For example, the M_{41} matrix may be regarded as a model in which we consider each condition and each occasion for each variable as a separate variable. In M_{14} we consider each condition and each occasion for each entity as a distinct entity. In M_{32} we regard each condition for each attribute as a distinct attribute and each occasion for each entity as a distinct entity. In M_{23} we regard each occasion for each attribute as a distinct attribute and each condition for each entity as a distinct entity.

Analysis of the other submatrices could be developed along similar lines. Certainly, the diagonal supermatrix indicated by M_{11} could scarcely be regarded as a parsimonious representation of the data. It implies that each condition and each occasion for each attribute is a distinct attribute, and also that each condition and each occasion for each entity is a distinct entity. In the measurement of change, our chief interest would seem to center around the matrices in the third row and the third column. The third column preserves occasions by attributes and the third row preserves occasions by entities.

There are also important considerations of parsimony with reference to the entity-attribute matrices. We may regard each entity-attribute matrix as a linear combination of four distinct types of matrices. These are indicated in equation (40):

$$(40) \qquad x_{ij} = m_a + m_{c_i} + m_{o_j} + m_{ij}.$$

Here m_a is an attribute matrix common to all of the x_{ij} matrices; m_{c_i} is a matrix common to all matrices of condition i; m_{o_j} is a matrix common for all matrices of occasion j; and m_{ij} is a matrix specific to x_{ij}. Conditions of parsimony may now be imposed by assumptions of minimal rank in the component matrices given in (40). We indicate the rank of these matrices by their basic structure representation in equations (41) through (44), respectively.

$$(41) \qquad m_a = P_a \Delta_a Q_a';$$

$$(42) \qquad m_{c_i} = P_{c_i} \Delta_{c_i} Q_{c_i}';$$

$$(43) \qquad m_{o_j} = P_{o_j} \Delta_{o_j} Q_{o_j}';$$

$$(44) \qquad m_{ij} = P_{ij} \Delta_{ij} Q_{ij}'.$$

Here the P matrices are nonhorizontal orthonormal matrices, the Δ matrices are diagonal with all positive diagonal elements, and the Q' matrices are nonvertical orthonormals. The orders of the Δ matrices in these equations indicate the respective ranks of the m matrices. Presumably the sum of these ranks should not exceed the number of entities n_e or the number of attributes n_a, whichever is the smaller.

The problem of solving for the unknown m's in (40) and their factors in (41) through (44) amounts to solving for attribute, condition, occasion, and specific factor scores and factor loadings. We may approach this problem in a number of ways. One of the models begins with equation (45), which implies a solution for m_a with resulting residual matrices indicated by the left-hand side of this equation:

$$(45) \qquad {}_a\epsilon_{ij} = x_{ij} - m_a.$$

We may then proceed to solve for m_{c_i} for the various conditions in terms of equation (46) and get a set of residual matrices with conditions eliminated:

$$(46) \qquad {}_c\epsilon_{ij} = {}_a\epsilon_{ij} - m_{c_i}.$$

In this way we may proceed to solve for the $n_\bullet$ occasion matrices and, finally, the specific m_{ij} matrices, as indicated by equations (47) and (48):

$$(47) \qquad {}_\epsilon_{ij} = {}_c\epsilon_{ij} - m_{o_j},$$

$$(48) \qquad \epsilon_{ij} = {}_o\epsilon_{ij} - m_{ij}.$$

A particular model for the solution of the m_a matrix is indicated in equation (49):

$$(49) \qquad V_{V_{x_{ij}}} - V_{V_{I_e}} m_a = V_{V_{a\epsilon_{ij}}}.$$

A particular solution for this model would be simply the least square solution, which can readily be shown to give m_a as the average of all of the

x_{ij}'s. This in general would not appear to be a very parsimonious solution, since in general such a solution for m_a would yield a basic, rather than a nonbasic, matrix.

From equations (41), (46), and (49) we can write equation (50), since by definition Q' is an orthonormal matrix:

$$(50) \qquad V_{V_{x_{ij}}}Q_a - V_{V_{I_e}}P_a\Delta_a = V_{V_{a^e_{ij}}}Q_a.$$

Equation (50) is now in the form of a two-set canonical model. It should be observed, however, that the solution for (50) implies the constraint of orthonormality in Q'_a and in P_a. The question of rank reduction for the residuals given in equation (45) requires further investigation. In any case, the order of Δ_a in (50), and therefore the rank of m_a in (45), should be much less than the smaller order of the x_{ij} matrices.

The solutions for the m matrices and their basic structure, given by equations (46), (47), and (48), and equations (42), (43), and (44), might follow along similar lines. Of course, more complex considerations would be involved. The rank of these matrices must, in general, have restrictions placed upon them. The extent to which it is possible to impose ortho-normality and mutual orthogonality on the various basic orthonormals in equations (41) through (44) also requires further investigation. For example, let us consider equation (51):

$$(51) \qquad x_{ij} = (P_a,\ P_{c_i},\ P_{o_j},\ P_{ij}) \begin{bmatrix} \Delta_a & 0 & 0 & 0 \\ 0 & \Delta_{c_i} & 0 & 0 \\ 0 & 0 & \Delta_{o_j} & 0 \\ 0 & 0 & 0 & \Delta_{ij} \end{bmatrix} \begin{bmatrix} Q'_a \\ Q'_{c_i} \\ Q'_{o_j} \\ Q'_{ij} \end{bmatrix}.$$

This, in effect, is the supermatric form of equations (40) through (44) expressed as a basic-structure solution. To what extent and under what conditions it is possible to solve for the basic-structure–type solutions indicated by equation (51) so that the outside factors of the right-hand side are orthonormal require further investigation.

Equations (40) through (50) indicate successive solutions for the component matrices of x_{ij}. A more elegant solution would be a simultaneous solution for all of the m matrices. It seems likely that equation (39) would provide the starting point for such a solution. It is also probable that extensions of the generalized canonical models involving m sets of variables would evolve in such a simultaneous solution (Horst, 1961a, 1961b). In any case, the generalized solution should enable us to come out with fewer attribute, condition, and occasion parameters than we started with. It should also relate the number of factors for each category to the predictable variance in the occasion dimension.

It would seem that predictability of change over time or successive occasions must ultimately indicate when we have enough attribute, condition, and occasion factors. Any overall solution for the latent parameters in equation (39) should yield measures of change and estimates of reliability considerably more fundamental and meaningful than those we use currently. These estimates of reliability must indicate when we have taken out enough factors of all types. Eventually an adequate model must also incorporate the instrument dimension or category. Such a model would have to integrate or synthesize in some way the results from the instrument and occasion dimensions to give a more complete analysis of variation with respect to sets of latent primary attributes, conditions, instruments, and occasions.

We may also explore a type of solution somewhat different from those already discussed. These might be along the following lines.

In equation (15) we replace every identity matrix with a null matrix except the one corresponding to the ith condition and the jth occasion. The resulting supervector we designate E_{ij}.

In equation (11) we replace every identity matrix with a null matrix except the one corresponding to the ith condition. The resulting supervector we designate E_{c_i}.

We let E_{o_j} be a supervector of superorder n_o in which all matrix elements are square null matrices of order n_c, except the one in the jth position, which is an identity matrix. We then define U matrices with appropriate subscripts, as in equations (52) through (55).

$$(52) \qquad D_{D_{x_{ij}}} V_{V_{I_a}} = U_a;$$

$$(53) \qquad D_{D_{x_{ij}}} D_{D_{I_a}} E_{ij} = U_{a_{ij}};$$

$$(54) \qquad D_{D_{x_{ij}}} V_{D_{I_a}} E_{c_i} = U_{c_i};$$

$$(55) \qquad D_{D_{x_{ij}}} D_{V_{I_a}} E_{o_j} = U_{o_j}.$$

In equation (52) we have a column supervector of all the x_{ij} matrices. In equation (53) we have a column supervector in which only the x_{ij} matrix for the ith condition and j^{th} occasion occurs; all remaining elements are null. In equation (54) only the x_{ij} matrices for condition i occur with other elements null. In equation (55) only the matrices for condition j occur with other elements null.

We next consider transformation matrices W with appropriate subscripts and with widths not greater than, and presumably much less than, n_a. We then define Y matrices with appropriate subscripts in equations (56) through (61).

$$(56) \qquad U_a W_{a_{ij}} = Y_{ij};$$

120   *Paul Horst*

(57) $$U_{a_{ij}}W_{a_{ij}} = Y_{a_{ij}};$$

(58) $$U_a W_{c_i} = Y_i;$$

(59) $$U_{c_i} W_{c_i} = Y_{c_i};$$

(60) $$U_a W_{o_j} = Y_i;$$

(61) $$U_{o_j} W_{o_j} = Y_{o_j}.$$

The problem now is to determine the W's with appropriate restrictions so as to maximize the functions given by equations (62), (63), and (64).

(62) $$\phi_{ij} = \frac{\operatorname{tr} Y'_{a_{ij}} Y_{a_{ij}}}{\operatorname{tr} Y'_{ij} Y_{ij}};$$

(63) $$\phi_i = \frac{\operatorname{tr} Y'_{c_i} Y_{c_i}}{\operatorname{tr} Y'_i Y_i};$$

(64) $$\phi_j = \frac{\operatorname{tr} Y'_{o_j} Y_{o_j}}{\operatorname{tr} Y'_j Y_j}.$$

If we assume the W's to be orthonormal, the solutions are given by equations (65), (66), and (67).

(65) $$U'_{a_{ij}}U_{a_{ij}}W_{a_{ij}} - U'_a U_a W_{a_{ij}}\Delta^2_{a_{ij}} = 0;$$

(66) $$U'_{c_i}U_{c_i}W_{c_i} - U'_a U_a W_{c_i}\Delta^2_{c_i} = 0;$$

(67) $$U'_{o_j}U_{o_j}W_{o_j} - U'_a U_a W_{o_i}\Delta^2_{o_i} = 0;$$

where the Δ's are diagonal.

Obviously, we have $n_c \times n_o$ solutions for (65), n_c solutions for (66), and n_o solutions for (67). All of these are principal-axis or basic-structure–type solutions. The $W\Delta$ matrices will correspond to factor loadings and the Y's to factor scores. There still remain unsolved and even unformulated problems similar to those resulting from the type of analyses indicated in equations (40) through (51).

One important problem which must be mentioned, if only briefly, is that of scale and origin. The general problem is extremely complex and no adequate solutions are currently available. We propose, however, that any multicategory data matrix may appropriately begin by consideration of the M_{14} superelement of equation (39), where the individual entity-attribute matrices are arranged in column form. It would seem appropriate to standardize the measures by supercolumns in this matrix so that the means for each attribute over all conditions and all occasions can be meaningfully compared both within and between attributes.

A practical, even though unsophisticated, approach for the initial reduction of multicategory data could begin with any of the supermatric elements of equation (39) which do not collapse data and which do not have zero matric elements. These would include the supermatrices M_{41}, M_{32}, M_{23}, and M_{14}. These are the minor diagonal elements, or the elements from lower left to upper right. One may carry out a preliminary principal-axis or basic-structure solution for one of these matrices to reduce the number of variables and solve for factor-loading and factor-score matrices. It should be remembered, however, that all columns of these matrices must be considered as distinct attributes and all rows as distinct entities.

The factor-score matrices may then be substituted for the original entity-attribute data matrices in the design indicated by equation (39). In general, the number of factors one obtains should be much less than the number of attributes or cases, whichever is smaller. This could be used as a criterion for selecting the appropriate minor diagonal matrix for preliminary analysis. Since the total number of elements in each of these matrices must be the same, one should probably select the one which is most nearly square. From such a matrix one could obtain the maximum number of factors without overfitting the matrix.

The difficulty in this preliminary approach is that if unsystematic occasion variance is regarded as the criterion that enough factors of all types have been removed, one must guess the occasion predictability of the data. An estimate of reliable variance might be an appropriate function of the average intercorrelations of a single variable for all occasions and all conditions. Or such a function might appropriately include only the intercorrelations of the same variables for different occasions. In any case, the estimates of reliable variance used as a basis for indicating how many factors to remove should be such that in the final set of solutions no appreciable residual variance is left, since it is assumed that all unsystematic variance has been removed in the preliminary analysis.

Seven | Implications of Factor Analysis
of Three-Way Matrices
for Measurement of Change

LEDYARD R TUCKER

The research discussed in this paper has been jointly supported by the Office of Naval Research under contract Nonr-1834(39) and the University of Illinois. Reproduction, translation, publication, use and disposal in whole or in part by or for the United States Government is permitted.

During the past two years I have been working on the development of a factor-analytic model to deal with observations classifiable in three or more ways. This is an extension of factor analysis which, in the past, has been conceived in terms of two-way classifications, usually the data being scores of individuals on a group of variables. These data have been recorded in a two-way table, or matrix. There are increasing numbers of situations of interest to research workers in psychology and education which involve data classifiable in more than two ways. For example, each of a number of individuals may rate each of a group of objects as to each of a number of attributes of objects. Such ratings would form a three-way table or matrix as suggested by Osgood, Suci, and Tannenbaum (1957) in connection with their research on the Semantic Differential. Such data might be extended to a fourth way of classification if similar ratings were obtained under each of several response sets established experimentally. An example of particular interest to this conference involves measures of a number of traits of a number of individuals at a number of occasions.

In this paper I shall discuss: (*a*) the general nature of the three-way factor-analytic model, (*b*) some implications of this model for investigation of the structure of changes in the performances of individuals over several occasions, and (*c*) possible procedures for analysis of observations. These discussions will be illustrated with a fictitious problem which has been set up to possess a number of possibly ideal properties.

Consider Table 7.1. This table presents the scores of 12 individuals on 9 traits measured on 5 occasions. For each occasion ($1k$, $2k$, $3k$, $4k$, and $5k$) there is a 12 by 9 matrix of observations. If these matrices were stacked one on top of another, they would form a parallelopiped, or three-way matrix. A point on notation is the use of postscripts to numbers to indicate the way of classification involved. Thus, the symbols $1i$, $2i$, etc. indicate the first individual, the second individual, etc.; the symbols $1j$, $2j$, etc. indicate the first trait, the second trait, etc.; and the symbols $1k$, $2k$, etc. indicate the first occasion, the second occasion, etc. A second notational point is the avoidance of the use of the word "dimension" in the present context. This is to avoid confusion with other uses of "dimension" in factor analysis. Instead, the parallelopiped of data may be termed a "three-way matrix." An alternative notation is to denote a way of classification as a "mode of classification," or a "mode" for a shorter term, and to denote the data matrix as a "three-mode matrix."

Let each cell entry in the data matrix be designated by x_{ijk} where

(1) $$i, i' = 1i,\ 2i,\ 3i,\ \cdots,\ I;$$

(2) $$j, j' = 1j,\ 2j,\ 3j,\ \cdots,\ J;$$

(3) $$k, k' = 1k,\ 2k,\ 3k,\ \cdots,\ K.$$

Note the use of capital letters to designate the orders of the modes. Capital letters, also, may be used to designate the different modes. Thus, mode I involves individuals, mode J involves traits, and mode K involves occasions. These modes will be termed "observational modes." The general elements in these modes are indicated by the lower case letters, primes being used to designate alternate general elements. These modes are indexing sets for various coefficients and their elements are used as subscripts to the coefficients. Sums of these coefficients will be taken over indicated ranges of the elements in the modes.

Consider, now, Table 7.2 which presents the intrinsic structure for the data matrix in Table 7.1. There is a two-mode matrix corresponding to each observational mode in Table 7.1: A with elements a_{im}, B with elements b_{jp}, and C with elements c_{kq}, where

(4) $$m, m' = 1m,\ 2m,\ 3m,\ \cdots,\ M;$$

(5) $$p, p' = 1p,\ 2p,\ 3p,\ \cdots,\ P;$$

(6) $$q, q' = 1q,\ 2q,\ 3q,\ \cdots,\ Q.$$

These modes may be termed "intrinsic modes." There is a central, or core, three-mode matrix G, with entries g_{mpq}. This matrix links together the

TABLE 7.1

Observations for Fictitious Problem

Oc-casion (k)	Indi-vidual (i)	Trait (j)								
		1j	2j	3j	4j	5j	6j	7j	8j	9j
1k	1i	120	120	80	160	160	80	0	40	40
	2i	120	112	80	128	136	64	0	40	32
	3i	72	80	48	128	120	64	0	24	32
	4i	156	120	104	64	100	32	0	52	16
	5i	144	104	96	32	72	16	0	48	8
	6i	36	56	24	128	108	64	0	12	32
	7i	36	56	24	128	108	64	0	12	32
	8i	0	40	0	160	120	80	0	0	40
	9i	60	56	40	64	68	32	0	20	16
	10i	72	64	48	64	72	32	0	24	16
	11i	24	32	16	64	56	32	0	8	16
	12i	24	24	16	32	32	16	0	8	8
2k	1i	240	245	175	340	335	200	30	95	115
	2i	231	221	168	268	278	162	28	91	95
	3i	153	171	112	276	258	158	20	61	89
	4i	294	232	205	144	206	90	18	107	54
	5i	276	205	193	84	155	60	18	101	39
	6i	72	112	61	256	216	154	26	37	90
	7i	84	124	61	272	232	146	10	33	78
	8i	12	89	17	324	247	180	18	13	99
	9i	126	120	93	144	150	90	18	51	54
	10i	141	129	98	140	152	78	8	51	43
	11i	51	67	42	132	116	82	16	25	49
	12i	48	49	35	68	67	40	6	19	23
3k	1i	390	410	320	600	580	420	120	190	270
	2i	354	352	292	464	466	344	112	174	228
	3i	270	304	220	496	462	328	80	130	204
	4i	435	358	326	272	349	208	72	181	140
	5i	420	326	316	184	278	164	72	176	118
	6i	117	182	130	416	351	312	104	91	208
	7i	165	230	130	480	415	280	40	75	160
	8i	48	166	68	536	418	340	72	52	206
	9i	219	214	182	272	277	208	72	109	140
	10i	222	212	164	256	266	160	32	90	96
	11i	90	116	92	224	198	176	64	62	120
	12i	78	82	64	120	116	84	24	38	54
4k	1i	510	545	445	820	785	620	210	275	415
	2i	447	455	396	628	620	510	196	247	353
	3i	369	417	316	684	636	482	140	193	311

Oc-casion (k)	Indi-vidual (i)	Trait (j)								
		1j	2j	3j	4j	5j	6j	7j	8j	9j
	4i	537	454	421	384	467	318	126	242	222
	5i	528	421	415	276	383	264	126	239	195
	6i	153	238	193	544	459	454	182	142	318
	7i	237	322	193	656	571	398	70	114	234
	8i	84	233	119	708	559	480	126	91	303
	9i	297	294	261	384	387	318	126	162	222
	10i	285	279	218	356	362	234	56	123	145
	11i	123	157	138	300	266	262	112	97	187
	12i	102	109	89	164	157	124	42	55	83
5k	1i	540	580	480	880	840	680	240	300	460
	2i	468	480	424	672	660	560	224	268	392
	3i	396	448	344	736	684	528	160	212	344
	4i	558	476	444	416	498	352	144	258	248
	5i	552	444	440	304	412	296	144	256	220
	6i	162	252	212	576	486	496	208	158	352
	7i	258	348	212	704	614	432	80	126	256
	8i	96	252	136	752	596	520	144	104	332
	9i	318	316	284	416	418	352	144	178	248
	10i	300	296	232	384	388	256	64	132	160
	11i	132	168	152	320	284	288	128	108	208
	12i	108	116	96	176	168	136	48	60	92

matrices A, B, and C, thus giving the relations among the intrinsic modes. The basic equation for the three-way factor-analytic model relates the observed matrix X to the intrinsic structure and may be expressed in summational notation as

$$(7) \qquad x_{ijk} = \sum_m \sum_p \sum_q a_{im} b_{jp} c_{kq} g_{mpq}.$$

A possible interpretation of the intrinsic modes is that they represent idealized entities. Thus, the matrix A describes the observed individuals in mode I in terms of the idealized individuals in mode M. Similarly, the matrices B and C describe the observed traits in mode J in terms of the idealized traits in mode P and the observed occasions in mode K in terms of the idealized occasions in mode Q. The matrix G gives the relations among the idealized individuals, traits, and occasions.

Consider the arrangement of the basic equation (7) as

$$(8) \qquad x_{ijk} = \sum_m \sum_p a_{im} b_{jp} \sum_q c_{kq} g_{mpq},$$

and define

TABLE 7.2
The Intrinsic Structure

$A\,(a_{im})$

	$1m$	$2m$	$3m$	$4m$
$1i$	5	0	0	0
$2i$	4	1	0	1
$3i$	4	-1	0	-1
$4i$	3	2	1	0
$5i$	3	0	2	0
$6i$	3	0	-1	2
$7i$	3	0	-1	-2
$8i$	3	0	-2	0
$9i$	3	-2	1	0
$10i$	2	1	0	-1
$11i$	2	-1	0	1
$12i$	1	0	0	0

$G\,(g_{mpq})$

$1q$:

	$1p$	$2p$	$3p$
$1m$	2	2	0
$2m$	2	0	0
$3m$	3	-2	0
$4m$	0	0	0

$2q$:

	$1p$	$2p$	$3p$
$1m$	2	3	3
$2m$	0	0	0
$3m$	1	-1	0
$4m$	-1	-1	2

$B'\,(b_{jp})$

	$1j$	$2j$	$3j$	$4j$	$5j$	$6j$	$7j$	$8j$	$9j$
$1p$	3	2	2	0	1	0	0	1	0
$2p$	0	1	0	4	3	2	0	0	1
$3p$	0	0	1	0	0	2	2	1	2

$C'\,(c_{ka})$

	$1k$	$2k$	$3k$	$4k$	$5k$
$1q$	4	7	1	0	10
$2q$	0	1	4	9	8

(9)
$$n_{mpk} = \sum_q c_{kq} g_{mpq};$$

then

(10)
$$x_{ijk} = \sum_m \sum_p a_{im} b_{jp} n_{mpk}.$$

Let X_k be the two-mode matrix, $I \times J$, of observations for the kth occasion and N_k be the two-mode matrix, $M \times P$, of n_{mpk} for the kth occasion; then equation (10) may be written in matrix form for the kth occasion as

(11)
$$X_k = AN_k B'.$$

The matrices N_k are given in the top section of Table 7.3 and are termed the core matrices for the occasions.

Rearrangement of equation (10) gives

(12)
$$x_{ijk} = \sum_p b_{jp} \sum_m a_{im} n_{mpk}.$$

Define

(13)
$$s_{ipk} = \sum_m a_{im} n_{mpk};$$

then equation (12) becomes

(14)
$$x_{ijk} = \sum_p b_{jp} s_{ipk}.$$

In matrix form, equation (13) is

(15)
$$S_k = AN_k$$

and equation (14) is

(16)
$$X_k = S_k B',$$

where S_k is a two-mode matrix, $I \times P$, of s_{ipk} for the kth occasion. The entries, s_{ipk}, in each matrix S_k can be thought of as factor scores of the individuals on factors in the intrinsic mode P. As indicated earlier, this mode may be considered to be composed of idealized traits and the matrix B to give the description of the observed traits in terms of these idealized traits.

A decision was made in the definitions leading to equations (14) and (16) to keep the relations of observed traits to intrinsic traits constant over occasions and to assign all changes to changes in the factor scores for the individuals for the several occasions. The definition of these factor scores can be summarized in a single equation by substitution of equation (9)

TABLE 7.3

Internal Matrices for Occasions (k) and Variable Factors (p)

		1k			2k			3k			4k			5k	
		1p	2p	3p	1p	2p	3p	1p	2p	3p	1p	2p	3p	1p	2p	3p
Variable factor core matrices for occasions	1m	8	8	0	16	17	3	26	30	12	34	41	21	36	44	24
	2m	8	0	0	14	0	0	18	0	0	20	0	0	20	0	0
	3m	12	−8	0	22	−15	0	31	−22	0	37	−27	0	38	−28	0
	4m	0	0	0	−1	−1	2	−4	−4	8	−7	−7	14	−8	−8	16
Mean cross-products for variable factor scores	1p	848	544	0	3241	2391	478	8061	7134	3088	13378	12990	7042	14868	14840	8512
	2p	544	704	0	2391	3116	508	7134	9500	3568	12990	17588	8512	14840	20208	10432
	3p	0	0	0	478	508	94	3088	3568	1504	7042	8512	4606	8512	10432	6016
Variable factor covariances	1p	272	−32	0	937	−57	46	1977	114	280	2974	444	616	3204	584	736
	2p	−32	128	0	−57	515	49	114	1400	328	444	2459	763	584	2784	928
	3p	0	0	0	46	49	13	280	328	208	616	763	637	736	928	832
Variable factor scores	Mean	24	24	0	48	51	9	78	90	36	102	123	63	108	132	72
	σ	16.5	11.3	0	30.6	22.7	3.6	44.5	37.4	14.4	54.5	49.6	25.2	52.8	56.6	28.8
Variable factor correlations	1p	1.00	−.17	—	1.00	−.08	.42	1.00	.07	.44	1.00	.16	.45	1.00	.20	.45
	2p	−.17	1.00	—	−.08	1.00	.60	.07	1.00	.61	.16	1.00	.61	.20	1.00	.61
	3p	—	—	—	.42	.60	1.00	.44	.61	1.00	.45	.61	1.00	.45	.61	1.00

into equation (13) to obtain

(17)
$$s_{ipk} = \sum_m \sum_q a_{im} c_{kq} g_{mpq}.$$

Given each matrix, S_k, of factor scores for occasion k, several statistics can be determined which are of major interest. These statistics are given in Table 7.3. First are the matrices of mean cross-products over individuals between the idealized traits, or variable factor scores; second are the corresponding covariances; third are the means and standard deviations of these scores; and fourth are the correlations between these factors. The example was set up so that all scores on factor $3p$ were zero for the first occasion. Consequently, the corresponding mean and standard deviation were zero also and the correlations of this factor were indeterminate. The implication is that the matrix of observations, X_k, for the first occasion did not involve the idealized trait $3p$ and, consequently, was of rank 2 instead of 3, the number of idealized traits necessary for the entire system. All of the other matrices X_k are of rank 3. The progression of mean scores on the idealized traits or variable factors is interesting. Means for the first factor increase rapidly over the first four occasions, followed by a relatively very small gain between occasions $4k$ and $5k$. Means for the third factor increase relatively less rapidly from occasion $1k$ to $2k$, followed by a rapid increase to occasion $4k$, followed by a smaller increase from occasion $4k$ to $5k$. These increases in means appear to follow different laws for the different factors. The same is true for the observed variables both in terms of the individual scores given in Table 7.1 and the means of these scores. In fact, however, all of the variety of forms of increase are linear combinations of the two rows of the matrix C' given in Table 7.2. The row for idealized occasion $1q$ represents one law of score increase while the second row represents another such law. The first law has large early increases, followed by no change from observed occasion $4k$ to $5k$. The second law has a small change from the first to second occasion, followed by relatively larger increases to occasion $4k$, followed by a lesser increase to the last occasion. The first law might represent early learning while the second law would represent delayed learning.

The progression of the standard deviations is to be noted also. All of these increase from occasion to occasion. We have already noted the zero standard deviation for variable factor $3p$ on occasion $1k$. Small values of these standard deviations indicate small influences of the factors on the individual differences in observed scores at given occasions.

Consider the progression in the correlation between factor $1p$ and factor $2p$ from occasion to occasion. This correlation starts out at a negative value and increases to a positive value. The correlations with factor $3p$ are indeterminate at first, but are almost constant from occasion $2k$ to occasion $5k$. These trends indicate the possible variety for the correlations of factors during the development of individuals and, when considered with the standard deviations, may account for the perplexing variety of results from factorial studies at several ages.

Let us consider the possibility of performing a factor analysis for each occasion and the relation of these analyses to the triple-mode model in the present development. In standard factor-analytic theory, the basic equation relates standard scores on the observed variables at each occasion to standard scores on the factors at that occasion. A form of this equation is

$$(18) \qquad Y_k = Z_k F'_k,$$

where Y_k is an $I \times J$ matrix of standard scores on the observed traits for occasion k, Z_k is an $I \times R$ matrix of standard scores on the factors (mode R) for occasion k, and F_k is a $J \times R$ matrix of factor loadings for occasion k. Our problem is to develop a corresponding equation from the triple-mode model. Standardization of the observed scores on each occasion can be accomplished by

$$(19) \qquad Y_k = [X_k - (1)\overline{X}_k](\sigma_{jk}^{-1}),$$

where (1) is a column vector of ones, $\overline{X}_k$ is a row vector of means of columns of X_k, and (σ_{jk}^{-1}) is a diagonal matrix containing the reciprocals of the standard deviations of the columns of X_k. At this point we make the inductive step of equating the factors for each occasion with the idealized traits. The validity of this step can be checked in terms of derived relations. With this step, the matrix of standard factor scores can be developed from the matrix S_k of the triple-mode model

$$(20) \qquad Z_k = [S_k - (1)\overline{S}_k](\sigma_{pk}^{-1}),$$

where the matrices have similar definitions to those in equation (19). Manipulation of equation (16) in terms of equations (19) and (20) yields

$$(21) \qquad Y_k = Z_k(\sigma_{pk})B'(\sigma_{jk}).$$

To complete the development of equation (18), let

$$(22) \qquad F'_k = (\sigma_{pk})B'(\sigma_{jk}).$$

This demonstrates the possible interpretation that the factor matrix for each occasion is obtained from the generalized factor matrix B as a result of scaling both observed scores and factor scores to standard scores for the occasion. The factors have different relative importance at different occasions as a result of the multiplication by the matrices of standard deviations. Whenever one of the standard deviations is zero, that factor disappears for that occasion. Then the number of factors for that occasion is less than the number of factors in the generalized factor matrix. An example is occasion $1k$ in the example for which the standard deviation is zero for factor $3p$. It is possible that a different factor could disappear for each occasion so that the factor matrices for the separate occasions would be of lower rank than the generalized factor matrix. In the extreme case, the factors for each occasion could be distinct from the factors for all other occasions. The generalized factor matrix would contain all of these factors and be of rank equal to the sum of the ranks for the occasions. The transitions from one occasion to another for actual data could be of very high interest.

Our final area of discussion involves possible procedures to be applied to observed data to investigate the intrinsic structure according to the triple-mode model presented earlier in this paper. This discussion will be limited to an extension of the principal-components–type analysis from the two-mode case to the three-mode case. This analysis may be generalized quite readily to the cases for four or more modes. An initial step in this development is to consider the possibilities of internal transformations of the matrices and of the intrinsic modes. Let T_m be a square, nonsingular matrix of order M with entries t_{m*m} where $m*$ are elements of a transformed intrinsic mode $M*$. The matrix A may be transformed to a matrix V_i with entries v_{im*} by the equation

$$(23) \qquad A T_m^{-1} = V_i.$$

For the present, let T_m be so defined that V_i is a section of an orthonormal matrix: That is, the sums of squares of the columns of V_i are unity and the sums of cross-products between pairs of columns are zero. This restriction may be satisfied in many ways, for, once one solution is known, many solutions may be obtained by postmultiplications by an orthogonal transformation. We may place further restrictions on this transformation in a following step.

Similar transformations may be defined for the other intrinsic modes P and Q such that

$$(24) \qquad B T_p^{-1} = V_j,$$

$$(25) \qquad C T_q^{-1} = V_k.$$

Both V_j and V_k are sections of orthonormal matrices. Entries in these matrices are v_{jp*} and v_{kq*}.

In order to maintain equivalence to the observed triple-mode matrix X, compensating transformations must be performed on the core matrix G to obtain the matrix G^* with elements g_{m*p*q*}:

$$\text{(26)} \qquad g_{m^*p^*q^*} = \sum_m \sum_p \sum_q t_{m^*m} t_{p^*p} t_{q^*q} g_{mpq}.$$

Then

$$\text{(27)} \qquad x_{ijk} = \sum_{m^*} \sum_{p^*} \sum_{q^*} v_{im^*} v_{jp^*} v_{kq^*} g_{m^*p^*q^*}.$$

An interesting property of this transformation is that, if the matrices V_i, V_j, and V_k are known along with the triple-mode matrix X, the matrix G^* may be obtained by the equation

$$\text{(28)} \qquad g_{m^*p^*q^*} = \sum_i \sum_j \sum_k v_{im^*} v_{jp^*} v_{kq^*} x_{ijk}.$$

In order to obtain matrices V_i, V_j, and V_k we define matrices P_i, P_j, and P_k with entries $p_{ii'}$, $p_{jj'}$, and $p_{kk'}$ by

$$\text{(29)} \qquad p_{ii'} = \sum_j \sum_k x_{ijk} x_{i'jk},$$

$$\text{(30)} \qquad p_{jj'} = \sum_i \sum_k x_{ijk} x_{ij'k},$$

$$\text{(31)} \qquad p_{kk'} = \sum_i \sum_j x_{ijk} x_{ijk'}.$$

The computation of P_j is most easily seen in Table 7.1. Results of the computations are in Table 7.4. The matrix P_j is square and symmetric with a row and a column for each of the traits. The first diagonal entry is the sum of squares of the observations in Table 7.1 for the first column, headed $1j$, over all individuals on all occasions. That is, each entry in column $1j$ is squared and the sum obtained down the entire column as it is laid out in Table 7.1. The off-diagonal entries in P_j are the sums of cross-products between columns of the matrix X as laid out in Table 7.1.

In order to compute the matrix P_i the observations in Table 7.1 may be recorded so that there is a section of columns for each occasion with columns in each section for each trait. There would be a row for each individual i. This amounts to moving the sections for each occasion from being below one another to being beside one another. The matrix P_i then contains the sums of squares of the rows of the rearranged matrix and the sums of cross-products between pairs of rows. The matrix P_k may be obtained in a similar way, following a rearrangement, so that there is one row for each occasion and a column for each combination of individual and trait.

We may now tighten our restrictions on the transformations so that the matrices V_i, V_j, and V_k contain characteristic vectors of the matrices P_i, P_j, and P_k, respectively. These matrices are given in Table 7.5. Once the V matrices are determined, the G^* matrix may be determined by equation (28). The characteristic roots of the P matrices have interesting relations to the G^* matrix as given in the following equations:

$$\text{(32)} \qquad \alpha_{m^*} = \sum_{p^*} \sum_{q^*} g_{m^*p^*q^*}^2,$$

$$\text{(33)} \qquad \beta_{p^*} = \sum_{m^*} \sum_{q^*} g_{m^*p^*q^*}^2,$$

$$\text{(34)} \qquad \gamma_{q^*} = \sum_{m^*} \sum_{p^*} g_{m^*p^*q^*}^2.$$

Thus, each characteristic root is the sum of squares of the entries in one plane of the matrix G^*. This matrix has interesting orthogonality properties for parallel planes in any of three possible directions for planes. For $m^* \neq m^{*\prime}$, $p^* \neq p^{*\prime}$, $q^* \neq q^{*\prime}$:

$$\text{(35)} \qquad \sum_{p^*} \sum_{q^*} g_{m^*p^*q^*} g_{m^{*\prime}p^*q^*} = \sum_{m^*} \sum_{q^*} g_{m^*p^*q^*} g_{m^*p^{*\prime}q^*}$$

$$= \sum_{m^*} \sum_{p^*} g_{m^*p^*q^*} g_{m^*p^*q^{*\prime}} = 0.$$

Once the V matrices and the G^* matrices are determined, there remain problems of transformations of the intrinsic modes. These transformations are the inverses of the transformations indicated in equations (23)–(26). In general they will not be known. For our example, however, we have a known starting structure, and the transformations given in Table 7.5 will return us to this structure. The determination of these transformations for the case of analyzing experimental data is similar to the problem of rotation of axes in two-mode factor analysis but must be repeated for each of the modes. The expectations might be that a simple structure would exist for the B matrix relating observed traits to the idealized traits and the example was constructed accordingly. For the matrix C, the ideal solution might be the indication of distinct laws of increase in performance as built into our example. The matrix A might be explored for a simple structure which would be indicative of different types of individuals. An alternative is to set up the transformation so that the core matrix is as simple as possible. There is no sure way of determining all of

TABLE 7.4

The P Matrices

Matrix P_i (Trace = 39517800)					
	1i	2i	3i	4i	5i	6i
1i	7834150	6438850	6095790	5156420	4469390	4587620
2i	6438850	5311104	4991056	4304300	3753530	3742368
3i	6095790	4991056	4762208	3945972	3397494	3597824
4i	5156420	4304300	3945972	3747100	3352492	2798932
5i	4469390	3753530	3397494	3352492	3034150	2366812
6i	4587620	3742368	3597824	2798932	2366812	2850756
7i	5044460	4094032	3977104	3130132	2643940	3040148
8i	4931590	3973090	3917454	2835212	2329118	3138332
9i	4013460	3312540	3108996	2699244	2363292	2320452
10i	3533610	2911396	2742380	2407332	2104338	2002016
11i	2733710	2239684	2134252	1717804	1471174	1668080
12i	1566830	1287770	1219158	1031284	893878	917524

Matrix P_j (Trace = 39517800)					
	1j	2j	3j	4j	5j	6j
1j	4362768	4272876	3596832	5457456	5547348	4105368
2j	4272876	4371552	3583704	6091872	5993196	4516176
3j	3596832	3583704	3003408	4743264	4756392	3582672
4j	5457456	6091872	4743264	9814272	9179856	7117056
5j	5547348	5993196	4756392	9179856	8734008	6706248
6j	4105368	4516176	3582672	7117056	6706248	5250048
7j	1376640	1470240	1211040	2209920	2116320	1691520
8j	2142576	2159412	1804464	2924112	2907276	2214216
9j	2741004	2993208	2396856	4663488	4411284	3470784

Matrix P_k (Trace = 39517800)				
	1k	2k	3k	4k	5k
1k	520512	1091088	1891920	2562624	2742816
2k	1091088	2308380	4050852	5520552	5919528
3k	1891920	4050852	7216788	9909744	10649736
4k	2562624	5520552	9909744	13658280	14694240
5k	2742816	5919528	10649736	14694240	15813840

TABLE 7.4 (*continued*)

The *P* Matrices

		Matrix P_i (Trace = 39517800)				
7*i*	8*i*	9*i*	10*i*	11*i*	12*i*	
5044460	4931590	4013460	3533610	2733710	1566830	1*i*
4094032	3973090	3312540	2911396	2239684	1287770	2*i*
3977104	3917454	3108996	2742380	2134252	1219158	3*i*
3130132	2835212	2699244	2407332	1717804	1031284	4*i*
2643940	2329118	2363292	2104338	1471174	893878	5*i*
3040148	3138332	2320452	2002016	1668080	917524	6*i*
3395940	3409412	2540484	2254144	1781424	1008892	7*i*
3409412	3588790	2452860	2135994	1809278	986318	8*i*
2540484	2452860	2072124	1817172	1393596	802692	9*i*
2254144	2135994	1817172	1624016	1202872	706722	10*i*
1781424	1809278	1393596	1202872	984096	546742	11*i*
1008892	986318	802692	706722	546742	313366	12*i*

		Matrix P_j (Trace = 39517800)	
7*j*	8*j*	9*j*	
1376640	2142576	2741004	1*j*
1470240	2159412	2993208	2*j*
1211040	1804464	2396856	3*j*
2209920	2924112	4663488	4*j*
2116320	2907276	4411284	5*j*
1691520	2214216	3470784	6*j*
586560	752160	1139040	7*j*
752160	1090272	1483188	8*j*
1139040	1483188	2304912	9*j*

the transformations to uniquely meaningful positions of the transformed modes. This is one of the remaining problems with the present model. It well may be that different solutions would be appropriate for different situations. The only point known for sure is that there exists freedom for transformation of the intrinsic modes.

Another major unsolved problem is the generalization of the communality problem to the three-mode situation. I am not sure as to the meaning and function of specific factors in the triple-mode case. One of the aspects of this problem comes from the repetition of measurements of given traits on the different occasions. A factor that is specific to one measure on one occasion may become common over the several occasions. These effects

TABLE 7.5

Analysis of the *P* Matrices

V_i

	1m*	2m*	3m*	4m*
1i	.455	.001	.017	−.025
2i	.374	.090	.233	.312
3i	.354	−.088	−.206	−.352
4i	.300	−.464	−.084	.423
5i	.260	.545	.066	−.198
6i	.267	−.285	.543	.211
7i	.293	−.259	−.579	−.058
8i	.287	−.544	−.046	.168
9i	.233	.081	.160	−.636
10i	.205	.103	−.335	.187
11i	.159	−.102	.348	−.207
12i	.091	−.000	.003	−.005

T_m

	1m	2m	3m	4m
1m*	10.93	.20	−.08	−.08
2m*	.03	1.15	3.27	−.08
3m*	.41	−.73	.34	3.37
4m*	−.60	3.18	−1.10	.81

Roots:
$\alpha_1 = 37769597$
$\alpha_2 = 1631421$
$\alpha_3 = 109504$
$\alpha_4 = 7278$

T_m^{-1}

	1m*	2m*	3m*	4m*
1m	.0911	.0002	.0034	−.0050
2m	.0166	.0957	−.0610	.2649
3m	−.0068	.2723	.0282	−.0915
4m	−.0067	−.0065	.2805	.0674

V_j

	1p*	2p*	3p*
1j	.315	.618	−.150
2j	.335	.293	−.180
3j	.269	.406	.175
4j	.500	−.474	−.321
5j	.480	−.150	−.291
6j	.369	−.250	.390
7j	.118	−.013	.550
8j	.164	−.200	.225
9j	.244	−.131	.470

T_p

	1p	2p	3p
1p*	2.80	4.76	1.89
2p*	3.30	−2.68	−.18
3p*	−.53	−1.09	3.22

Roots:
$\beta_1 = 37686730$
$\beta_2 = 1642559$
$\beta_3 = 188511$

T_p^{-1}

	1p*	2p*	3p*
1p	.1049	.2060	−.0500
2p	.1250	−.1186	−.0802
3p	.0592	−.0064	.2752

V_k

	1q*	2q*
1k	.111	−.507
2k	.239	−.680
3k	.428	−.313
4k	.589	.181

T_q

	1q	2q
1q*	18.19	11.14
2q*	−3.91	2.44

Roots:
$\gamma_1 = 39382020$

T_q^{-1}

	1q*	2q*
1q	.0278	−.1267
2q	.0445	.2068

may result in greatly increased complexity of solutions when an attempt is made to utilize communalities in the model.

This paper should be considered as a progress report on the development of a model for handling the cases when data are collected such as to involve multiple ways in which to classify the data. The parts of this model may have properties that succinctly summarize the structure of relations existent in the data and may help us in understanding the effects of change when multiple measures are taken on many individuals at a number of occasions.

Eight | Canonical Factor Models for the Description of Change

CHESTER W. HARRIS

This paper has a limited scope and purpose. It is intended to review the notion of canonical factor analysis, which is a development due to Rao (1955), but one that is related to the earlier development known as the maximum likelihood solution for factor analysis first presented by Lawley (1940). We shall take certain liberties with the work of Lawley and Rao, primarily by underplaying the tests of significance associated with their formulations and emphasizing the features that appear to us to be important considerations in any attempt to describe a population of persons. The point of view implied here is that a careful examination of descriptive procedures is a necessary, if primitive, step in the eventual development of generalizations about populations that are based on samples. We do not intend to assert that the descriptive problem is the only problem; we do, however, believe that at the present time the modes of describing change need further examination in an effort to clarify alternatives and to emphasize their psychometric strengths and limitations. In this respect we are adopting a point of view that underlies certain work of Guttman (1954b, 1956), namely, that there is a legitimate set of problems centered around the question of how various descriptive measures behave when certain measurement procedures—rather than samples of persons—are varied. A major limitation, then, of this paper is its emphasis on psychometric problems, as distinguished from inferential problems—in the sense of sampling persons.

A long-term interest in the idea of factor analysis provides motivation for the paper, but also prompts the introduction of another limitation. It seems to be a reasonable inference from the books, monographs, and journal articles which include the words "factor analysis" somewhere in the title that this is not a unitary concept. One rather gross, but quite

138

meaningful, distinction that can be made is the distinction between the analysis of the data in hand—either completely or incompletely in the sense of accounting for the total variance in these data—and what has often been labeled a "communality solution." It might assist us—at least in communication—to call the analysis of the data in hand "component analysis" and to leave "factor analysis" for the second category. This crude distinction does not solve all the problems of variant meanings, however. For example, Harman's recent volume (1960) adequately documents the point that there are varieties (some of them probably quite trivial variations) within the second category. The limitation imposed here is that of considering only an analysis that might be classified in category two. Further, we shall focus attention on only one of the "methods," but we shall try to show that this is a distinctive method conceptually, as well as differing in computation routine. It is quite evident that the canonical factor model has not been used extensively and has not been discussed widely; however, discussion or use is not an infallible guide to methodology.

A third limitation being imposed is that of concern primarily with problems of describing change in "pattern" or "profile" as distinguished from change in "scale" or "elevation." Let us suppose that for a group of students being introduced to a particular instructional program we secure a number of measures of status, as of that time, and then at the conclusion of the instructional program we repeat these measures. This practice would make available data from a set of pretests and a comparable or possibly "identical" set of post-tests for a specified group of students. Presumably these data contain at least a modest amount of information about change (or lack of change) in these students, and the question of how to extract or summarize this information arises. One distinction that can be made is between changes in elevation, as represented, say, by changes in mean score, and changes in pattern or profile. Concern with changes in pattern or profile would be represented by a question of whether or not the abilities or achievements represented in the battery tend to become "integrated" during the period, tend to remain related in the same fashion, or tend to become more specific. That this is a question of some interest is evident in the speculations about the pattern of growth of intelligence. Let us ignore the many problems connected with the assessment of changes in elevation and focus attention on this problem of changes in pattern. Very roughly, we are slighting the question of the constancy of the IQ in order to attend to the question of whether g increases or decreases. Undoubtedly, Cattell (1962) would insist on elaborating the question to include two g's.

The canonical factor model

This section merely describes the canonical factor model without particular reference to the problem of measuring change; in the following section we shall attempt to show the relevance of certain characteristics of the model to this problem. This first section therefore is somewhat abstract.

There appears to be more than one way in which the canonical factor model may be developed. Rao's approach is to consider a set of factor measurements that are uncorrelated with each other. He wishes to choose these arrays in such a way that given a certain restriction, each has a maximum possible correlation with the observed data. Define W as the set of observed data scaled and deviated so that $W'W$ yields the matrix of intercorrelations of the observed variables with units in the diagonal. Throughout we use R to symbolize this matrix of intercorrelations. If S symbolizes these factor measurements, then

$$(1) \qquad \begin{bmatrix} W' \\ S' \end{bmatrix} \cdot [W \quad S] = \begin{bmatrix} R & F \\ F' & I \end{bmatrix}$$

yields a supermatrix for which a canonical solution results by solving the determinantal equation:

$$(2) \qquad |FF' - aR| = 0.$$

The roots, a_i, of (2) are the squares of the canonical correlations between the set W and the set S. The matrix F symbolizes the correlations between the observed data, W, and the factor measurements or factor scores.

What we earlier called a component analysis can now be defined with respect to (1) and (2). Suppose we require that $FF' = R$; then (2) has a solution for which every root, a_i, equals unity when R is nonsingular. (If R is of rank less than its order, then one or more a_i may be zero.) Under these conditions, the matrix S is a linear transformation of the observations, W, and consequently is a set of factor measurements, or factor scores, that can be computed rather than estimated. If, however, we require that FF' reproduce only the off-diagonal elements of R (reproduce the correlations, but not the unit diagonals), we in effect define $FF' = R - U^2$, where U^2 is a diagonal matrix of unique variances. With this definition we may modify (2) thus:

$$(3) \qquad |R - U^2 - aR| = 0,$$

or

$$|R - bU^2| = 0,$$

where $b_i = 1/(1 - a_i)$. It should be evident that (3) cannot be developed from (2) when any a_i is permitted to equal unity. One way to define a communality solution is to specify that (3) holds as well as (2). The restriction on the arrays of S that is implicit in the Rao procedure is that they be hypothetical, i.e., that W' approximate rather than equal FS'. See Harris (1955). When this restriction is introduced, we also restrict the squares of the canonical correlations, a_i, to less than unity.

Another treatment of the supermatrix of (1) would yield the determinantal equation:

$$(4) \qquad \left| F'R^{-1}F - aI \right| = 0.$$

The roots of (4) are identical with the roots of (2); see T. W. Anderson (1958, pp. 340–41). Once again, a component analysis is implied by (4) when F is the complete set of correlations yielded by a linear transformation of the elements of R. Note that (4) may be written only if R is nonsingular; if so, then $FF'=R$ implies $F'R^{-1}F=I$, and each $a_i=1$. When $FF'=R-U^2$, equation (4), following the standard canonical analysis, indicates that the characteristic vectors of $F'R^{-1}F$ give the relative weights to be used in making linear combinations of the elements of S that will have the maximum, next to maximum, etc., correlation with the appropriate linear combinations of W.

Equation (4) may be derived in a slightly different fashion. Let us now consider a set of hypothetical factor measurements, or factor scores, S, and their least squares approximations, $\overline{S}$. The standard procedure (Harman, 1960, pp. 338–48) directs that $\overline{S}$ be estimated by

$$(5) \qquad \overline{S}' = F'R^{-1}W',$$

with the result that

$$(6) \qquad \overline{S}'\overline{S} = \overline{S}'S = S'\overline{S} = F'R^{-1}F.$$

Therefore the supermatrix generated by the hypothetical and the estimated factor scores is

$$(7) \qquad \begin{bmatrix} I & F'R^{-1}F \\ F'R^{-1}F & F'R^{-1}F \end{bmatrix}.$$

A canonical solution for this matrix is given by the determinantal equation already written as (4). For the case of $FF'=R$, (7) reduces to a set of four identity matrices, each of the same order, and the roots of (4) must each be unity. The case of $FF'=R-U^2$ can be solved with $F'R^{-1}F$ equal to a diagonal matrix of the roots, a_i; for such a solution, the least squares estimators of the hypothetical factor scores have zero covariances with each other and with all but one of the set of hypothetical factor scores. We shall show below in (13) that under the restriction $FF' = R - U^2$, a canonical factor matrix F is such that (7) becomes

(7a)
$$\begin{bmatrix} I & D_a \\ D_a & D_a \end{bmatrix}.$$

This point may not have been made explicit before. It is a meaningful one for those who would seek to "rotate" or transform the least squares estimators of hypothetical factor scores into arrays that have maximum correlation with the hypothetical factor scores.

A third approach to canonical factors is by way of the relationship between factors of R itself and factors of $R - U^2$. Since this relationship has been examined in some detail elsewhere (Harris, 1956), it will not be repeated here.

Let us now return to equation (3) and require that the diagonal matrix of unique variances, U^2, to be admissible, be positive-definite. This device rules out communalities of unity. Our preference is to regard an analysis that admits one or more communalities of unity as belonging to category one—component analysis—rather than category two—factor analysis. We shall also require that R be positive-definite. With both R and U^2 positive-definite (Gramian and nonsingular), (3) may be transformed into

(3a)
$$| U^{-1}RU^{-1} - bI | = 0,$$

and we deduce that all the roots, b_i, are greater than zero. The complete set of normalized characteristic vectors of $U^{-1}RU^{-1}$ may be symbolized as Q, and we may write

(8)
$$U^{-1}RU^{-1} = Q[b_i]Q',$$

(9)
$$R = UQ[b_i]Q'U,$$

and

(10)
$$R^{-1} = U^{-1}Q[1/b_i]Q'U^{-1}.$$

The internal matrices, $[b_i]$ and $[1/b_i]$, are diagonal. For any positive-definite U^2, then, we may write

(11)
$$R - U^2 = UQ[b_i - 1]Q'U,$$

noting that some of the entries in the diagonal matrix, $[b_i - 1]$, may be negative. Equation (11) locates for us the major problem: that of choosing a matrix U^2 such that $R - U^2$ will be Gramian, with the related conditions that F is real and no b_i is less than unity.

Let us assume for a moment that we can choose a matrix U^2 such that $R - U^2$ is Gramian. If so, we can write as the factors of $R - U^2$

$$(12) \qquad\qquad F = UQ[b_i - 1]^{1/2},$$

and then, using (10), observe that

$$(13) \qquad\qquad F'R^{-1}F = \left[\frac{b_i - 1}{b_i}\right].$$

The relationship $b_i = 1/(1 - a_i)$, established above, shows that the right side of (13) is the diagonal matrix of roots, a_i. Equation (13) holds generally for any $R - U^2$ expressed as in (11), but when $R - U^2$ is not Gramian, some of the a_i's are negative, corresponding to imaginary canonical correlations.

One feature of the canonical factor model that may be deduced from (3a) and our operations on it to secure (11) is that the communality problem can be translated into the problem of rescaling the standardized data by a diagonal matrix, U^{-1}, to achieve roots, b_i, of (3a), none of which is less than unity. This may seem incongruous, since we typically consider communalities in the context of reducing the rank of $R - U^2$, i.e., requiring some of the b_i to be unity. The canonical factor model permits this reduction of rank, which has as a consequence that some of the a_i's are zero. However, a real F, as in (12), can be secured without rank reduction. Later we shall comment on the functional utility of the requirement that $R - U^2$ be Gramian in estimating the elements of the matrix U^2; we shall also point out that adding a requirement that $R - U^2$ be singular or of minimum rank gives no obvious assistance in this estimation process.

A second feature of the canonical factor model is its independence of the original, and possibly arbitrary, scale of the variables. Let us assume that instead of beginning the analysis with R, the correlation matrix, we began with the variance-covariance matrix CRC, say. (C is diagonal.) We could arrive by regular steps at an analog of (3):

$$(3b) \qquad\qquad |CRC - bCU^2C| = 0,$$

which would transform into the (3a) we have already written. In other words, the roots, b_i, of (3) are invariant when the equation is premultiplied and postmultiplied by a nonsingular matrix. Consequently, when we "control" our solution by specifying the desired characteristics of the roots, b_i, we need not be concerned with the original scale of the data. It may be more convenient to work with R than with CRC, though this is not necessarily true since a machine program might be written either way.

Convenience is not the issue, however. This feature is extremely important in the case where we can conceive of various meaningful patterns of weightings of the variables and wish to examine the factor results for these several weighting systems. This will be considered again in the next section where we take up difference scores that vary as functions of weightings applied to the original variables and show that from one canonical factor analysis we can recover the analyses that would have been secured for the various weighting schemes. The general principle, illustrated with the covariance matrix, is that if the F of (12) is a satisfactory solution for $R - U^2$, then CF is the comparable solution based on the covariance matrix.

INITIAL ESTIMATION OF U^2

The mode of attack used here translates the problem of estimating communalities into the problem of rescaling the data so as to achieve a desired set of roots of (3) or (3a). The representation given in (11) indicates that $R - U^2$ will be Gramian if, and only if, no b_i is less than unity. Translating this into a requirement on the a_i, we have $R - U^2$ Gramian when all a_i's are in the interval $1 > a_i \geq 0$, and consequently all the canonical correlations are real.

Let us manufacture a matrix whose roots are the a_i. We invert $U^{-1}RU^{-1}$, of (3a), and then write

(14)
$$| I - UR^{-1}U - aI | = 0$$

to achieve this. For $R - U^2$ to be Gramian, it is necessary that every diagonal element of $I - UR^{-1}U$ be positive, providing we have not included in the set of variables one or more that is uncorrelated with all the others. This procedural rule will be assumed in what follows. Therefore:

$$1 - u_j^2 r^{jj} > 0,$$

which is equivalent to

(15)
$$u_j^2 < 1/r^{jj}.$$

We are using u_j^2 as a symbol for the diagonal elements of U^2 and r^{ii} for the diagonal elements of R^{-1}. Inequality (15) gives the familiar squared multiple correlation of each variable with the remaining variables in the set as a lower bound to the communality of the variable. Here we have written this relation as an upper bound to the unique variance, u_j^2. Guttman (1954b) developed our (15) without the procedural rule and consequently allowed u_j^2 to equal $1/r^{ii}$.

Let s_j^2 designate $1/r^{jj}$, and write U_s^2 to symbolize the diagonal matrix of these upper bounds to the unique variances. If we substitute U_s^2 for the essentially unspecified U^2 of (3a), we can deduce several generalizations. One is that Guttman's "best" lower bound to the number of common factors is exactly equal to the number of roots of $U_s^{-1}RU_s^{-1}$ that equal or exceed unity. Another is that at least one of these roots must be less than unity, and consequently no F consisting only of real columns can reproduce $R - U_s^2$; this is equivalent to saying that $R - U_s^2$ cannot be Gramian. A third is that the characteristic vectors and roots of $U_s^{-1}RU_s^{-1}$ can be employed to generate the factors of Guttman's image covariance matrix (1953), and that the real portion of an F that reproduces $R - U_s^2$ is in a particular sense merely an approximation to the factors of this image co-variance matrix. The proofs of these statements have been given else-where (Harris, 1962). The pertinent conclusion here is that U_s^2 is not a "proper" set of unique variances, though it may be a satisfactory set of initial estimators that can be modified in some regular manner to yield a U^2 for which $R - U^2$ is Gramian. This statement should not be mis-interpreted as a criticism of the s_j^2 quantities. They are excellent numbers for certain purposes, and we are now at work collecting some empirical examples which we hope will show that the factors of the image covariance matrix, which itself depends only on R and U_s^2, have certain virtues. Our criticism is of the use of the s_j^2 as if they were equivalent to the u_j^2 short of the limit reached as the number of variables increases indefinitely.

We can manufacture another matrix whose roots are $(a_i^2 - a_i)$; this matrix is $(UR^{-1}U - I)(UR^{-1}U)$. Now if $1 > a_i \geq 0$, then every trace element of $(UR^{-1}U - I)(UR^{-1}U)$ must be negative. In detail, this is the requirement that

$$u_1^2 \left[\sum_{j=1}^{j=p} (u_j r^{1j})^2 - (r^{11}) \right] < 0,$$

$$u_2^2 \left[\sum_{j=1}^{j=p} (u_j r^{2j})^2 - (r^{22}) \right] < 0,$$

(16) $\qquad \cdot \quad \cdot \quad \cdot \quad \cdot \quad \cdot \quad \cdot \quad \cdot \quad \cdot \quad \cdot \quad \cdot \quad \cdot \quad \cdot \quad \cdot \quad ,$

$$u_p^2 \left[\sum_{j=1}^{j=p} (u_j r^{pj})^2 - (r^{pp}) \right] < 0.$$

Let us assume that U^2 is positive-definite; then the inequality

(17) $$[u_j^2] \cdot [(r^{jk})^2] < [r^{jj}]$$

must hold. Here $[u_j^2]$ is a row vector of the unique variances; $[(r^{jk})^2]$ is the square matrix, of order p, whose elements consist of the *squares* of the corresponding elements of R^{-1}; and $[r^{jj}]$ is a row vector of the diagonal elements of R^{-1}. A matrix U^2 might therefore be estimated by solving (17) in some fashion. One approach would be to consider this a standard linear programming problem, subject to a restriction such as maximizing the trace of $I - UR^{-1}U$. We have not yet had time to explore this approach, first with artificial problems for which the "true" u_j^2's are known and then with empirical data that have been studied in some detail by other factoring procedures; however, we intend to.

Another approach is to modify (17) to

$$(17a) \qquad [v_j^2] = [r^{jj}] \cdot [(r^{jk})^2]^{-1},$$

where we use a new symbol, v_j^2, to indicate estimates of the u_j^2. The matrix $[(r^{jk})^2]$, which was constructed from the elements of R^{-1}, is nonsingular and has an inverse; therefore (17a) is possible. The results of solving (17a) can, however, present a problem of negative values for one or more v_j^2. Table 8.1 illustrates this. We took a "Heywood case" from Thomson (1939, p. 231) and made the calculations presented in Table 8.1. Note that the "true" U^2 is not positive-definite; thus (16) should hold, but not (17) or (17a). From Table 8.1 it is evident that for variable 1 we have a negative value of v_j^2 corresponding to the negative "true" u_j^2. Apparently the v_j^2's are, in some as yet unexplained fashion, sensitive to the rank of the off-diagonal elements of R. This would seem to be a good feature. However, the warning that negative values can be secured is important to keep in mind in exploring this relatively unknown territory. In contrast to the "Heywood case," we have had apparently good success with the v_j^2 for empirical data.

Although our development of the v_j^2 was independently arrived at, we find that Guttman (1957) proposed these same quantities as estimators of the unique variances earlier. He arrived at them by considering $I - UR^{-1}U$, rather than by our route. He set the requirement that the sum of squares of the elements of $I - UR^{-1}U$ be a minimum, and then by partial differentiation developed the v_j^2 of (17a) as the quantities which, when substituted for the u_j^2, achieve this minimum. The rationale is that $UR^{-1}U$ is the matrix of covariances of the estimated unique factors; the minimization secures estimated unique factors whose covariances fit the identity matrix as closely as possible. This quite different approach to the development of the v_j^2 throws additional light on them as estimators of the u_j^2

TABLE 8.1

Estimates of the Unique Variances for a "Heywood Case"[a]

R	1.000				
	.945	1.000			
	.840	.720	1.000		
	.735	.630	.560	1.000	
	.630	.540	.480	.420	1.000
R^{-1}	38.128395				
	−22.144176	15.504227			
	−10.387650	4.803767	5.031187		
	−6.415902	2.967033	1.391812	2.820433	
	−4.382278	2.026583	0.950652	0.587166	1.963557
$[(r^{ik})^2]^{-1}$	.004608				
	−.007680	.017551			
	−.011323	.014995	.071525		
	−.012119	.016051	.023712	.163912	
	−.011032	.014610	.021539	.023053	.291640
s_i^2	.0262	.0645	.1989	.3546	.5093
v_i^2	−.0562	.1287	.2698	.4136	.5504
"true" u_i^2	−.1025	.1900	.3600	.5100	.6400

[a] Matrix R from Thomson (1939, p. 231).

Another problem is buried in here. It is the question of under what conditions the v_j^2 will, individually, be upper bounds to the "true" u_j^2. We were led to the v_j^2 by an attempt to find new and more restrictive bounds than the familiar s_j^2 quantities. However, this appears to be a complicated problem that will take additional study. One would like to be able to show a systematic bias of the form $v_j^2 > u_j^2$, since then it would be possible to specify the conditions necessary for the chain of inequalities of the form $0 < u_j^2 < v_j^2 < s_j^2 < 1$ to hold. A similar boundary question will arise for estimates derived from a linear programming solution to (17). At present, then, we see the Guttman-Harris v_j^2 as estimators of the unique variances that have certain desirable characteristics and certain limitations. For example, the necessary condition of (17) is not satisfied by substituting v_j^2 for u_j^2.

Further, it does not seem possible, using the techniques of analysis we are employing here, to improve these estimates by adding a requirement that $R - U^2$ be singular or of minimum rank. The reason is that in our development we restricted the a_i to the interval $1 > a_i \geq 0$, thus permitting but not requiring singularity of $R - U^2$. The deduction of the necessary character of trace elements follows from the requirement that $R - U^2$ be Gramian, and cannot be strengthened by adding a singularity requirement. Apparently improved estimators, if there are such that are functions of R, will have to be developed along other lines.

In summary, two different diagonal matrices might be taken as the initial estimators of U^2. One is U_s^2, whose nonzero elements are the Guttman s_j^2; the other is U_v^2, whose nonzero elements are the Guttman-Harris v_j^2. It is generally true that each v_j^2 is less than the corresponding s_j^2; consequently the v_j^2 *may* be better initial estimators of the u_j^2. Recall, however, that the boundary problem has not yet been solved satisfactorily. As for U_s^2, we can also show that $R - U_s^2$ is not Gramian; this follows immediately by noting that the v_j^2's, when substituted for the u_j^2's, give trace elements of zero for $(UR^{-1}U - I)(UR^{-1}U)$, and thus force at least one a_i to be negative. Both sets of estimators, therefore, should be modified in some fashion if we are to secure a canonical factor solution with a maximum number of real columns of F.

MODIFICATION OF THE INITIAL ESTIMATES

Rao (1955) provides a scheme for taking initial estimates of the unique variances and then converging them to a stable set for a fixed number of factors. The procedure is to introduce the initial set of estimates into (3a), solve for the roots and vectors, and then construct a new set of estimates by

$$(18) \qquad {}_2u_j^{-2} = \sum_{i=1}^{i=m} ({}_1b_i - 1)\,{}_1q_{ji}^2 + 1,$$

where ${}_1b_i$ designates the roots of (3a) secured with the initial set of estimates, and the summation is for some fixed number, m, of roots and columns of the normalized characteristic vectors. The elements ${}_1q_{ji}$ appear in the jth row and i^{th} column of the initial Q. Repeated application of (18) for a fixed m, each time securing the new characteristic vectors and roots associated with the new estimates of uniqueness, should, according to Rao, converge the initial estimates to a stable set of values, within some chosen tolerance range.

All this is quite easy to say; however, merely saying it does not necessarily guarantee that certain problems have been solved. As one example, it is relatively simple to show that if one fixes m as the number of roots greater than unity in the solution of (3a) when the initial estimates of the unique variances are employed, then the second set of estimates of the unique variances will each be less than the corresponding initial estimate. Thus a rule such as this for choosing m is most appropriate when it can be demonstrated that the initial estimates are each too large. Recall that this is true for the matrix U_s^2 and may be true under certain conditions for the matrix U_v^2. In the illustration given in the second section we have adopted this rule. With U_s^2 as the initial set of estimates, this rule is consistent with the fact that the number of positive roots of $R - U_s^2$, which equals the number of roots of $U_s^{-1} R U_s^{-1}$ that exceed unity, is a lower bound to the number of common factors. We have also used this rule when we take U_v^2 as the initial set of estimates of the unique variances; this use is tentative and not completely justified.

Another interesting problem arises. Even though we fix m in the fashion described above for the purpose of iteration, the "final" set of uniqueness estimates, U_f^2 say, are likely to be such that $U_f^{-1} R U_f^{-1}$ has more than m roots that are greater than unity. If we then construct our factors in the fashion outlined in (12), we may choose either m real columns for our F, or some larger number that corresponds to this number of roots greater than unity. We have done the latter, and then relied on a rotation process to identify factors that are essentially null. These procedures clearly move in the direction of extracting what ordinarily would be regarded as a very large number of factors, relative to the number of variables. We believe, however, that this is a strategy that is growing in acceptance.

These comments emphasize the point that several specifications must enter into any clear description of how a particular set of canonical factors was developed. The general need for clearer descriptions of how any particular set of factors was arrived at is evident in many of the reports of research. We can summarize here the canonical factor model as we have used it in the work reported in the next section:

Type A: We use U_s^2 as the initial set of estimates of uniqueness.

We specify m to be the number of roots of $U_s^{-1} R U_s^{-1}$ that are greater than unity, and we use (18) to converge the estimates with a .005 tolerance.

We construct, by (12), all the real columns of F, which is generally greater than m.

Type B: We use U_v^2 as the initial set of estimates of uniqueness.

We specify m to be the number of roots of $U_v^{-1} R U_v^{-1}$ that are greater than unity, and we use (18) to converge the estimates with a .005 tolerance.

We construct, by (12), all the real columns of F, which is generally greater than m.

Note that m may differ for *Type A* and *Type B*, with the m for *Type B* being larger. Following the analysis, we have used Kaiser's "normal" varimax procedure (Kaiser, 1958*b*; Harman, 1960, pp. 302–308) to yield a derived set of orthogonal factors.

Application to the description of change

Our interest in the profile or pattern problem has been stated above. Given, for the same set of individuals, the "same" battery administered on two occasions, the relationships both within and between batteries over the two occasions may be expressed as correlation coefficients, yielding the supermatrix:

$$(19) \qquad \begin{bmatrix} R_{11} & R_{12} \\ R_{21} & R_{22} \end{bmatrix}.$$

The intercorrelations for the first administration appear in R_{11}, which is assumed to have units in the diagonals. R_{12} and its transpose R_{21} give the correlations across occasions. R_{22} designates the intercorrelations, with units in the diagonal, for occasion 2. If we substitute (19) for the R of equation (3*a*), we can develop a set of canonical factors which for convenience can be written as the supermatrix:

$$(20) \qquad \begin{bmatrix} F_1 \\ F_2 \end{bmatrix},$$

with

$$(21) \qquad \begin{bmatrix} F_1 F_1' & F_1 F_2' \\ F_2 F_1' & F_2 F_2' \end{bmatrix}$$

reproducing

$$(22) \qquad \begin{bmatrix} R_{11} - U_1^2 & R_{12} \\ R_{21} & R_{22} - U_2^2 \end{bmatrix}$$

to a satisfactory degree of approximation.

We have taken data studied by Meyer and Bendig (1961) as an illustration of our methods. Professor Bendig kindly provided all the correlations necessary for the analysis, since the complete R_{12} matrix of (19) does not appear in the journal article; we wish to express our appreciation to him. The data are based on observations from 49 boys and 61 girls and were gathered at Grade 8 and Grade 11. The Primary Mental Abilities Test, Intermediate Form, yielded scores on V, S, R, N, and W for each of the two occasions. In addition, the Myers-Ruch High School Achieve-

TABLE 8.2

Rotated Canonical Factors—Girls

		1	2	3	4	5	6	7	h^2
					Type A solution				
Grade 8	V	.32	.25	.04	.77	.13	.10	.17	.83
	S	.11	.80	.23	.16	.04	.26	.13	.83
	R	.16	.15	.79	.18	.23	.16	.02	.81
	N	.77	−.05	.13	.25	.13	.01	.27	.76
	W	.12	.07	.18	.12	.66	.18	.01	.53
Grade 11	Ach	.01	.13	.26	.70	.08	−.13	−.09	.63
	V	.61	.27	.14	.56	.07	.07	−.01	.84
	S	−.02	.88	.11	.22	.08	.11	−.11	.87
	R	.32	.19	.76	.16	.09	.01	−.01	.77
	N	.81	.04	.26	.00	.05	−.01	−.18	.76
	W	.00	.23	.09	−.04	.18	.69	.00	.58
					Type B solution				
Grade 8	V	.25	.21	.05	.84	.11	.13	.12	.87
	S	.09	.81	.23	.18	.01	.29	.15	.87
	R	.15	.14	.81	.18	.24	.16	.03	.84
	N	.75	−.06	.12	.30	.13	.01	.33	.80
	W	.11	.06	.19	.14	.62	.19	.01	.49
Grade 11	Ach	.01	.14	.28	.65	.12	−.21	−.06	.58
	V	.57	.26	.14	.63	.03	.11	−.06	.84
	S	.02	.87	.11	.23	.09	.09	−.13	.87
	R	.32	.20	.76	.17	.08	.01	−.01	.78
	N	.83	.04	.25	.03	.07	−.02	−.14	.79
	W	−.01	.24	.09	−.03	.21	.60	.00	.47

ment Test was administered to the students in Grade 11. Eleven variables (five PMA measures on each of two occasions and the achievement test) were available for analysis. Meyer and Bendig used a centroid analysis, extracting five factors that were rotated to an oblique solution. Boys and girls were treated separately. Their results yield the expected first-order factors, V, S, R, N, and W, and two second-order factors.

Our analysis of the Meyer and Bendig data gives a slightly different picture. The results for girls are presented in Table 8.2 and the results for boys in Table 8.3. Both Table 8.2 and Table 8.3 give two analyses: our *Type A* and *Type B*. The varimax rotated solutions rather than the original canonical factors are presented. In each instance eight factors were

152   *Chester W. Harris*

produced and rotated, and then one factor with no coefficients outside
the ±.15 range was dropped. Table 8.2 indicates that the *Type A* solution, which uses U_s^2 as the initial estimate of uniqueness, and the *Type B*
solution, which uses U_v^2 as the initial estimates, yield very similar results
for all seven factors. However, Table 8.3, the data for the boys, shows that
factor 7 differs somewhat for the two types of solution. At this stage, one
might have slightly more confidence in the *Type A* solution, and so it will
be chosen for the interpretation below.

Factors 2, 3, and 4 have sufficient similarity for both boys and girls
to be regarded as essentially the same. Factor 1 differs at least slightly
for the two sexes: note the differences for Grade 11, Achievement and V.
For the girls, factors 5 and 6 split W into two factors: one for Grade 8

TABLE 8.3

Rotated Canonical Factors—Boys

		1	2	3	4	5	6	7	h^2
Type A solution									
Grade 8	V	.31	.25	.24	.74	.31	−.13	.09	.89
	S	.12	.71	.20	.13	−.02	.08	.24	.65
	R	.15	.11	.80	.39	−.10	−.01	−.08	.86
	N	.81	−.05	.21	.32	.11	.08	.04	.84
	W	.02	.03	.00	.22	.81	−.09	.23	.77
Grade 11	Ach	.27	.18	.29	.66	.14	.27	.02	.72
	V	.29	.23	.21	.81	.20	−.06	−.06	.89
	S	.04	.75	.02	.21	.07	−.06	−.19	.65
	R	.34	.14	.82	.14	.16	.03	.10	.87
	N	.86	.10	.23	.23	.07	−.04	−.02	.88
	W	.12	.02	.04	.09	.67	.08	−.18	.51
Type B solution									
Grade 8	V	.29	.19	.23	.76	.33	−.22	.15	.93
	S	.10	.49	.19	.17	−.03	.00	.62	.70
	R	.15	.11	.83	.39	−.11	−.02	−.01	.92
	N	.81	−.10	.20	.33	.13	.08	.08	.89
	W	.01	−.02	.00	.19	.89	−.10	.12	.85
Grade 11	Ach	.25	.11	.28	.68	.15	.26	.15	.73
	V	.28	.24	.21	.83	.21	−.03	.00	.91
	S	−.02	.80	.04	.19	.07	.00	.13	.70
	R	.32	.03	.84	.15	.17	.04	.20	.94
	N	.90	.09	.22	.23	.07	−.05	.03	.95
	W	.12	.07	.04	.11	.59	.09	−.09	.39

and one for Grade 11; whereas factor 5 is a single W factor for the boys. These differences are consistent with the original cross-correlations; for girls, the first and second administrations of W correlate only .27, whereas for boys the correlation is .52. For the girls, factor 7 suggests that the first administration of N has a modest specificity; there is no such evidence for the boys. There is, for the boys, an analogous suggestion of specificity for the Grade 8, S score in factor 7; this is particularly evident in the *Type B* solution. Finally, factor 6 for the boys suggests a specific for the Achievement variable which is not evident for the girls.

Let us now propose a somewhat unorthodox mode of interpretation. First, since these are canonical factors that have been rotated by the normal varimax procedure, we might multiply any row of the factor matrix by any constant we would choose and regard these new values as the ones we would have secured by using our procedure on the weighted variables. Note that the separability of scale that characterizes the Rao procedure and the normalizing feature of the varimax rotation both are required for this to be true. Second, since we rotated all eleven variables simultaneously, we have in effect kept the factor scores the same but allowed the correlations of the variables with these hypothetical factor scores to differ for the two occasions. This procedure has in effect fixed the individuals' hypothetical measures of ability in a given factor, and then allowed variables that are indexed by the same symbol to have different correlations with the factor at different times. This may seem strange, since in effect we are stating that the individuals have not changed, but the variables may have. Under this restriction of fixed factor scores it is quite legitimate to look at differences in factor coefficients for the "same" variable on the two occasions with respect to the same factor. Note that when (21) adequately reproduces (22), we can derive the difference matrix $F_2 - F_1$ (restricted, of course, to only those variables common to the two occasions) by operating on (22) with the signs of the elements of R_{21} and R_{12} all reversed. Thus, $F_2 - F_1$ reproduces $R_{11} + R_{22} - R_{21} - R_{12} - U_1^2 - U_2^2$. We are here advancing the speculation that had we begun the analysis with $R_{11} + R_{22} - R_{12} - R_{21}$ as our matrix of interest, we would have secured $U_1^2 + U_2^2$ as the appropriate uniqueness estimates, and thus can regard $F_2 - F_1$ as the factors that would have resulted from taking differences in standard scores across occasions as the five variables of interest. If this is correct, we can also apply diagonal matrices of weights as premultipliers of F_2, F_1, or both of them, to secure factors of differentially weighted differences in standard scores.

It is obvious from Tables 8.4 and 8.5 that this unorthodox approach to interpretation has given us seven factors for the five variables (pairs of tests). This undoubtedly is distasteful to some. Further rotations on the

TABLE 8.4

Approximate Factors of Covariances of Differences in Standard Scores

	1	2	3	4	5	6	7
				Girls			
V	.29	.02	.10	−.21	−.06	−.03	−.18
S	−.13	.08	−.12	.06	.04	−.15	−.24
R	.16	.04	−.03	−.02	−.14	−.15	−.03
N	.04	.09	.13	−.25	−.07	−.02	−.45
W	−.12	.16	−.09	−.16	−.48	.51	−.01
				Boys			
V	−.02	−.02	−.03	.07	−.11	.07	−.15
S	−.08	.04	−.18	.08	.09	−.14	−.43
R	.19	.03	.02	−.25	.26	.04	.18
N	.05	.15	.02	−.09	−.04	−.12	−.06
W	.10	−.01	.04	−.13	−.14	.17	−.41

derived matrices of Tables 8.4 and 8.5 might be made in the hope of
nullifying at least two of the factors in each instance and thus bringing the
results in line with the conventional doctrine that one should not have
more *common* factors than variables. Someone may wish to do this. Here
we merely present the tables and make some crude observations.

TABLE 8.5

Approximate Factors of Covariances of "Residual" Gains

	1	2	3	4	5	6	7
				Girls			
V	.37	.08	.11	−.01	−.03	.00	−.14
S	−.11	.26	−.07	.10	.05	−.09	−.21
R	.21	.08	.20	.03	−.07	−.10	−.02
N	.32	.07	.18	−.16	−.03	−.02	−.35
W	−.03	.21	.04	−.07	.00	.64	.00
				Boys			
V	.02	.01	.00	.16	−.07	.05	−.14
S	−.02	.39	−.08	.14	.08	−.10	−.31
R	.23	.06	.21	−.16	.24	.04	.16
N	.19	−.14	.06	−.04	−.02	−.11	−.05
W	.11	.00	.04	−.02	.25	.13	−.30

The simple differences, $F_2 - F_1$, appear in Table 8.4. For girls, variables N and W, and possibly V, appear to be measuring something different on the two occasions; for boys, variables R, S, and W appear to function differently. If, as we believe, the material of Table 8.4 approximates the factors of the covariances of the differences in standard scores taken as variables, then the familiar point that factoring the covariances of such differences may not be very informative is given some support. It should be noted that the variance for a difference between standard scores can readily be calculated when one knows the correlation across occasions for the designated variable, and thus one could multiply each row of Table 8.4 by the appropriate constant to approximate the results of factoring the normalized covariances, or correlations, of these differences in standard scores. Since the variance for such a difference equals $2(1 - r_{12})$, where r_{12} designates the correlation across occasions, we note that the appropriate weights (the reciprocals of the standard deviations) are unity when r_{12} equals $+.50$, and greater than unity when r_{12} exceeds $+.50$. For variables that are substantially correlated across occasions, the effect of this transformation is to increase the magnitudes of the nonzero entries in Table 8.4, but not to change sign.

In Table 8.5, we give the differences between the entries in F_2 and the entries in F_1 when these are weighted by the correlation across occasions for the designated variable. Thus Table 8.5 approximates what would have been secured had we factored not the covariances of the differences in standard scores for the two occasions, but the covariances of the portions of the variables on occasion 2 that cannot be predicted (linearly) from the data of occasion 1. In this case the variance of these "residual" scores is $1 - r_{12}$; consequently an analogous transformation of the data of Table 8.5 might be made to approximate the values that would have been secured from a factoring of the correlations of these residuals. For nonzero r_{12}^2, the variance is less than one; consequently, for the data of Table 8.5, the adjustment would consist generally of increasing the magnitude—often substantially—of the nonzero values.

The major point of this example has been that—given a certain methodology—one can derive at least an approximate factorial description of "change" from the factorial description of the data for the two occasions. Here we illustrated with two somewhat different definitions of change; other definitions, as long as only linear combinations of the standard scores are involved, might have been used. Our methods explicitly rest upon fixing the factor measurements (factor scores) for the individuals and then observing differences (weighted in some fashion) between the correlations with the factor of the variable on the two occasions.

Nine | Image Analysis

HENRY F. KAISER

In the measurement of change, traditional factor analysis and Guttman's simplex theory (Guttman, 1954a) are often used procedures. With both of these methods, the hoary question of communalities may arise, for it may be desirable to study *not* the observable variables (e.g., scores on successive trials, ordered in time, of a learning experiment) but rather the *parts* of these variables which can be said, in some sense, to be in common with the remaining observable variables. These common or "communality" parts of the original variables are not observable and thus must be determined—or approximated—from the observable data.

In this paper, I shall outline what appears presently to be the theoretically most defensible solution for the communality problem: Guttman's image analysis (Guttman, 1953). After image theory is described in some detail in the following section, its relationship to classic factor analysis and to the simplex model is taken up in subsequent sections.

Image theory

Consider n observable random variables (generically called tests) $z_j, j = 1, 2, \cdots, n$, standardized so that each has mean zero and variance one. Then, for each test, consider its linear least-squares predicted value p_j, as determined by the remaining $n - 1$ tests:

$$(1) \qquad p_j = \sum_{k=1}^{n} w_{jk} z_k,$$

where w_{jk} is the (standardized) regression coefficient for predicting test j from test k in this multiple regression equation, and where $w_{jj} = 0$ by definition, as we are not considering the regression of a variable on itself. The random variable p_j is called the *image* of test j; geometrically it is the

projection or image of the test on the space of the remaining $n - 1$ tests.
The anti-image e_j of test j may be defined simply as

$$(2) \qquad\qquad e_j = z_j - p_j,$$

and is that part of z_j *not* predictable from a knowledge of the scores on the
remaining tests. Geometrically, the anti-image is orthogonal to the space
of the remaining tests. This situation is shown in Figure 9.1.

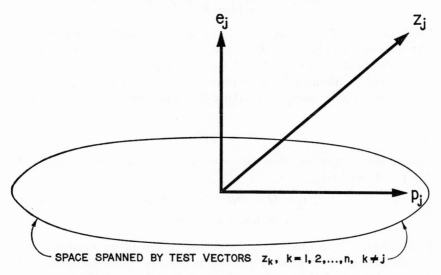

Fig. 9.1.—Geometrical representation of an anti-image.

What has been described thus far is well known and extremely elementary. Guttman's image theory consists of a detailed and penetrating
further exploration of the properties of the set of all n images simultaneously.

We may write (2) more generally as

$$(3) \qquad\qquad z = p + e,$$

where z is the (column) vector variable of all n observable tests, p is the
vector variable of the corresponding n images, and e is the vector variable
of the n anti-images. Equation (3) is usually termed the "fundamental
postulate" of image analysis.

The n images p in (1) are given by

$$(4) \qquad\qquad p = Wz,$$

where W is the matrix of multiple regression coefficients, each row of which gives the coefficients for predicting a given test from the remaining tests. From the theory of multiple regression (Guttman, 1940), it may be shown that

$$(5) \qquad W = I - S^2 R^{-1},$$

where R is the correlation matrix of the z's, and

$$(6) \qquad S^2 = [\text{diag } R^{-1}]^{-1},$$

the diagonal matrix of variance errors of estimate or anti-image variances. (We have assumed here that R is nonsingular. This will almost always be —and should of course always be—the case in practice.)

To study simultaneously the interrelationships of the images, we find G, their covariance matrix, by taking the expectation, over individuals, of pp':

$$(7) \qquad G = \mathcal{E}(pp'),$$

where $\mathcal{E}$ is the expected value operator. From (4) and (5) and noting that $\mathcal{E}(zz') = R$, we find

$$(8) \qquad \begin{aligned} G &= (I - S^2 R^{-1})R(I - R^{-1}S^2) \\ &= R + S^2 R^{-1} S^2 - 2S^2. \end{aligned}$$

In developing (8) we have taken expected values, rather than summing and dividing by the degrees of freedom, in order to emphasize that we are dealing with populations and population parameters.

Similarly, the anti-image covariance matrix Q may be found:

$$(9) \qquad \begin{aligned} Q &= \mathcal{E}(ee') \\ &= \mathcal{E}(S^2 R^{-1} zz' R^{-1} S^2) \\ &= S^2 R^{-1} S^2. \end{aligned}$$

Note again from (6) and (9) that

$$(10) \qquad \text{diag } Q = S^2$$

or that S^2 is the diagonal matrix of anti-image variances.

Formulas (8) and (9) may be combined to give the "fundamental theorem" of image analysis:

$$(11) \qquad R = G - Q + 2S^2;$$

that is, the observable correlation matrix is partitioned into the image covariance matrix minus the anti-image covariance matrix plus twice the diagonal matrix of anti-image variances.

What we have called images and anti-images, Guttman terms *partial* images and *partial* anti-images; for we may also consider *total* images and *total* anti-images, the corresponding hypothetical variables which may be said to exist in the universe of tests (or content) as $n \to \infty$. Thus, corresponding to (1), the total image of test j, π_j, is given by

$$(12) \qquad \pi_j = \lim_{n \to \infty} \sum_{k=1}^{n} \omega_{jk} z_k, \qquad (\omega_{jj} = 0),$$

where ω_{jk} is the universe regression coefficient.

The limit in (12) is a mathematical limit (as contrasted with a limit in probability or a probability limit), implying that the selection of n variables from the universe is nonrandom and that the infinity of tests in the universe is denumerable. (I am indebted to Albert Madansky for pointing out the nature of this limit.) Guttman (1955) has proved that this limit always exists. The corresponding total anti-image ϵ_j is simply

$$(13) \qquad \epsilon_j = z_j - \pi_j.$$

Since total images and anti-images bear an intimate relationship to— and provide profound insight into—factor-analytic theory, their properties will be outlined in the next section.

Application to factor analysis

Let r be the number of common factors for a given n. Guttman (1956) has proved that if

$$(14) \qquad \lim_{n \to \infty} \frac{r}{n} = 0,$$

then image analysis *in the universe* ("total" image analysis) and factor analysis are the same thing. More specifically, he has proved, given condition (14), that

$$(15) \qquad p_j \to \pi_j = c_j,$$

where c_j is the factor-analytic common-part of z_j, i.e., that part of the observable test z_j which lies in the common factor space—the part of the test which subsequently may be expanded into common factors. Similarly,

$$(16) \qquad e_j \to \epsilon_j = y_j,$$

where y_j is the unique-part of z_j $(z_j = c_j + y_j)$.

Equations (15) and (16) then imply the conventional factor-analytic assumptions of zero covariance,

$$(17) \quad q_{jk} = \mathrm{Cov}\,(e_j, e_k) \to \mathrm{Cov}\,(\epsilon_j, \epsilon_k) = \mathrm{Cov}\,(y_j, y_k) = 0, \qquad (j \neq k),$$

(18) $\mathrm{Cov}\,(p_j,\,e_k) \to \mathrm{Cov}\,(\pi_j,\,\epsilon_k) = \mathrm{Cov}\,(c_j,\,y_k) = 0,$

and the fundamental theorem of factor analysis,

(19) $g_{jj} = \mathrm{Var}\,(p_j) \to \mathrm{Var}\,(\pi_j) = \mathrm{Var}\,(c_j) = h_j^2,$

(20) $q_{jj} = \mathrm{Var}\,(e_j) \to \mathrm{Var}\,(\epsilon_j) = \mathrm{Var}\,(y_j) = u_j^2,$

(21) $g_{jk} = \mathrm{Cov}\,(p_j,\,p_k) \to \mathrm{Cov}\,(\pi_j,\,\pi_k) = \mathrm{Cov}\,(c_j,\,c_k) = r_{jk},$ $(j \neq k),$

where h_j^2 is the communality of test j, u_j^2 is the uniqueness of test j ($h_j^2 + u_j^2 = 1$), and r_{jk} is the correlation between tests j and k.

More compactly, then, we can say that, given condition (14),

(22) $G \to R - U^2,$

(23) $\mathrm{diag}\,Q = S^2 \to U^2,$

(24) $Q \to U^2,$

when U^2 is the diagonal matrix of uniquenesses.

The preceding material suggests that G, the image covariance matrix, might well be a good approximation to $R - U^2$, the so-called "reduced correlation matrix" (actually the covariance matrix of the common-parts of the tests). How can we tell if the approximation is good? Most simply by looking at the off-diagonal elements of the anti-image covariance matrix Q. From (17) and (24) a good approximation is indicated by all these elements' being close to zero: In this case our n is essentially infinite—we have a comprehensive selection of tests from the universe of tests. If, on the other hand, Q is not near-diagonal, we know that the approximation is poor. However, when this occurs, we have evidence that factor analysis is perhaps not appropriate for the data at hand—we may not have thoroughly covered the universe under consideration, or the factor-analytic model may not apply even as $n \to \infty$. Thus, not only can the image approach provide an excellent approximation to factor analysis, but it also routinely tells us of the validity of factor-analytic inferences regarding the structure of a universe of tests, the problem with which factor analysis is most fundamentally concerned.

Given, then, that we take G as an ideal approximation to $R - U^2$, how may one best then proceed to factor G, determine the "number of factors," and handle the rotation problem?

Note how G differs from the ideally desirable, but unobtainable, $R - U^2$ in the following two respects: (a) In the diagonal cells appear the squared multiple correlations of each variable, in turn, on the remaining $n - 1$; this, of course, is Guttman's well-known universally strongest lower bound (Guttman, 1954*b*, 1956) and often advocated "best estimate" for the communalities. (*b*) In the off-diagonals, the observed correlations have been replaced by image covariances—values whose differences from the correlations approach zero, but, for finite *n*, differ by an amount equal to the anti-image covariances. This amount is sufficient to make the image covariance matrix Gramian. Traditionally, the communality problem operationally has been thought of as finding numbers to "insert" in the diagonal; from this crude viewpoint, we are inserting squared multiples in the diagonal and adding the new wrinkle of adjusting (usually slightly lowering) the off-diagonals "just enough" to keep the matrix honest, or Gramian.

The first attempt to answer this question of making image analysis operational in a factor-analytic setting was outlined in an Air Force Research Report of mine in 1958 (Kaiser, 1958*a*). At that time, principal axes of about 30 *G*'s derived from correlation matrices appearing in the literature were found. Invariably, these *G*'s were positive-definite—there was no exact rank reduction. But the eigenvalues determined behaved very much as one would expect from "good" estimates of $R - U^2$: In each study the majority of these eigenvalues were infinitesimal. Still, however, the "number of factors" problem persisted, for these very, very small eigenvalues were not zero. It turned out, however, that the number of factors question could be effectively avoided by the following device. Rotate analytically all *n* principal axes of *G*, the image covariance matrix. Without exception, under *orthogonal* analytic rotation, e.g., quartimax (Neuhaus and Wrigley, 1954) or varimax (Kaiser, 1958*b*), it did not matter whether these minute principal axes were rotated (except for a somewhat cavalier attitude toward computer time). Their being included did not affect the structure of the major rotated factors. Thus, the question of the number of factors was avoided until the final, most important stage of any factor analysis, psychological interpretation. This dodge for avoiding the number of factors question before rotation applies only to orthogonal rotation; any known analytic procedure for the oblique case invariably appears extremely sensitive to the number of factors. Nevertheless, it would seem that there is something uncomfortable about rotating, say, $n = r = 120$ common factors, when one knows *a priori* that ultimately the number of interpretable common factors will be perhaps 20. This consideration led me to abandon temporarily the image approach to the communality problem—until a most important paper burst upon the scene.

In this paper Harris (1962) not only has answered the number of factors question in an image-analytic content, but has added immense theoretical justification for the approach. Harris considers Rao's canonical factor analysis (Rao, 1955), surely the definitive *statistical* method of factoring. Rao's solution is equivalent to Lawley's (1940) maximum-likelihood solution. Rao's procedure consists of a solution of the eigenequation

(25) $$[U^{-1}RU^{-1} - \beta I]\xi = 0.$$

If we take S^2 as an initial approximation to the diagonal matrix of uniquenesses U^2, equation (25) becomes

(26) $$[S^{-1}RS^{-1} - bI]x = 0,$$

where b is the corresponding first approximation to β and x is the corresponding first approximation to ξ.

A direct solution of (26) implies that $XB^{\frac{1}{2}}$ is a principal-axes factor analysis of $R^* = S^{-1}RS^{-1}$, where X is the matrix of unit-length eigenvectors of R^* and B is the diagonal matrix of eigenvalues of R^*. A factor matrix F_r of R itself is then

(27) $$F_r = SXB^{\frac{1}{2}}.$$

Then Harris finds, as the reader may verify using (9) and (11), that the eigenvectors of $G^* = S^{-1}GS^{-1}$ are the *same* as the eigenvectors of R^*—although the eigenvalues of G^*, rather than being B, are $[(B - I)^2B^{-1}]$. Thus, a factoring F_g of G is

(28) $$F_g = SX[(B - I)^2B^{-1}]^{\frac{1}{2}}.$$

From (27) and (28) it is clear that these factor matrices for R and G are the same except for the scale of the columns. That is, $F_g = F_rD$, where D is the diagonal matrix,

(29) $$D = I - B^{-1}.$$

More importantly, Harris goes on to prove that the factors implied by these two factor matrices are the same in the sense that the correlation between the factors represented by corresponding columns in these two matrices is one. And even more importantly, it may be shown that the "Harris factors" represented by F_g, like canonical factors, are invariant under changes in the original metric. Were we to start the analysis with KRK, where K is diagonal and nonsingular—i.e., *any* covariance matrix associated with R—then F_g would become KF_g and the factors represented by F_g and KF_g would be the same. The importance of this metric invariance cannot be overemphasized: We are freed from the traditional agnostic confession of ignorance implied by standardizing the observable tests z. Here, this standardization is merely a convenience to which we are in no way tied.

At this point it is instructive to explore the difference between the size of the eigenvalues of G^* and R^*. As shown in Figure 9.2, $(b - 1)^2/b$, possible eigenvalues of G^*, are plotted as a function of b, possible eigenvalues of R^*. From the figure it is seen that the value $b = 1$ is crucial: When $b > 1$, $(b - 1)^2/b$ is a monotonically increasing function of b; i.e.,

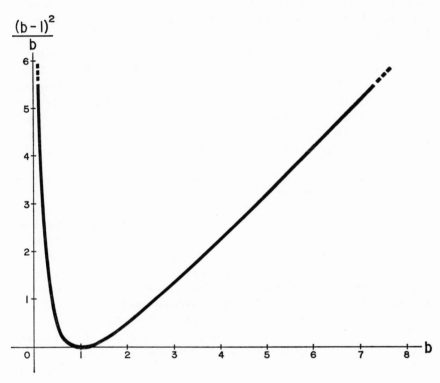

Fig. 9.2.—Eigenvalues of G^* as functions of eigenvalues of R^*.

there is a positive correspondence in the size of the factors of R^* and G^*. On the other hand, factors of R^* and G^* for which $b < 1$ have the confusing property of being negatively related in size. (In the extreme case, it is seen that as a factor of R^* approaches its smallest possible size of zero, the corresponding factor of G^* becomes infinitely large.) Thus, it looks as if these factors may be of dubious value and should be rejected. There are other substantial reasons why factors with b less than or equal to one should be rejected.

First, in solving Rao's eigenequation (25), for a given number of common factors r, successive iterations to find U^2 will lead, upon convergence, to $n - r$ eigenvalues β in (25) as close as possible to one, representing the factors which statistically are hypothesized to be nonsignificant.

Second, a direct solution of the first approximation to (26) of Rao's eigenequation (with uniqueness estimates S^2) gives a number of eigenvalues b greater than one exactly equal to Guttman's (1954b) classic strongest algebraic lower bound for the number of common factors. Also, when $b > 1$, Rao's canonical correlations are real; for $b < 1$, they are imaginary (Harris, 1962).

Finally, if G is to be a good approximation to $R - U^2$, as Guttman (1940, 1953, 1956) repeatedly shows, it must be that R^{-1} or $Q \; (= S^2 R^{-1} S^2)$ or the anti-image correlation matrix $SR^{-1}S$ should be nearly diagonal. Now the negative of $SR^{-1}S$ is the matrix of partial correlations between any two variables with the remaining $n - 2$ held constant. But clearly these partials should be close to zero if Guttman's assertion is to hold; i.e., the off-diagonals of R^{-1} should be small. But Harris has shown that

$$(30) \qquad \sum_{j \neq k} \sum (s_j \overset{jk}{r} s_k)^2 = \sum_{s=1}^{n} (b_s - 1)^2 / b_s^2,$$

where r^{jk} is the jk^{th} element of R^{-1}. Thus, if any of the eigenvalues b are very small, the right-hand member of (30) becomes large, implying, of course, that the left-hand member of (30) is large; but this is precisely the situation for which Guttman points out that factor analysis is not applicable or that the selection of n variables is not a comprehensive selection from the universe of content under consideration.

Thus, we have Guttman's algebra and psychometrics corresponding with Rao's statistics corresponding with Harris' marriage of the two as a device for answering the question of the "number of factors."

How many factors is this? Hunka and I have systematically investigated this number and found that typically the number of common factors indicated by this Guttman-Rao-Harris rule of behavior is, for 64 correlation matrices from the psychological literature ($n \leq 40$), about $n/2$. It may be said that this is "too many" factors for ultimate psychological interpretation. However, while this almost certainly is true, it is possible analytically to rotate this number of factors of F_g orthogonally without the inclusion of the trivial factors affecting in any substantial way the rotated position of the major psychologically interpretable factors, just as when I had earlier rotated all n principal axes of G. This contention—verified by a great deal of empirical experience—does *not* apply to analytic rotation applied to F_r: The size of "trivial" factors of F_r, given by their eigenvalues b, is not so trivial, and their inclusion under any rotational scheme, orthogonal or otherwise, is invariably disastrous.

The question arises of "polishing" the Harris factors in F_g into canonical factors by iterating with Rao's eigenequation (25) (keeping the number of factors suggested above). Harris suggests the possibility of this, but I feel that "fighting" the communality problem in this fashion exacts a terrible price, beyond the horrible computational problem involved; for the Harris factors of G are linear functions of the images which, in turn, are linear functions of the observable variables z, and thus factor scores may be calculated exactly for the data at hand. Once we start such polishing, à la Rao, we are in "pure" factor analysis, and we can only express factors as linear functions of the nonobservable common-parts c of the observable tests, and the calculation of factor scores is impossible (Thomson, 1951).

A practical summarization of what is recommended above follows: Determine S^2 from (6) and find the unit-length eigenvectors X associated with eigenvalues b greater than one of $R^* = S^{-1}RS^{-1}$. Scale each of these eigenvectors by multiplying each by its associated $[(b-1)^2/b]^{\frac{1}{2}}$ and scale the resulting row vectors by premultiplying this matrix by S; this yields F_g, the rescaled principal axes—or Harris factors—of G associated with eigenvalues b greater than one. There will be approximately $n/2$ such factors. Subject this matrix to analytic orthogonal rotation, e.g., varimax, and then, if desired, attack the problem of oblique rotation by adjusting, either graphically or analytically, those orthogonally rotated common factors which appear to be of psychological interest.

Application to the simplex

Guttman's simplex model seems particularly applicable to the analysis of repeated measurements in time. In this model, each test is ordered such that its content contains everything in the preceding tests in the hierarchy plus perhaps something more. In factor-analytic terms, the common-factor matrix here would be a lower-triangular matrix. However, the model is predicated upon only one psychological dimension: To each test is attached a single parameter a_j, and the "fundamental theorem" for the simplex is that

$$(31) \qquad r_{jk} = a_j/a_k, \qquad j \leq k.$$

There are two ways in which image-analytic ideas may be brought to bear in a simplex analysis. First, it may be that there is some doubt whether a simplex analysis is appropriate—as opposed to a standard factor-analytic treatment of data. As we saw above, for factor analysis to be applicable à la Guttman, it must be that $r^{jk} \to 0$ for all j and k, $j \neq k$. From this viewpoint, for finite n, if all r^{jk} are small, we have a situation which may call for factor analysis. However, for a perfect simplex

$$(32) \qquad \begin{aligned} r^{jk} &= 0, & |j - k| &> 1, \\ r^{jk} &\neq 0, & |j - k| &\leq 1. \end{aligned}$$

Equation (32) holds for the observable variables as well as in the limit. Thus (32) says that the inverse of the correlation matrix, for a perfect simplex, is tridiagonal; it has nonzero elements only on the diagonal and in the immediate secondary diagonals. If, in practice, R^{-1} essentially has this form, it suggests that traditional factor analysis is not appropriate but that a simplex model may be appropriate. Thus, the first stage of any image analysis, i.e., finding R^{-1}, serves to adjudicate between the factor-analytic model and the simplex model.

Second, it may be that (32) does not seem to hold for the observable variables z. But this may be because of a "communality problem." It may be that the common-parts of the observable variables do indeed closely follow (32), where in (32) the subscripts j and k refer not to z_j and z_k but rather to their common-parts. Thus, rather than look for a simplex in R, it could be desirable to look for a simplex in G. If G^{-1} is essentially tridiagonal, the subsequent simplex analysis may then more conveniently be carried out on

$$(33) \qquad (I - S^2)^{-\frac{1}{2}} G (I - S^2)^{-\frac{1}{2}},$$

the image *correlation* matrix. A procedure for fitting a simplex and determining the loadings a_j in (31) is available (Kaiser, 1962). This method provides a measure of the efficacy of the fit and could thus alternatively indicate whether the simplex analysis of R itself or of the image correlation matrix (33) is the more appropriate.

The material presented in this last section on the application of image theory to the simplex model must be considered as somewhat speculative. It is based only on logical and theoretical considerations: The application of these ideas to real data has not yet been undertaken.

Ten | The Structuring of Change by *P*-Technique and Incremental *R*-Technique

RAYMOND B. CATTELL

To orient the reader to the particular flavor of the approach it should be said that, unlike many of the accompanying chapters which are concerned purely with some mathematico-statistical model, it is closely bound to many years of systematic substantive research in personality, motivation, and social psychology (Cattell, 1946, 1957, 1961*a*). This tie is deliberately developed in the belief that models and the modification of models should occur through intimate connection with experimental data. However, the reader perhaps needs additional alertness here, where the exposition of a beautiful model is apt to be cut short at any moment by a brutal fact, and where deductive and inductive directions of reasoning interact so rapidly.

The theme of this paper may be described as the application of factor analysis to the measurement of change, but since it does not cover that whole area the title is restricted. Other factor-analytic applications will be mentioned in passing. The especial claims of factor analysis to consideration are the same here as in other fields, namely, that to a greater extent than correlational or mean difference statistics it permits resolution of the diverse influences at work. On the other hand, it also makes demands on more complex reasoning and technical skills which require more experience for their effective use.

Throwing mathematical elegance to the winds, I propose to start with the psychological end of the problem, by describing briefly a system of experiments, and even something of their history. For it is my prejudice that since there is an infinite possibility of models, whereas only two or three are going to work well, models should grow from the beginning in sensitive relation to emerging research findings. The psychological problem was that of discovering human traits and states, and the model was that particular form of factor analysis (to be distinguished mainly from component analysis) in which a factor is defined as an influence, cause, or causal dimension. This means that we deal only with those factors which emerge from unique resolutions by simple structure or confactor rotation (Cattell and White, 1962) and which should consequently possess a definable kind of constancy across the matrices from different experiments, populations, and conditions (Cattell, 1957).

The argument with which our experiments began was that a personality source trait, so defined as a factor influence upon a set of behavioral variables, should appear in both R- and P-technique. If we define the *efficacy* of a concept (Cattell, 1952a) as the number of distinct multivariate systems or facets in nature in which its pattern appears, then it seemed desirable that a trait concept should manifest its functional unity at the level of efficacy of having at least *two* facets. That is to say, it should have a unity of growth (or fluctuation) as well as a unity of structure in terms of static individual differences.

In 1944 I entered on a theoretical exploration of the possible sources of variation and covariation observable through psychological measurements. My aim was to see what we meant by "error" in various experimental designs (one man's error evidently being another man's meat, if a metaphor may be advantageously mixed!) and to ask in how many facets of covariation a real influence should be expected to show itself if it is indeed a real influence in nature. This issued in my 1946 book (Cattell, 1946) as the Covariation Chart, in which persons, tests, and occasions were set down as Cartesian coordinates, yielding three facets of covariation relations, and, since each yielded two alternative transposes, six factor-analytic techniques, which I named R and Q, P and O, and T and S (Cattell, 1952b). This revelation of possibilities showed that only two—R and Q—had previously been used, and, of the new ones, P-technique seemed to have the greatest possibilities for personality and social research.

Incidentally, further reasoning has suggested that five Cartesian coordinates, rather than three, are required, and for this more fully developed "covariation chart" I have suggested the expression Basic Data Relation Matrix or BDR matrix. The implications of this for further factor-analytic developments are discussed in this volume particularly in the chapters by Horst and Tucker and have been presented systematically by the present writer in 1957 (Cattell, 1957) and in the *Handbook of Multivariate Experimental Psychology* recently gone to press (Cattell, 1963). Suffice it, however, that this alters in no fundamental way the particular matter discussed here, namely, the past use of P-technique, R-technique, and incremental R-technique, and their fundamental interrelationships.

P-technique takes a facet on the BDR matrix adjacent to *R*-technique. It may be visualized as hinging on the same set of variables but extending their measures across occasions instead of across people. That is to say, one takes a set of psychologically significant variables and measures them repeatedly for, say, a hundred days on one person. The series are correlated and factored. My wife was gallantly the first subject for such an experiment, in 1945, and the outcome of the factorization was most encouraging, for it clearly showed several one-to-one correspondences of personality factors previously found in *R*-technique with trait-states, i.e., daily-trait-level change factors, in *R*-technique. As a result of this opening experiment a systematically interlocking set of researches were set up, now extending to nearly twenty cases in the literature, normal and abnormal, in which trait structures have been replicated both in general personality and in the motivational (erg and sentiment) realm. The personality data extends across questionnaire (*Q*-data) and ratings (*L*-data), as well as objective test (*T*-data) and physiological measures. See Cattell (1951*a*, 1951*b*, 1953, 1955, 1957), Cattell, Cattell, and Rhymer (1947), Cattell and Cross (1952), Cattell and Luborsky (1950), Cattell and Williams (1953), and Mefferd, Moran, and Kimble (1958). The dynamic motivational analyses have led to a particularly valuable objective model for the therapeutic location of conflict areas (Cattell and Scheier, 1961) and for objectively determining intensities of conflict; but clinicians, unfortunately, have not yet awakened to these possibilities of the computer. I have paused briefly to show the nature of these studies, with widely chosen but interlocking sets of variables, to make clear the inductive basis for certain features I shall later describe in the model. Incidentally the method has worked, in terms of consistent and scientifically meaningful results, not only in psychology, but also when applied to countries and communities as organisms, in cultural sociology (Cattell, 1953; Cattell and Adelson, 1951).

Still keeping contact with the substantive, psychological field, I would like to try to remove some obscurities in the verbally defined concepts of trait and state by creating for them more exact mathematico-statistical models. To the psychologist it is apparently obvious that a state and a trait are different, and he will even confidently say that *X* is at a certain characterological *trait* level in anxiety and at another, temporary level in the *state* or mood of anxiety, despite the high similarity of the concepts and their patterns. To the statistician the problem does not look so simple.

In our comparisons of *R*- and *T*-technique results we were soon compelled to ask, "What is the difference between fluctuation on a trait level and fluctuation in a state?" In answering this it should be noted that ordinary *R*-technique picks up both states and traits (Cattell, 1952*a*,

1957). R-technique, perfectly carried out, is, as it were, an instantaneous snapshot, and, as such, it catches people at different state levels as well as at their different trait levels. In statistical terms it includes both across-people and across-occasion variance. Incidentally, the proper way to approach a factoring of *traits* only—and a way which no one has ever used—would be to test every individual a great number of times, and factor *averages* of his scores on each variable. Thus the inter-occasion variance, while not totally disappearing, would fall to negligibility compared with inter-person variance. Indeed, at first we thought that the greater part of the remarkable agreement found between R-technique and P-technique might be due simply to our aligning *state* factors in R-technique with *state* factors in P-technique. But evidence shows this is not the whole story. T. W. Anderson (1961), as a mathematician, criticizes the title "P-technique" because "the name itself gives no hint of what it represents." This illustrates the differences of mathematical and psychological use. P-, Q-, and R-technique titles have deep roots in psychological statistics, and to the clinician P-technique conveniently conveys directly the notion of factoring the single person.

A simple operational, statistical way to separate traits from states would be to cut the knot by saying that a trait is something that does not vary at all and which therefore appears only in R-technique analyses ("averaged R-technique," to be exact). Unfortunately for this simplicity, it might produce an empty class! So far the only major trait in R-technique not found in P-technique is general intelligence, and, if recent indications are correct, even this is likely to appear in experiments which insert variables for both fluid and crystallized general ability factors (Cattell, 1962). All traits may be expected to generate trait-states.

Conceptually we can certainly speak of *traits* (derived from averaged–variable-level R-technique), of *states on traits* or *trait-states* (ordinary R, incremental R, and P-technique), and of *states* (incremental R and P-technique). However, no sharp line can be drawn, on the basis of differential emergence by techniques, between trait-states (occasion variance on a mood or dynamic condition) and states, since both appear on both techniques (incremental R and P). However, they can be contingently *defined* as opposite ends of a continuum, the continuum being the ratio of averaged–variable-level R-technique factor variance and the incremental or P-technique variance. And if the distribution of this ratio should prove to be bi-modal, as is quite likely, the definitions of state and trait-state could be made practically nonoverlapping.

Further discussion of the separation of instances of these concepts requires more detailed reference to assumptions and their verification. The notion of a trait-state factor, for example, implies that a relatively fixed state will in some sense vary in level from day to day. If there is a characteristic level of "elasticity" running through all manifestations of a given trait (but not necessarily the same magnitude for different traits), then, this being interpreted as a constant *coefficient of variation*, over time, for variables insofar as they are affected by the same trait, the loading pattern for the factor corresponding to trait fluctuation should be the same as that for the fixed trait, examined by R-technique on individual differences. If this is so, it provides a basis for distinguishing trait-states from states as they emerge together in P-technique or incremental R-technique, but makes a greater problem in separating traits from trait-states in ordinary R-technique, since the paired factors will now be cooperative in form and difficult to rotate apart.

The particular statistical problems of P-technique will be examined in a moment. Meanwhile let us take a brief look at the problems of incremental R-technique. In this method all persons are measured on each of a series of tests on two occasions. The difference scores are then correlated and factored. This line of research began with Woodrow (1939a) and has been carried forward in our laboratory in relation to P-technique and in relation to cross-sectioning abilities at various levels. The main problems raised here concern (a) the reduced reliability due to the measure's sharing both initial and final errors of measurement, (b) the question whether the gain score should be corrected for initial, or initial and final levels, and (c) the tendency of initially high and low scores to make the usual regression to the mean on the second measurement. The answers offered seem in the writer's opinion to share the frequent error of confusing function fluctuation with error of measurement. For example, if the statistical regression to the mean is largely true, homeostatic function fluctuation, then it is something not to be gotten rid of but to be analyzed. If we could correct gain score *only for that degree of correlation with initial score which arises from the shared error of measurement*, this would be desirable. But to remove all correlation of gain with initial status is undesirable, since it may be in the nature of things *at certain stages* that "to him that hath shall be given." In a word, our argument would be that where the scale has no artificial ceiling, and where measures are long enough greatly to reduce measurement error, ordinary uncorrected scale scores should be used in incremental R-technique.

When such scores are used, alignments are found, on the one hand, between trait-states from incremental R and trait-states or traits in R-technique, and on the other, with trait-states and states in P-technique. An example of the first is the alignment of second-order factors in the 16

P.F. Test from these two approaches (Cattell, 1957), and an example of the second is the alignment of incremental R and P-technique anxiety factor pattern (Cattell and Scheier, 1961). However, it should be noted that both theoretically and in confirmatory empirical findings, incremental R-technique gives a loading pattern which is common to all people whereas the P-technique loading pattern defines a trait psychologically and statistically unique to one person. Our empirical evidence shows that these unique trait patterns tend to range fairly closely about the central common trait pattern. The restriction on the P-technique pattern that it is unique to one person is balanced, however, by the restriction on incremental R that it deals with the type of change that may occur only over *one occasion*, whereas P-technique samples occasions liberally. Parenthetically, we could avoid some semantic confusion between psychologists and statisticians if the latter would use the term *specific* instead of unique for variance peculiar to a *test;* for the term *unique trait* has long been used, e.g., by Allport (1938), for a pattern unique to a person. For completeness and clarity we would then have *unique* variance to a *person, specific* variance to a *test*, and *instance* variance peculiar to an *occasion*.

To complete this story of interrelations of techniques, however, we must consider also what has been called group-mean P-technique, in which a whole group is treated as a unit for successive measures, the scores for N people on test t being averaged for each of the occasions. This would have the advantage of yielding a *common* trait pattern of change for all people but the serious disadvantage of losing much variance through the different individuals' being out of phase in their changes. Its best field of use would seem to be where all subjects are subjected to the same powerful manipulated influences, in manipulative P-technique discussed below. A better derivative design related to these is that of *Chain P-technique*, used by Cattell and Scheier (1961), in which with too few observations on any one case for an adequate P-technique, one strings the cases along in an extended score matrix, one beyond another. In the actual experiments, which have given consistent results, all subjects were brought to the same mean and sigma on all variables, i.e., standardized, thus allowing each to contribute equally. A reasonable argument could be made, however, for having only the same mean and not throwing away the evidence of extreme variability which some cases actually show.

However, the main combined use of methods will be those of R, incremental R, and P-techniques, with the aims of (*a*) checking factor structure, (*b*) separating traits, trait-states, and states, and (*c*) discovering the variability of unique from common traits (especially in dynamic traits and clinical practice). As to the second, one further way (additional to the inter- and intra-person variance ratio) for distinguishing a trait-state from a state is available by comparing the averaged *R*-technique pattern with the incremental *R* or *P*-technique pattern. Thereupon some patterns in the latter—the trait-states—should strongly resemble corresponding patterns in the former; whereas others—the states—would not. Although, as stated, no true *averaged* R-*technique* on an adequate occasion-sample seems ever to have been made, yet already, by ordinary, single-occasion *R*-technique we have a research example, namely, in anxiety (Cattell and Scheier, 1961), where sufficient difference is evident between trait-state and state to justify the hypotheses that they are distinct factors. For example, systolic blood pressure loads the anxiety state much more than the trait of characterological anxiousness, and presumably than the trait-state. Parenthetically there are difficult factor rotation problems here because, if the trait-state level reacts to the same situations as the pure state, one has to separate factors which will not only be substantially cooperative but also highly correlated.

In conclusion on the matter of total "setting," it should be added that the separation of trait, trait-state, and state factors will also rest on facts beyond these immediate statistical ones, namely, history of development, criterion associations, etc., for the trait factor. The state should correlate with no permanent criteria.

Statistical properties and problems of the P-*technique model*

With this glance at the statistical setting of *P*-technique in relation to other possibilities in the BDR matrix and at the psychological aims in its use (namely mood state, dynamic conflict indices, etc.), we can turn to the particular statistical problems and properties of *P*-technique as a mathematico-statistical model.

In factoring that variance which arises from repeated application of the same test, we are operating in the region which most users of the reliability coefficient have been accustomed to think of as error. It is therefore perhaps not surprising that the first criticism of *P*-technique by the conservative was that we were merely factoring error. A more sophisticated view of the reliability coefficient, namely, the recognition that it regards function fluctuation as error, makes comment on this criticism unnecessary. A related point which needs comment, however, is T. W. Anderson's (1961) argument that because all measures are made on one *occasion* they may share some experimental error of measurement. This risk is not peculiar to *P*-technique. In *R*-technique all measures on one *person* may share experimental error, e.g., because he came late or felt "out of sorts," or, in *T*- and *S*-techniques, one *test* apparatus may be acting up and affecting a whole row of the score matrix. This is a matter of the experimenter's being alert to the type of error which is most deadly to his proposed form of analysis. If, as Anderson cites, the weather may affect all *P*-technique measures on one day, such an uncontrollable has equivalents in the other techniques and can be set aside as a definite exogenous factor in the final analysis.

However, the longitudinal reliabilities to be expected in *P*-technique will tend to be systematically lower than those we are accustomed to in *R*-technique, because the same size of true error is here contrasted *only* with that part of the real variance which is function fluctuation, instead of function fluctuation plus individual difference variation; i.e.,

$$(1) \qquad r_{r_R} = \frac{\sigma_i^2 + \sigma_f^2}{\sigma_i^2 + \sigma_f^2 + \sigma_e^2},$$

but

$$(2) \qquad r_{r_P} = \frac{\sigma_f^2}{\sigma_f^2 + \sigma_e^2},$$

where σ_i^2 is individual difference variance, and σ_f^2 is real function fluctuation.

The second criticism, which, by contrast, is a real and interesting one, was that the sampling of occasions in time is an unexplored statistical problem and may not fit the same assumptions as the sampling of people. Admittedly, the whole question of sampling on the five possible main series or tags of the BDR matrix is still under examination. The five series are people, stimuli, responses, observers, and conditions extra to the stimulus. The last can be divided into endogenous and exogenous conditions. These are the five sufficient "tags" or entity series to identify a psychological event and measurement in the BDR matrix. It may be that empirical as well as theoretical considerations will finally be needed to settle issues. For, basically, these issues can be settled only when we know something about the type groupings of the kind of nodes which constitute each Cartesian coordinate or tag series in the BDR matrix. The term nodes— meaning intersection points—is perhaps the best possible term for the single entries in the various series which constitute the Cartesian coordinates of the BDR matrix; e.g., a person, a stimulus, or a response is a node. Each entry in each series can be regarded as a node or intersection point of a set of parameters of properties.

The sampling problem is only one of several in regard to which some clearer thinking on the role of *time* in *P*-technique has to be done. The main confusion arises from considering the occasions axis as a simple time axis. Actually it is several things. In the present case—the sampling of occasions—our object is really to *sample the environment*. If this has any reference to time, it is only in the sense of time as a distance, not a direction. We may decide to sample the environmental stimuli representatively with regard to "chunks" of time, as one might in regard to sections of space. One possible view of what the minimum "chunk" of time should be to constitute a "population of occasions" is that it is the life span of the organism or organization being studied. This has been argued, for example, by Kish (1953). The life span of the system is certainly one firm definition of the total population we are concerned to sample appropriately, but there are others. For example, any physiological use of *P*-technique needs to sample for the seasons, and many cultural processes also indicate the calendar year as a natural unit.

As mentioned above, the writer would suggest that an even more important need, before the sampling laws of people are applied to other modes of the BDR matrix, is to discover by species-type analysis whether one is sampling from a homogeneous population or one with subsets of species types (Cattell, 1961a). The mathematical statistician's assumption that human beings constitute a homogeneous total population, which is very questionable in psychological measurements, is probably still moːe questionable for occasions, responses, etc. However, with these provisos that certain effects are quantitatively more emphasized in occasions, the sampling problem and laws of *P*-technique cannot be considered fundamentally different in any respect from those of *R*-technique.

However, other problems particular to the use of time in *P*-technique exist, and will be discussed in the following order: (*a*) effect on degrees of freedom, (*b*) the effect of special time-related influences, as in trends and cycles, (*c*) the cumulative effects, in psychological use of *P*-technique, of the repeated-measurement effects themselves upon the subject, and (*d*) the adjustment of the analysis to the model of causal action assumed to be operative.

The problem of degrees of freedom

Serial correlation has been defined as the correlation of one series of time-identified measures with another, when the second is lagged (or advanced) by one, two, or more intervals on the first. If the serial correlation is that of a variable with itself, we speak of an *autocorrelation*, and if with another variable, as a *lead-and-lag cross correlation*. It is convenient to speak of one-lag, two-lag, etc., serial correlation, according to the number of periods by which one is stepped forward on another.

In two variables with n occasion measures lagged by b periods the sample of occasions is obviously reduced to $(n - b)$ by this lag arrangement alone. (One cannot, meaningfully, arrange the two series in two rings.) However, it is further argued by Quenouille (1952, 1957), Bartlett (1935), and other leading statisticians that the degrees of freedom in the typical P-technique serial correlation, *even without lag*, is reduced by the fact that any variable is likely to have a significant autocorrelation, extending perhaps to a lag of several periods. That this would, in the ordinary sense, reduce degrees of freedom is evident from the fact that one does not have independent pieces of information in the measurements in any series. Typically we have, indeed, what is known as first-degree and some higher degree Markoff processes (Bartlett, 1935; Danford, Hughes, and McNee, 1960; Quenouille, 1952). In a first-degree Markoff stochastic process, measurement n in a series accounts for some of the variance in $n + 1$ and contains in itself *all* the determination from preceding measures. Most P-technique data runs to third- or fourth-order Markoff processes, for the partialing out of n from $n + 1$ measures still leaves some correlation with $n - 1$, $n - 2$, etc.

Assuming significant autocorrelation exists, the solution which Holtzman (1962) offers, following Quenouille, is as follows. Suppose the cross correlation, i.e., without lead and lag, of two variables, x and y, is .30; the first four serial coefficients for x are .70, .50, .40, and .20; and the same coefficients for y are .50, .40, .30, and .10. Following Quenouille's suggestion (1952, p. 170), we may use Bartlett's formula for estimating the number of observations equivalent to one independent observation. For the present example, the number of paired observations needed to equal one degree of freedom for purposes of statistical inference is *at least* 2.38. Thus,

$$1 + 2r_{x1}r_{y1} + 2r_{x2}r_{y2} + \cdots = 2.38 + \cdots,$$

where r_{x1} is a one-lag autocorrelation in the x variable series, and so on.

If serial correlation beyond the fourth coefficient had been included in the equation, the estimate would have been still higher. In other words there are fewer than 42 degrees of freedom, instead of 98, for testing the significance of the obtained correlation: too few for a correlation of .30 to prove significant beyond the .05 level.

For the moment, I shall let this stand, but after we have dealt with the general issue of trend factors, I propose to show what I believe to be a fallacy in generally applying this procedure.

The problem of trends and cycles

It may help in understanding the nature of my subsequent arguments against psychologists' following the procedure of Quenouille and others if the history and philosophy of the differing viewpoints are first briefly sketched. The chief analysts of time-series other than psychologists have been economists and, lately, meteorologists. But it is the traditional interests and approaches of economists which tend to be unquestioningly carried over when mathematical statisticians like Anderson or Quenouille attempt mathematical abstractions which they believe should apply to both economists' and psychologists' usages. Now although economists may have been a little longer in the time-trend business, their interests and suppositions have been very different from ours. For example, they have very fixed ideas about something called a *trend* and something called a *cycle*, and often they are little interested in anything else.

I think some economists will admit a mild obsession with trends and oscillations, but on my argument that our differences go deeper, because classical economics has been an armchair discipline with far less of a general empirical scientific approach, there may be disagreement. Some will deny and others—the die-hards at Oxford and elsewhere—will proudly claim that economics is a purely deductive science (whatever that can be!). The psychologist has used factor analysis supremely as a method of discovery. But, at least until quite recently, the economists have not used factor analysis to find out, but only to check upon the influences they believe are operating over time. They have even *told* the statistician what conceptual entities are important and have asked him to use them, by canonical correlation or simpler devices, to predict what future measures they want to predict. Thus the treatment of any apparent monotonic trend visible to the economist in his data is first to apotheosize it as "the trend" and then to partial it out, to look for the lesser deities—the cycles —which he expects to dance attendance on the greater deity. It is this difference of philosophy which justifies the psychologist's questioning the degrees of freedom model which the statistician has developed for the economist.

Concentrating for a moment on the trend concept, let us note that the psychologist sees it very differently. *It may represent one, two, or more time-associated factors acting together, and we want to know what they are.* There is no reason why any *real* factor or factors should *not* show a time trend. Spearman's "*g*" will show a monotonic trend in growing children, and we have shown that three distinct personality factors show a common trend in the course of successful psychotherapy (Cattell and Scheier, 1961).

Time is associated with factors but there is no reason to posit that it is itself a factor or to treat it in this respect as a privileged variable. If it *is* a factor, we shall discover this fact in a simple structure rotation. Its status should properly be initially that of any other variable in the correlation matrix and, although it is in certain respects a unique variable, those respects do not require any arbitrarily different treatment of it *at this stage.*

Consequently, (a) to partial out "time trend" from the correlations among other variables in the matrix before factoring, or (b) to rotate to set aside a factor running through the time vector after factoring, is to wreck the whole purpose of the analysis. In the first case, according to Thomson and Ledermann's (1939) theorem, selection on one variable will distort all the correlations among the factors and, of course, obliterate their relation to time. In (b) we are most likely to rotate to a quite artificial factor—a monster possessing no natural hyperplane—thus adding, to the distortion of the factors left by (a), the final confusion of entertaining a truly nonexistent factor. In either case we throw away a great deal of valuable information about the covariance of variables. Anything that happens over time is excluded from our science. It is the supreme example of throwing away the baby with the bath water.

The alternative and far better procedure is surely to recognize that the influences which we aim to locate as simple structure factors will naturally, in several cases, tend to have significant relations with time. These relations can be plotted or expressed as correlations *after* the factors have been found and estimated.

However, it is well to face the fact that the time associations in P-technique do create special problems at the technical level and aggravate what are minor difficulties in R-technique into difficulties requiring unusual levels of technical skill. What I have frequently seen happen is that an investigator pursuing simple structure encounters a tendency to far larger correlations among the factors than he is accustomed to find. Perceiving that the large correlations among certain factors are all due to their correlation with time, he may resolve his panic at the unusual, improbable-looking situation by deciding first to partial out time and start again. The objections to this, as stated above, are fundamental. Yet the fact remains that these substantially time-related factors often at first produce a C_R matrix which is singular, or so ill-conditioned and near-singular, as to be uninvertible to obtain C_F. The fact is that when several vectors are thus intercorrelated, there is considerable danger of one of them being so near the time axis that it is bound to come near being a linear combination of the others. The only remedy is superb accuracy in simple structure attainable by unusual patience in trial and error search, for our experience has shown that the true position is always invertible whereas any error deviation has a tendency to produce uninvertible, near-singular C_R matrices.

However, the possibility must next be considered that the model may sometimes require time to emerge from the data as a genuine second-order simple structure factor. Below it is pointed out that perfectly time-correlated trends and cycles may be expected. For example, in a developmental use of P-technique with children it can be reasonably hypothesized that such factors as intelligence, body height, basal metabolic rate, and inhibition will each have part of its variance contributed by time, as an aging process. Consequently, time *could* appear as an influence, and, since it accounts for part of the variance in each of these factors and has a distinct hyperplane if there are a number of other, quite time-unconnected factors in the study, it could show up as a simple structure second-order factor. It is mainly in this sense that time has a uniqueness as a variable which needs to be watched in the factor-analytic process. The special problem of separating two perfectly time-correlated factors is discussed under the causal model below.

With this preamble, revealing trends and cycles as the consequences of interaction of several factors *organic to the system*, we can return to the degrees of freedom problem. At the risk of seeming to disagree with statistical authorities, one must raise the question of what is meant by degrees of freedom. It is curious that mathematical statisticians have written very little on this as a general problem, but it seems to the present writer that the constraints are of at least four different kinds, as follows:

(*a*) Those inherent in the laws of algebra; e.g., a mean and one of two components being known, only one degree of freedom remains, or, in Q sort, the placing of one variable above average rank increases the probability of a later variable's falling below.

(*b*) Those given by distribution, when *experience* in a field tells us that a certain distribution can infallibly be expected.

(*c*) Those given by *experimental* dependence of variables, as when two measures are bound to share variance due to a particular instrument.

(*d*) Those imported when an experimenter agrees that he will interpret only according to a particular model; whereupon if the model denies the independence of two measures, the analyst should not assume it.

Regardless of origin, the decision on degrees of freedom should precede the experiment; i.e., it should not depend on the particular experimental, numerical values which emerge. *Any constraint on numbers which occurs in the experimental data constitutes the scientific law one is seeking.* One may question the use of (b), (c), and (d)—i.e., of anything but algebraic necessity (a) above—as the real basis for degrees of freedom. Instrument and model effects could be part of the hypothesis being tested, as also could distribution effects. In the present case, have we the right to assume that significant autocorrelation (Markoff process) will exist? Obviously not, because with suitable intervals it disappears. The significance test with greatly reduced degrees of freedom proposed by Bartlett, Quenouille, and Holtzman is testing the null hypothesis involved in the question, "Assuming autocorrelation exists in the series a and b, is the correlation between a and b significant?"

The analyst who wants first to get rid of trends and cycles, and then to examine the significance of any connections that remain, rightly uses the degrees of freedom which these statisticians indicate. But the factor analyst, regardless of whether he is using this multivariate method for discovery of hypotheses or testing of hypotheses, is asking a different question. He is asking, "What are the number and nature of the factors required to account for the observed correlations?" and his null hypothesis is that there are no factors. His only assumption is the behavioral science equivalent of Newton's first law of motion, statable as, "If there are no influences at work, all variables will persist at the same unchanging level and the correlation matrix (and the autocorrelations) will be all zeros." Parenthetically, it may be objected that the correlation of two fixed series is not zero but is indeterminate. A "method of limits" argument, however, would point to its being zero, for when any actual correlations are plotted between two randomly related series, as each approaches the horizontal the trend is to smaller and smaller values. In other words, the serial cross correlations in P-technique and the autocorrelations are both due to the existence of the same influences—the influences which negate the null hypothesis that no influences are at work. Consequently, the statistical test for the null hypothesis should not be one which assumes the existence of significant autocorrelations. If these appear, they are part of the hypothesis being tested, and the degrees of freedom should consequently be $N - 2$ where N is the number of occasions.

Another way of looking at this problem is to refer to two kinds of time, which in conference debate we have jocularly called Holtzmanian and Cattellian time! The latter removes the unidirectional property from time and considers it, like space, simply as a dimension occurring in various quantities necessary for events to take place. Holtzmanian time is unidirectional. Suppose we have scores for all tests on one occasion punched on one IBM card. If, now, unknown to the experimenter, someone shuffles the IBM cards (or the secretary drops them on the stairs), any autocorrelation that existed will be unknown to the experimenter and he will not, following Holtzman, feel it necessary to test significance with reduced degrees of freedom. The "organic" correlations among the variables will, however, be completely unaltered by this shuffling!

The meaning of thus operating in Cattellian time can be shown further by analogy with *R*-technique, into which Holtzmanian time cannot enter. If 200 boys are tested on ten school subjects and ranked, as usual in school lists, in order of general achievement, then, by virtue of Spearman's "*g*," there will be significant autocorrelations down the list of boys as down the list of days in *P*-technique. But again they can be removed by shuffling and, indeed, we see that in both *R*-technique and *P*-technique the order which gives significant autocorrelations is only one very special one among a very large number. The ordinary *R*-technique experimenter does not feel required to throw away degrees of freedom because of the existence of this possible order, and it may be argued from this independent approach that the *P*-technique investigator is also under no such obligation.

A word may also be desirable on the curious tendency to regard instrumental dependency as somehow a greater peril in *P*-technique than in *R*-technique. Most *P*-technique measures are as *experimentally* independent as those of *R*-technique. Different measures may use the same instrument wielded by the same observer, but so does *R*-technique. And for every special connection that can be cited in *P*-technique there is an equivalent, symmetrical connection of the two measures in *R*-technique. The assumption that there is a causal connection between event n and event $n + 1$ would, of course, involve something asymmetric to the *R*-technique model where the nth person's effects on the $n + 1^{th}$ are reciprocated.

Incidentally, yet another way of getting rid of irrelevant autocorrelation, and operating with full degrees of freedom, has been suggested to the writer by the statistician Mikulski. If the conditions of a stationary time-series can be met, namely, the mean and sigma for all measures together have no significant differences from day to day—an acceptable assumption in any well-sampled *P*-technique—then a linear transformation for the series on any one variable can be made which will eliminate the autocorrelation. This involves calculating the covariances of all possible autocorrelations and obtaining therefrom the beta weights of the various lagged series which will produce a set of values in the derived score series orthogonal to all lagged series. The objection to this ingenious approach is, however, still the same in principle as to Quenouille's approach; namely, if the factors we are interested in are partly or wholly responsible for the autocorrelation, then its existence is part of the evidence for the hypotheses to be tested.

Incidentally, the issue of degrees of freedom is not a merely academic one. The main single reason that so few *P*-technique studies have been done in areas greatly needing such studies is that subjects cannot be found to endure the 100 or so days of experimentation needed. The effect of requiring, for statistical reasons, an extension to 200 days can be imagined! However, the discussion, for this practical reason, of degrees of freedom, has done us service in clarifying the whole issue of the time dimension. It has been seen that there are some aspects of the introduction of time measurement into *P*-technique which require real modifications of statistical analytical procedures and others which are, as it were, merely hypnotic, requiring us to be awake to what we are really assuming and asking in the experiment. With so large a digression we are now disposed to agree with Donne and Huxley that "time must have a stop," and to resume the main exposition.

The special problem of effects from repetition

Let us now turn to the third of the four debatable issues: the effect of repetition of measurement. Those interested in models may object that this is a purely psychological problem, but a model must offer to fit all psychological effects, even though they be minor. So far the kind of simplification we have accepted, namely, that a stimulus of the same meaning is repeated, is no worse than that in the reliability coefficient concept. For the latter supposes a symmetrical relation between test and retest measures whereas in fact we know that the meaning of the retest has been changed by the experience of the test.

Here, in *P*-technique, we can hypothesize from a psychological standpoint that the repetition of the stimulus will bring in its train certain significantly time-correlated effects, mainly classifiable under (*a*) learning and (*b*) changes in interest, notably boredom. That the nature of the perceptual and motor ability factors resulting in a given response to a given stimulus changes with repetition in an orderly way is well known from the work of Fleishman and Hempel (1954) and Tucker (1959). It would be interesting and valuable in prolonged *P*-technique studies to factor the first and the second halves of the series separately, to check on the magnitude and nature of these effects in longer series than those studied by Fleishman or Tucker. However, inasmuch as *P*-technique variables have generally been carefully chosen to avoid those effects which are obviously susceptible to learning, we might expect the ability-achievement factor changes to be less than those in the learning studies just quoted. On the other hand, the changes in the loadings of variables on personality factors might be appreciable. Such changes, if they exist, should result in more specific error of prediction of particular responses at the beginning and end of the period when the whole period is factored as one. In other words, we might get more complete and powerful prediction (higher communality) from common factors if we factored separately for two halves. Certainly one might argue for more completely meaningfully and fully resolved *P*-technique studies if the practice were introduced of chopping off and throwing away the early period of, say, the first ten or more days, involving maximum adjustive change to the experimental instrument situation *per se*.

In a general way the special effects of having to repeat measurements with the very same instruments will be some loss of general personality trait and state variance into apparent specific test variance. But this lost variance may also turn up in common factors, of the general class of instrument factors (Cattell, 1961*b*). However, these will be somewhat unusual, hybrid instrument factors in that they represent instrument learning and instrument boredom factors in the subject—and, in this situation of *P*-technique, they would be expected to be highly time-correlated. Whether such factors should be expected to consist of one general learning and one general boredom factor running across all variables, or of several such factors localized to various content areas, it is hard to say on theoretical grounds alone. Curiously enough, empirical findings so far offer no evidence even for the existence of such factors. The definite presence in most of our studies and those of Mefferd, Moran, and Kimble (1958), Williams (1959), and Haverland (1954) of psychological variables, on the one hand, which *could* show learning, and physiological variables, on the other, which almost certainly would not, has provided good conditions for the simple structure rotational resolution in terms of such factors to emerge. Moreover, that the analyses have been, statistically, *sensitive* enough to yield fainter extraneous factors is shown by the discovery of a seasonal-trend factor (Cattell, 1957), associated with sunlight, in two of our studies, and also of weather-condition factors, associated with pressure change, in Haverland's study (1954).

Because there may thus be a sporting chance that learning-boredom factors can be kept trivial by proper experimental conditions, and because the alternative procedure of trying to separate them later might be difficult, in that they should share an almost perfect time correlation, there is much to be said for a determined attempt to make such factors negligible by experimental control, instead of pulling them out later by statistical, factorial analysis. One way of doing this is, as in our own researches, by careful search for those test situations which get at what one wants, yet are repeatable. An instance of this is the measurement of motivation by reaction time and by fluency—i.e., by formal properties rather than content, as in, for example, opinionnaire or information tests. Another is that pioneered by Moran (1959) in which, say, twenty or more equivalent forms of a test are standardized for mutual equivalence on adequate population samples.

If this latter course is to be followed—and I firmly believe it is the better solution—then it is imperative that some research foundation come to the rescue, for the task is a large one and needs to be systematically organized with the best technical advice coordinated from various fields. Incidentally, experiment may show that *P*-technique experiments with a hundred or two hundred repetitions may be practically pursued with what we may designate *serial equivalent* test forms consisting of no more than twenty tests, repeated in a cycle through the experiment. Gross effects of familiarity could be expected to disappear after twenty days, and anything remaining in the form of a cyclical effect could be recognized and pulled out by correlating into the study a numerical, calendar variable, the cycles in which keep time with those of the test cycle. This should be superior to randomly altering the order of the twenty tests. Indeed, the very idea of *serial equivalence* is that the standardization shall be made in the same order as that in which the test is going to be administered to the individual. This means that, say, a sample of 300 subjects should take the twenty equivalent forms in a standard order. The resulting standardization aims at making standard scores equivalent on subsequent days. Whether it also gets rid of sequential learning and boredom effects is more questionable, since these learning-boredom trends might be different in the individual and the group; but at least serial standardization should greatly reduce unwanted variance from such sources.

In summary, it is advocated that learning-boredom effects be handled by (*a*) a resourceful choice of repeatable tests, (*b*) developing *serial equivalent forms*, over at least a twenty-cycle range if possible for at least the markers for the main known factors, (*c*) introducing calendar variables in phase with the test cycles to examine significance of repetition cycles, (*d*) throwing away the first dozen scores, or whatever experiment shows to be an "abnormal" adaptation period, (*e*) factoring the total period in two parts as a check on trends, etc., (*f*) rotating to separate such learning-boredom factors as may remain from the personality-state real variance. This is an arduous task, but I firmly believe that such equivalent, prescribed-sequence test form batteries have to be built up on all tests used in *P*-technique if we are to do really good work, and some foundation should be organizing this. These steps of developing equivalent forms, throwing away the first week or so of special adaptation effects, and factoring first and second periods separately as a check on any trends in structure—and any others calculated to leave the final analysis experimentally clear of unnecessary complicating factors—offer the best solution to the repetition problem.

The causal scientific model from which the mathematico-statistical model is abstracted

There remains the last of the four major problems listed earlier, namely, the adjustment of the mathematical model, and its statistical analysis and testing, to the required properties of a hypothetical scientific causal model. The ultimate aim in the use of *P*-technique is, after all, to gain interpretations in terms of scientific concepts, and this can be done only if definite hypotheses about causal action can be checked in the form of the mathematical model.

Causality has been such a subject of contention when scientists, mathematicians, and philosophers get together, in this generation, that a word on operational definition is necessary. Incidentally, the mathematician in particular has something like a phobia in regard to coming to terms with causality, which may be due to the fact that in the whole menagerie of relations kept by the mathematician this particular creature does not exist. Psychologists also have their problems, insofar as the so-called experimental psychologists have long pursued a wild-goose chase, in which they have asserted and assumed that causality investigation belongs only to bivariate, dependent-independent variable designs but not to multivariate, correlational, and factor-analytic experiment. Elsewhere I have systematically classified experimental designs (Cattell, 1963) showing that this is a superficial and historically quite accidental association, and that the capacity of a design to investigate causality has really nothing to do with whether correlation or analysis of variance or any other relation-testing statistic is finally used. Nor does capacity to infer causality depend on the introduction of *manipulative control*—sometimes too broadly described as "controlled experiment." *The capacity of a design to yield evidence on causality depends entirely upon the presence or absence of evidence of time sequence in the measurement data.* If anyone objects to the definition of causality as invariable sequence, e.g., that this makes night the cause of day, one must complete the definition with restrictions which it is unnecessary to mention here, except to say that they are essentially of the kind which resides in the argument that makes simple structure evidence of a causal factor.

If time sequence is the essential touchstone of causal inference, our discussions in this volume on change measures are so deeply interwoven with the concept of causality that discussion beyond the above brief introduction would be appropriate. However, the present chapter lacks space for such fuller treatment. What the meaning of time sequences in P-technique may be for causal inference we shall discuss in a moment. But before we do so, it is necessary to notice that some inference about causality is possible in P-technique before any time sequences are considered and for purely the same reasons as exist in any other form of uniquely rotated factor analysis. In R-technique or any other form, unique rotation by simple structure or confactor rotation carries the implication that the factor is a causal influence operating upon variables. The argument in simple structure, for example, is that a cause would be likely to influence only a limited set of any total, representative array of variables. Consequently, when such a simple structure position is found, the factor is, or rather has been, the influencer of the variables, not vice versa. R-technique investigates either presently acting causes or evidence that particular causes have been at work there. But in either case there is no direct and immediate time-sequence evidence. It is a form of archaeology or geology in which frozen history tells by the positions in which things have been caught what causal sequences occurred. However, the initial use of simple structure in P-technique simply at this level of inference about causes can, unlike the similar use in R-technique, actually be verified in a way I hope to show.

But by reason of the evidence on time sequence in the actual experiment, P-technique (and incremental R-technique) has additional resources for analyzing causal connection. Originally, I suggested handling this analysis in terms of variables. What I called *time-corrected P-technique* was to determine the deviation of causal action among variables a and b by discovering whether the correlation between them increased when the measurement in a was made before that on b, or vice versa. It was proposed that the experimenter would carry out an equi-interval P-technique experiment, i.e., one with even intervals between observations, and discover by trial and error those leads and lags in the correlations of one variable with another that would maximize particular correlations and ultimately the mean correlation within the whole matrix. The assumption here is that the maximum correlation will correspond to that with least "error" in the contributory measures since the effect of error is to attenuate the correlation. The error in this analysis is considered to consist of two parts: the usual random error of experimental measurement, and an *incorrect time interval between a value attained on one variable and its causal effect on the value of another variable.* If we assume that the latter is a substantially larger effect, the time-correction procedure would not capitalize on random error of measurement, for the position required by causal lag to produce a maximization would be unlikely to coincide with that required by random error.

This time-corrected or lead-and-lag *P*-technique proposition has since been considered, with qualified favor, by T. W. Anderson (1961), Holtzman (1962), and a number of others. It has also found expression—but at the level of simple correlations rather than treatment of a whole matrix—in the proposals of Lazarsfeld (1947). However, it now seems altogether less adequate, to me, than the *iteration for displaced factors* which I have since suggested to supersede it. In the first place, my own earlier proposal restricts the possibilities to x acting on y or y acting on x, whereas any truly comprehensive and realistic model should include and be responsive to the third correlational possibility, namely that a third influence affects both x and y. Further, if the restricted model is handled in the total correlation matrix system, instead of in the inconclusive examination of single, atomistic relations, it happens to become impracticably time consuming, even for high-speed computers. The particular time lag of variable x on its observed time which maximizes its correlation with y is unlikely to be the same as that which maximizes it with z. Since each variable must preserve its identity in the matrix, though no longer the identity of the originally observed time, these unequal lags might produce, in a 100 variable matrix, 99 different versions of each variable, i.e., 9,900 variables. One escape from this is to find for each variable that one time-lagged substitute variable which maximizes its *average* correlation with all other variables, i.e., which is the best compromise. Strictly, however, this is a case of a compromise which satisfies no one clear theoretical position. Moreover, even then the procedures are impractical, for in a matrix of merely 100 variables one would have to try factorial 100, i.e., several billion, time-rank orders of the variables to discover that which possessed the maximizing property.

The more important consideration, however, is that this causal model is inadequate or even definitely wrong. If we are to be consistent with our assumption that variables are normally the dependent variables and factors the independent variables, i.e., the assumption of simple structure, it is *the lag of the variables on the factors* with which we should be concerned. Before pursuing this, let us note that the theoretically possible range of causal models in this field is as follows:

(*a*) That some variables are dependent and some independent.

(*b*) That factors are dependent and variables are independent.

(*c*) That factors are independent and variables are dependent.
(*d*) That among factors, some are dependent and some independent.
(*e*) That among factors, all are dependent variables of higher order factors which are independent influences.

These five models must later be considered additionally in terms of influences endogenous and exogenous to the system observed, but for the present we shall state that only (*c*) and (*e*) are acceptable and consistent both with our other assumptions in factor analysis and with the empirical findings on psychological states and trait-states. In short, we adopt the model that factors are causal influences on variables and that factors will themselves be correlated as the result of higher order factors being causal influences upon them. This does not rule out the occasional instance where a variable will turn out to be itself a factor, i.e., loaded unity on a factor. Incidentally, in this oblique model the factor *loadings*, and not the *correlations* of variables with the factors, will be a statement of the extent of the contributory action of the factor to the variance of each variable.

The procedure to which this assumption leads may be called *iteration for factor displacement*. Instead of looking into the correlation matrix for the significant lagged correlations which betoken causal action, we look at the *factor* matrix. The aim is now to discover the interval between a change in the factor level and the change in the variable level which it causes. The method is to try various leads and lags of each variable on the factor, as first estimated from the unlagged variables, in order to maximize the correlation—with a probability, incidentally, of improving the factor estimation from the variables.

The transformations and relations of factors and variables will be representable by the usual equations for oblique factors only at the beginning, before staggered correlations are begun. For once they are begun, each variable will probably become a different variable, in terms of phase, for each factor with which it is connected. Initially, therefore, the procedure is to obtain the matrix for estimating factors from variable scores, V_{fe}, thus:

$$(3) \qquad V_{fe} = R^{-1}V_{fs},$$

where V_{fs} is the factor structure, and then make the first estimate of the factor scores, in the matrix, S_{fo}, from the original test occasion scores, S_{to} (the subscript o indicating values at the *original* experiment, with no lags), thus:

$$(4) \qquad S_{fo} = S_{to}V_{fe}.$$

From general scientific considerations of causal action it seems likely that the lead of any factor on the variables, i.e., the number of measurement intervals by which a change in its level will precede its effects, will differ from factor to factor. For example, a rise in the alertness or arousal factor should affect reaction time within a matter of seconds whereas the effects of, say, a rising estrogen level might take hours or days to bring about changes in sexual perceptions. For the same factor, also, different leads should be allowable for different variables. For example, rising anxiety might immediately affect metabolic rate and tremor, but only after some lag affect the "tendency to self-depreciation" and the "lack of confidence" variables with which we know the anxiety-state factor to be associated.

Accordingly, different lag correlations must now be tried, for each and all of the variables, with each factor, to determine the lags at which the maxima occur. Obviously, this can only be done by using the estimated factor scores from equation (4), for no correlation matrix exists from the numerous staggered variables (nor could one exist without the hopeless complications of a so-called simplex!). However, when the optimum lags of the whole series of variables on a given factor have been determined, the basis exists for making a fresh estimate of this factor. For a correlation matrix, $R_{f_{k1}}$ can be computed among the uniquely lagged variables and the new weights in the column matrix $V_{fe_{k1}}$ calculated thus:

$$(5) \qquad V_{fe_{k1}} = R_{k1}^{-1} V_{fs_{k1}}.$$

(The subscript indicates a lagged matrix referred to factor k, at the *first* occasion of its lagged estimation. R_{k1} is the matrix of correlations of variables appropriately lagged on one another for factor k at 1.)

With the second factor scores for f_k, obtainable by substituting $V_{fe_{k1}}$ for V_{fe} in (4), the lags of all variables on this factor which will maximize the correlations can be calculated again. They will presumably now be more accurately determinable, since the factor is more reliably estimated, and they will tend to result in higher correlation. Thus, by an iterative process, which will presumably converge, one should obtain both the unique variable lags and the correlations corresponding to the causal connections hypothesized in the model. This is perhaps best called the method of *iteration for factor-variable displacement;* for the displacement is relative. Indeed, it is the variable measures that are actually displaced, relative to the original position of the factor. This must be remembered when one comes to calculate and plot the factor scores over time, and in relation to other factors.

For the mathematician there may be some disappointment in the lack of completeness in this outcome. For there is no "closure" in the sense of a way back from the single-column vectors which express these factor-variable correlations and loadings to any general correlation matrix, because the variables have now become different variables. Each variable is differently lagged, for each factor, and there are now $k \times n$ variables. To the chemist, however, there is no great disappointment in the fact that there is no easy way back from the pure element to the crude one from which it has been extracted. So here the obtaining of the factors, of their causal contributions to variables, and of the various causal lags constitutes the understanding desired. One can still get at the rest of the variance of each variable, in that equations permit one to find the contribution of other factors to each of the variables at a time when they are maximally affected by the one factor in which an experimenter is particularly interested. For example, one can accept the variables as defined by the lags for the focused factor and with these variables proceed to a consistent correlation matrix, and to all that can be derived therefrom.

Here, and at several other points in P-technique procedure, e.g., in Mikulski's method of eliminating autocorrelations, above, where higher order lead-lag correlations are employed, one must always watch for two statistical complications. First, as stated early above, the degrees of freedom of the correlation on a series n lagged on a similar series by d will be reduced to $n - d - 2$. Second, the use in a single correlation matrix of decidedly different subsamples, i.e., when d becomes large, can lead to a non-Gramian matrix. In the writer's experience when d becomes as large as about $n/3$, a non-Gramian, unfactorizable matrix is not uncommon, but theoretically this can occur from $d = 1$ onward.

Our model, it will be remembered, admits other influences acting upon the influences just found, and this higher order causal action can be investigated, either from the factor obliquities found from the original R matrix or, better, from actual correlations (attenuation-corrected) of the estimated factors, estimated as above from the iteratively improved correlations of each factor with its variables. In the latter case it is imperative to *synchronize* all factors by fixing each at the same original phase (the interval is already fixed). This involves using each variable, for estimating a given factor, at the phase lag accepted for that variable for that factor only. The procedures and inferences for determining the second-order factors among first-orders are just the same as for those deriving the first-orders from variables.

The relations and separation of endogenous, exogenous, and feedback influences

It remains to take account of those more complex features of our recommended model which have to do with (*a*) circular causal action or positive and negative feedback, and (*b*) the concepts of endogenous and exogenous influences. A division of the latter kind has perennially entered into discussions of analysis of time-series, but it would be a mistake for psychologists uncritically to take over the definitions of economists, or perhaps even the particular implications accepted by writers like T. W. Anderson (1961), Hood and Koopmans (1953), Quenouille (1957), and Whittle (1951). Indeed, what some economists apparently mean by exogenous is nothing more than that some authority, from Keynes to Ricardo or Adam Smith, has declared the data to be irrelevant. It is possible, and constitutes some advance, to say, as Holtzman does, that by exogenous we mean "outside the system," but again there might be arbitrariness in defining the boundaries of a system. Certainly to define a system *A* as meaning that variables from "the universe minus *A*" may act on it but not conversely is to make a perilous, unstable definition. For interaction is the rule of our universe, up to the speed of light, and a system so defined is unlikely to leave any universe!

In the discussion elsewhere of the BDR matrix (Cattell, 1963) a division has been made between *inmodulators* occurring spontaneously in the organism and *exmodulator* conditions originating outside of it. Endogenous and exogenous might well be made synonymous with this. Once again, consistent with our definition of factors, it is *factors* which will be endogenous or exogenous, whereas variables will experience changes which derive from both sources.

It happens that most of the earlier *P*-technique studies did not seek to manipulate environment; i.e., they did not *deliberately* introduce exogenous sources of variation. "Stimuli" have been only brief tests which elicit a response for test purposes, much as one takes a small blood sample, considering it as a test which *measures*, rather than *affects*, the state of the whole organism. Day-to-day real life events have been depended upon to do the tugging and shoving which shakes the organism up and reveals the functionally unitary response and adjustive mechanisms which we are interested to observe. But there is no reason why powerful stimuli should not also be either manipulatively introduced or, at any rate, measured as they occur, and such a wider use of the design has been made already in four of our studies (Cattell and Cross, 1952; Cattell and Luborsky, 1950;

Cattell and Scheier, 1961; Cattell and Williams, 1953) and in that of Mefferd, Moran, and Kimble (1958).

However, if this is done, our method of analysis should reflect the model we believe to be operating. The absence of measured or manipulated variables extra to the organism has never meant that exogenous factors are not operative and experimentally located, but it does mean that the external influence has been only an inference. By contrast there have been more recently a number of very interesting and enlightening multivariate experiments in which stimuli and criteria have been examined in the same factor analysis as test variables and responses. The intention of these clearly designed studies threatens to be clouded by a spate of imitations by band-wagoners who seem to believe that by simply lumping together any stimuli and responses in the same matrix, a desirable design is being achieved. Merely including stimuli and responses in the same matrix is not enough—except perhaps to generate confusion. If we want to find the *dimensions of the stimulus world*, it would be best first to factor the physical measures of the stimuli on their own, and introduce these factors in correlations with response factors. Of course, if the stimuli can be freely manipulated, they can be introduced in a balanced design, as in analysis of variance effects, so that they are deliberately uncorrelated. Unless this is done, and where one wishes evidence that a stimulus actually affects factors, it might be best to refrain from introducing the stimulus variables into the *variable* correlation matrix and to introduce them only into the *factor* correlation matrix, for by hypothesis they are acting as, and should mark, second-order factors.

However, even when exogenous stimuli have deliberately been introduced into the analysis, it does not guarantee that these account for all the changes of the organism due to exogenous influences. Researchers are seldom that lucky. Consequently, the identification and differentiation from other factors of the same general appearance of factors which are exogenous must rest on more general evidence about characteristics of endogenous and exogenous influences.

A truly endogenous influence must appear completely spontaneous as far as any events in the environment are concerned. Known examples would be a maturational growth factor, in a long-term *P*-technique, and appetitive, ergic factors, like hunger and fatigue, in a shorter *P*-technique, as well as a number of obviously physiologically determined changes like those of the menstrual cycle. Such processes must arise by (*a*) some internal time clock or probability function, (*b*) the homeostatic reaction of the organism to its own endogenous processes or externally originating upsets, and (*c*) some memory or storage effect, where the process is triggered by an interval event.

Although some exogenous influences *could* be time bound—for example, night and day, spring and fall, and the psychological state known as Monday morning are exogenous—the endogenous processes above will have time correlation as their most characteristic feature. Perhaps the nearest relative to this in inorganic science is the spontaneous decay of radioactive substances, and the case of U^{238} and U^{234} may be taken to illustrate the peculiar difficulties that would be expected to arise in separating endogenous factors of this kind. For although U^{238} and U^{234} have different half-lives and produce different effects which, in a *P*-technique analysis, would generate distinct factors and loading patterns, yet each is perfectly correlated with time. The paradox of two distinct factors being perfectly correlated is less disturbing to the psychological-factor analyst than to the mathematical-component analysts, but it still presents some fundamental rotation problems!

The technical difficulties which arise in properly separating several factors which are highly correlated with time trend ("calendar factors") and therefore with one another have already been faced, and it may now be noted that they concern largely endogenous influences. Our attention remains to be directed, however, to the technical problems of *cycles*. It is many years since Yule (1926) pointed out as a sort of statistical curiosity that two sine curves of the same frequency would nevertheless yield a serial correlation of zero if separated by a quarter phase, and, of course, a correlation of minus one if lagged by half a cycle. Arguing that two such cycles of the same frequency must spring from some common source, T. W. Anderson (1961) has considered this to indicate a blind spot in the *P*-technique method. However, as we have seen, if the earlier of two such variables is a factor or loads highly on a factor, the second, if truly connected with it, is almost certain to have its connection established by the systematic experimenting with lagged variables as described in the factor-displacement method. Indeed, the real danger is the converse one of mistaking two essentially independent cycles which happen to have the same period, and which happen also to be virtually in phase, for the same factor—a danger we have just discussed for time-trend–bound factors. If they are truly different, however, they will affect different variables and be separable by their different hyperplanes. There is no denying, however, that the bugbear of *P*-technique theoretically is bound to lie in separating the various highly intercorrelating factors, mainly endogenous, that are correlated with time trend, or show similar cycles. However, although the former danger has actually already materialized in our own work, the confusion of cycles has not occurred in any existent experiment.

Finally our model of endogenous and exogenous influences has to be complicated by a realistic necessity, namely, the recognition of a circular action of influences, or feedback. Let us face the fact that no one has yet worked out how feedback effects could be caught by factor analysis—in the *P*-technique form or any other. Our analysis would be that feedback is to be detected only by taking higher order factor analysis to more orders than has yet typically been done. If a first-order factor *A* is influenced by a second-order factor *B* when *A* has a positive or negative feedback on *B*, we would expect *A* to appear also as a third-order factor (provided it operates also upon some *other* factors at the second-order level). Whether our present methods of resolution are capable of coping with this problem we do not know, because it has never been tackled. However, the only realistic thing to do is to set up the *P*-technique on the assumption that the system contains not only factors endogenous to the organism and exogenous factors reflecting known and unknown impinging influences from the environment, but also feedback or more remote circular effects within and between exogenous and endogenous systems.

Some miscellaneous problems:
Sampling, standardization, transpose analysis

Although the general position has already been stated that sampling in *P*-technique is a sampling of the population constituted by the environmental and internal situations encountered in the life span of the system or organism, some peculiarities remain for discussion. Equi-interval *P*-technique, if the interval be made a 24-hour one, will give less satisfactory sampling than unequal interval, or equi-interval at, say, 8-hour periods; for the exogenous rhythm of the day, with measurement at the same clock hour, will give a narrower sampling.

What are the differences, also, between two otherwise similar *P*-technique experiments where one samples at very short and another at very long intervals? The situation still remains similar to *R*-technique where high and low density of variables differentiates two studies. The former may recognize as common factors what are only specifics in the latter, and the latter may sometimes go directly to what are second-order factors in the former. If rhythms are involved, the latter will tend to miss fine oscillations and the former those of long period. The greatest difference will show in relation to the displaced-factor method, where intervals of too gross a size may prevent discovery of the best maximizing lag of variable on factor. It has been said earlier that increasing the length of retest interval abolishes autocorrelation, and this has been true of variables and intervals in the few studies where comparisons have been made. But theoretically one would expect that one would move from autocorrelations associated with short-term rhythms and causal effect to autocorrelations associated with longer effects. If the autocorrelations are, as argued, only expressions of the main systematic influences at work, then an interval which obliterates autocorrelations may be inaptly long in relation to the causal processes actually at work in that area. Thus although there is need for systematic exploration at different intevals, since different substantive hypotheses are being checked at the different intervals, yet that interval which gives the largest mean r for the matrix is initially cutting into the connections with the most apt interval.

It remains to look a little more closely at certain relations in the BDR matrix. First it will be noted that the proposal for using *serial standardized* tests in P-technique amounts to the same thing as testing N people on n tests over p occasions, i.e., utilizing all parallel facets—each person a facet—of test-occasion matrices. Just as we sometimes in R-technique standardize within each person before correlating over tests, i.e., we use ipsative scores, so here we could ipsatize the score of each occasion over a set of people before starting the usual P-technique correlations. Such a procedure of performing the experiment over occasions with *several* people, even though all but one are used only for standardization purposes, would have certain advantages.

Just as Q is the transposed technique from R, so O-technique is the transpose of P-technique. O-technique is the correlation of occasions, and the immediate indication at the level of *surface traits* (correlation clusters) is a grouping of occasions according to their similarity (in shape, not level) in the person's life. However, just as in Q and R-technique, if one uses covariances, the effect is to get essentially the same factors (Cattell, 1951a). The decision to proceed by P or O-technique to these factors is therefore best left to convenience, principally, whether it is easier to get in more tests or more occasions of testing. Since stability on the test factors is usually more desired, P-technique is generally preferable to the O-technique design.

Summary

P-technique can be properly understood only in relation to the total covariation chart or BDR matrix, and in particular to those factor techniques which correlate test variables, namely, R-technique and incremental R-technique across time and people. Its relation to incremental R-technique is that it deals with person–unique factors instead of common factors (whence its label P, or single *person* analysis).

Three kinds of pattern are theoretically distinguishable from correlational examination of the organism—traits, trait-states or time-variational patterns in traits and states, or dimensions of variation with no corresponding permanent trait. They can be separated partly by observing their different variance contributions in P, incremental R, and averaged

R factor analyses, and partly by considerations external to factor analysis, e.g., growth curves and criterion relations. The chief direct means of distinguishing a trait-state from a state dimension, however, are (*a*) the congruence of pattern of the former with the corresponding true trait pattern and (*b*) the higher ratio of inter-occasion to inter-person variance in the latter.

As a mathematical-statistical model *P*-technique needs special examination in respect to (*a*) the distribution properties of the measurements; (*b*) the effect which time sequence may have upon the independence of the measures and the degrees of freedom for significance testing; (*c*) the different role of error of measurement and consequent different ranges of reliability concepts; and (*d*) the problem of sampling. As to (*a*) it is assumed that we have a normal distribution, and as to (*c*) that reliabilities will consistently run lower than in *R*-technique, but of the same order as in incremental *R*-technique.

As to degrees of freedom, issue is taken with Quenouille and Bartlett— or at least with the conclusions psychologists have drawn from their statements that degrees of freedom should be reduced because of serial correlation. If one is testing the significance of the correlation of *a* and *b* when a manipulative influence has been introduced which hypothetically could cause them to correlate, then the prior existence of an autocorrelation would reduce the degrees of freedom as stated. However, the factor analyst is not asking, "What would be the distribution of a zero *r* of *a* and *b* when a prior autocorrelation exists in both?" but "What is the statistical significance of the evidence for factors which cause both the autocorrelation and the cross correlation?" In these circumstances, where a trend or cycle is not taken for granted, the proper null assumption, made *a priori* and before any experiment begins, is that no causal influences exist and that no necessary relations exist among the figures. The only necessary relations, i.e., restrictions on degrees of freedom, are then those imposed by the laws of algebra, and point to $N - 2$ degrees of freedom, as in evaluating any other correlation coefficient. In any case, by shuffling or other procedures, autocorrelations can always be abolished without upsetting the intrinsic correlations.

On the question of sampling: (*a*) The symmetry of occasion sampling to person sampling is upset by the apparent fact that occasions may prove to come from several species types instead of one, as is assumed with people. This is precisely similar to the problem of sampling of tests (measurement variables), but in both the difference from person sampling is really one of degree since, in the last resort, persons also fall into species types. (*b*) The shorter or longer intervals of sampling in *P*-technique are equivalent to closer and broader sampling of variables in tests. For example, very short cycle phenomena will be missed in longer spaced P-technique intervals, just as more narrow factors will be missed when a low density of test representation is used. The effect springs in P-technique from the fact that no lag adjustment can possibly catch the causal dependence of a on b if the measurement interval is of a different order from the $a - b$ dependence. It is very important, therefore, in exploring and interpreting factors by P-technique to adjust the interval to the matter being investigated, and to make comparative studies of results from experiments systematically varying the interval.

The handling of trends and cycles must depend on the causal model with which one operates. The model advocated here is one in which both endogenous and exogenous causes are recognized. The former, for reasons of scientific structure, will tend to appear as substantially time-related trends and cycles. Indeed, it is conceivable that two distinct endogenous influences will be perfectly correlated with time and, at least over certain periods, with each other. The latter will be more "accidental," but *could* also include trends and cycles. Measures of stimulus conditions, manipulated and unmanipulated, correlated in the P-technique matrix, may locate some exogenous factors, but others will be known only from their factor effects. It is desirable to factor, at the second order, in a single matrix, both the factors which appear to be endogenous and those initially identified as exogenous; for, if the supposition is correct, the two sets should be substantially orthogonal. However, it is possible, through certain mutual influences of organism and environment, that a second-order factor in one system will occasionally prove to be a first-order in the other. Hunger in a tiger (first-order endogenous factor) may produce such behavior as makes game scarce, i.e., reduces the frequency of environmental, exogenous factors. Thus in addition to a factor structure consisting of a hierarchy of causal influences, certainly circular, positive and negative feedback effects would be expected, insufficiently explored formally in the factor-analytic model, but probably producing an identity of certain first-order and third-order, etc., factors.

Consistent with this scientific model, a statistical analysis is proposed by simple structure-order hierarchies, as stated, with, additionally, what has been called *iteration for factor displacement*. This procedure by iterative cycles seeks to maximize the loading of each factor on the variables by giving the latter lags which will be peculiar to each variable and each factor. Incidentally, this handles Yule's dilemma that equal frequency but out-of-phase cycles from the same cause may not show the correlation necessary to recognize their connection.

It follows from the above that, except for special applied purposes in a well-known field, one should not remove trends or cycles before proceeding with one's analysis. Time is initially only a variable, not a factor, and its special properties as a variable need to be regarded only at later stages. A trend will commonly be the result of more than one time-correlated factor. The special difficulty of P-technique is the unusual simple structure rotational problem presented by the existence of several probably strongly time-correlated factors. These might yield, at the second order, a factor virtually identical with time, especially for the endogenous, internal-clock influences. But the main difficulty is that quite small inaccuracies in simple structure rotation, which would pass without difficulties in most R-technique studies, are likely to make the C_R matrix near-singular and cause repeated failures when inverting to get the C_F.

The special difficulties of P-technique at the practical level arise from learning and boredom effects through repeated measurement. The best attacks on this problem are (a) to exercise ingenuity in setting up new kinds of tests for the same psychological traits, which will permit effectively repeatable measurements in areas where such tests cannot at present be found; (b) to insert markers to recognize learning and boredom factors, so that they can be set aside; and (c) to produce serial standardized tests. These need not run to the whole length of the experiment but can be cycled, with a "calendar number" variable added to recognize any remaining time effect. So far the effects do not appear as large as might *a priori* be expected. Especially by using serial equivalent scales standardized in the given serial order, there is hope of reducing these disturbers.

The aim of P-technique is to discover the influences at work, to assign them to their endogenous and exogenous origins, to work out their patterns of causal interaction, and to note individual uniqueness by comparing the individual's factor-loading pattern and second-order structure with those from incremental R-technique for the general population. These aims cannot, however, be wholly achieved by any techniques applied to a single data matrix. Using the usual strategic interrelation of factor-analytic experiments, P-technique can broaden its inferences and, in addition, it has its own peculiar advantages in inference through being able to plot the estimated factors over time in order to recognize their characteristic trends or cyclical or causal connections.

In the systematic advance of P-technique and incremental R-technique structuring of human states and trait-states, it is most important at this juncture to carry from research to research certain identical variables which have been shown consistently to mark the main factors. For this purpose the seven most substantial of some nine known state factors have been made available in a standard marker battery (Cattell and Nesselroade, 1962).

Eleven | Statistical Models for
the Study of Change in the
Single Case

WAYNE H. HOLTZMAN

Appreciation is expressed to Roy Mefferd, Louis Moran, and James Kimble for their generosity in supplying the original data for the three time-series that serve as examples.

Any approach to the study of change must involve two or more measurements of the same variable at different times in order to provide a basis for inferring that change has or has not taken place. In all such designs, time is the master variable against which everything else is ordered.

In the usual situation with only one repeated measurement, time is generally ignored as a variable, and replication is obtained by using a large enough number of independently behaving individuals to employ statistical inference as a basis for reaching decisions concerning change. If only very few individuals are available for study, however, replication may be obtained by increasing the number of repeated measures through time. In the extreme case of a single individual, the only possible way to obtain the replication necessary for statistical inference is by many repetitions of the measurement. A number of problems arise in the analysis of such time-series, most of which are unfamiliar to the great majority of psychologists and social scientists who have always obtained replication of observations for statistical inference by studying a number of individuals rather than the single case.

In recent years, however, there has been growing awareness of the need for greater attention to statistical models that will be appropriate for the single case. Because of this focus on the single individual or system, the field of time-series analysis, so important in econometrics, demography, meteorology, communications engineering, and a number of other sciences, is a rapidly growing branch of statistics that psychologists would do well to study carefully.

199

Everyone is familiar with such time-series as the annual rainfall, the gross national product, or the family income over a number of years. The study of change is commonplace in countless dynamic systems, although forecasting future trends is still only approximate at best for most such series. Unlike the usual situation in psychology, the statistical population is the life span of the system and the statistical sample is a relatively short time-series within this total life span. The main purpose of the analysis is to gain enough insight into the internal structure of the time-series to permit valid generalizations about the system's behavior.

Three general characteristics of time-series have special ramifications for the development of statistical models from which to draw generalizations. First, time as the major ordering dimension can bring with it countless other variables, only some of which may be taken into account systematically by the investigator. Second, the time interval between observations is arbitrary and for continuous variables can be made infinitely small. For example, the time-series formed by repeated measurements of brain-wave activity in a particular area of the cortex can vary from monthly measures of delta wave activity collected over a number of years to the continuous recording of electrical potential over a short period of one minute or less. Since the time interval is arbitrary, the number of observations constituting a series of given duration is also arbitrary. And third, repeated observations through time are often sequentially dependent, rendering invalid many of the usual statistical models which require independence of observations. While the degree of this dependency can usually be reduced by lengthening the time interval between successive observations, it is difficult to eliminate it entirely without first separating the time-series into orthogonal components and treating the residual scores as independent of major trends and oscillations. Most of the remainder of this paper is devoted to the problems introduced by such sequential dependencies in time-series analysis.

Analysis of the single time-series

Before the problems encountered in the analysis of multiple time-series are taken up, it may be instructive to look closely at the internal structure of single time-series and some of their general properties. The usual method of plotting a time-series involves the simple coordinate graphing of the N observations with equal time intervals on the abscissa and values of the function on the ordinate. Three such time-series are presented in Figures 11.1–11.3.

The particular series chosen for purposes of illustration were constructed from daily measurements of three functions over a period of 245 successive days on a single schizophrenic patient who had been studied intensively by Mefferd and his colleagues. Two of these variables— Relatedness Score on the Word Association Test (z) and Perceptual Speed (y)—are scores on simple mental abilities tests for which Moran (1959) and Moran, Mefferd, and Kimble (1960) had developed a large number of standardized parallel forms that can be given in daily testing. The third variable, creatinine (x) output in daily samples of urine, is included to illustrate a biochemical variable studied in connection with the two psychological measures. These three variables were selected from over a hundred different daily measures actually obtained from one schizophrenic patient by Mefferd and his co-workers (1960).

Inspection of the time-series plotted for creatinine in Figure 11.1 shows the typical rapid fluctuation characteristic of most time-series, together with the slow, undulating trend over a long period of time.

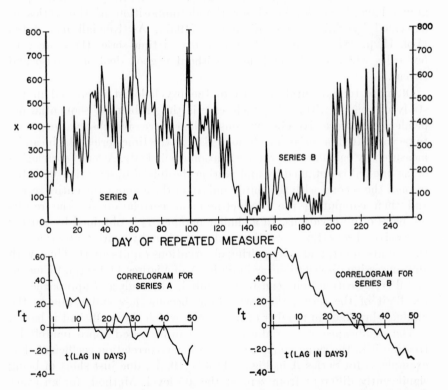

Fig. 11.1.—Time-series and correlograms for daily measures of creatinine (x) in the urine of one schizophrenic patient.

Most systems that show long-range growth and decay as well as cyclical fluctuations or seasonal oscillations require at least three kinds of components to describe the obtained time-series: (*a*) a trend or long-term movement; (*b*) an oscillation about the trend; and (*c*) a "random" or residual component. Although considerable progress has been made in the development of methods for the decomposition of time-series into orthogonal components, several important problems still remain unresolved. For example, how does one distinguish between a long-term trend and an oscillation without being arbitrary? What may appear like a trend (such as the movement in Series A for creatinine) may indeed be an oscillation about a still more stable trend if the time span were greatly lengthened. Some methods of trend elimination, such as moving averages, may actually generate artificial oscillations that obscure subsequent analysis (the Slutzky-Yule effect). A good review of the problems in trend analysis of time-series is given by Kendall (1948). More recently, computer programs have been developed for the decomposition of time-series as described by Shiskin and Eisenpress (1957). As Kendall has stated (Vol. II, p. 387), however, "In the theory of time-series there are very few rules which can be laid down without a good deal of proviso and caveat."

Of more fundamental concern to the psychologist interested in the study of change within the single case is the problem of sequential dependency in successive observations. When successive observations tend to be correlated, a serial correlation exists in the time-series which can be measured by calculating serial correlation coefficients. A serial correlation of lag one (r_1) is obtained by first pairing the initial observation with the second, the second with the third, and so on throughout the entire series, and then computing the product-moment correlation for the resulting pairs of observations. In a similar manner, r_2 is obtained by pairing successive observations two time-units apart, r_3 by pairing observations three units apart, and r_t by pairing observations t units apart. Thus, with 100 successive observations as in Series A of Figures 11.1–11.3, 97 meaningful serial correlations can be computed, although as t approaches n, the limit of the series, the correlations become less stable due to the gradual shrinkage in number of pairs upon which the coefficient is based.

The significance of a serial correlation can be tested approximately by treating it in the same manner as an ordinary correlation coefficient. For example, r_1 for Series A in Figure 11.3 is .19, a value just short of being significantly different from zero at the .05 level. Methods for an exact test of the significance of a serial correlation have been given by R. L. Anderson (1942).

Since the serial correlation coefficient serves as an index of the degree of sequential dependency in successive observations, it is highly useful for obtaining further insights concerning the internal structure of a time-series. By plotting r_t against t for successively lagged coefficients, a correlogram can be obtained which shows the amount of dependency throughout the series. Correlograms for r_t lagged up to 50 observations are given in the lower half of Figures 11.1–11.3 for the series used in the illustration.

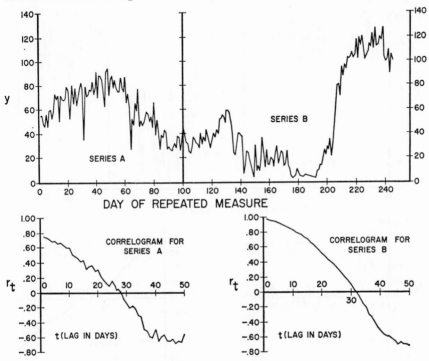

Fig. 11.2.—Time-series and correlograms for daily measures on Perceptual Speed (y) for one schizophrenic patient.

The differences in these six correlograms are quite striking and reflect the contrasting character of the several time-series involved.

The amount of serial correlation in Series A for creatinine drops off sharply in four lags to the insignificant value of .25. For the remainder of the correlogram, r_t hovers sufficiently close to zero to prove insignificant for the $100 - t$ pairs used in computing r_t. In spite of an obvious, bow-shaped trend in Series A, the amount of serial correlation is relatively minor, disappearing after four lags.

By contrast, the correlogram of Series A for Perceptual Speed (Fig. 11.2) drops off very gradually, crossing the zero line at lag 29 and continuing to march downward to values almost as large in the negative direction ($-.68$ for r_{47}) as the first serial correlation in the positive direction (.75). The reason for this difference between creatinine (x) and Perceptual Speed (y) on Series A is fairly simple. Although both show a somewhat similar bow-shaped trend, x has much greater daily fluctuation about the trend relative to the trend itself, flattening out its correlogram. In addition

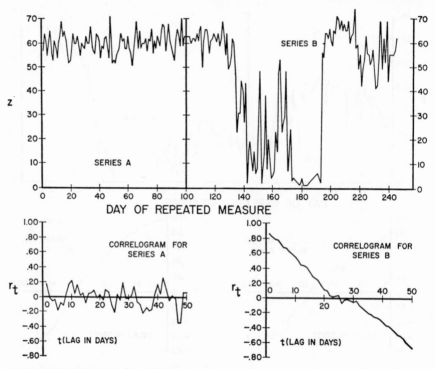

Fig. 11.3.—Time-series and correlograms for daily measures on Word Association, Relatedness Score (z), for one schizophrenic patient.

y shows a more accentuated trend than does x, particularly in the marked drop from the sixtieth to ninetieth day, resulting in more negative r_t with a high amount of lag.

　Still a different picture is shown by the correlogram of Series A in Figure 11.3. Unlike the first two series, the daily measures on Word Association, Relatedness Score (z), show no trend for the first 100 days. A time-series of this type in which the distribution function of measures is not affected by a translation in time of the set of observations is known as a stationary time-series. Since there is no trend in Series A for z, the mean and variance are independent of t. Much simpler statistical models apply to stationary time-series than to the usual nonstationary type found in most social or natural systems (Grenander and Rosenblatt, 1957). The correlogram is comprised entirely of insignificant serial correlations, indicating that the observations in Series A for z can be treated as independent.

An important question to ask in the analysis of any time-series is the extent to which a given observation is dependent upon the observations preceding it. Where the systematic variance in a given observation depends only upon the preceding observation, the time-series forms a Markoff process of the first order. If more than one previous observation is needed, a higher order Markoff process is present. Quenouille (1952) has suggested that the order of Markoff scheme to which the observations in a single time-series may belong can be estimated by the use of partial serial correlation coefficients. To test for a first-order Markoff chain, $r_{13.2}$ is computed, where r_{12} and r_{23} in the usual formula for computing a first-order partial correlation coefficient are serial correlations lagged one observation (herein designated as r_1) and r_{13} is a serial r with a lag of two (r_2). The formula as simplified for use with serial correlations is as follows:

$$r_{13.2} = \frac{r_2 - r_1^2}{1 - r_1^2},$$

where r_1 and r_2 are serial correlations computed in the usual manner.

When applied to the six series in Figures 11.1–11.3, this method suggests that Series A for x is the only first-order Markoff chain in the group. The partial serial correlation of lag two, corrected for lag one, is only .19 as compared to the lag-one coefficient of .60. In a similar manner, higher order, partial serial correlations can be computed to determine approximately the number of preceding observations necessary to account for the nonrandom, time-determined aspects of the series. In the remaining examples, Series B for y and z are probably second-order Markoff processes, $r_{14.23}$ being .02 and $-.14$, respectively; while Series B for x and Series A for y are of still higher order. Although it is possible to calculate higher order, partial serial correlations, the instability of the results do not justify the work involved.

Analysis of the internal structure of a single time-series is of particular importance as a preliminary step to dealing with the more interesting problem of inferring the cause of the observed change in the individual through time. Looking at only the one series tells us nothing about why the change has taken place or what other variables may have changed concomitantly with the one in question.

Multiple time-series analysis

With time as the master ordering variable, any number of factors other than the primary series in question may be changing concurrently with the primary series as a part of the total system. Variables which can logically interact with each other in a mutually dependent way are usually referred to as endogenous since they are all conceivably part of the same system. Variables which act upon the system without in turn being influenced by it are called exogenous. The term, endogenous, has similar connotations to the term, dependent, and an exogenous variable is similar to an independent variable as used in experimental design.

A series of learning trials with a predetermined reinforcement schedule can be thought of as two concurrent time-series. The reinforcement schedule is an exogenous variable, coded in binary form in the familiar case where reward is present or absent. The individual's response constitutes an endogenous variable which is expected to change as a function of the reinforcement schedule. If the experiment is one in which the reinforcement schedule is altered as a result of the individual's response, both resulting time-series are endogenous in character. When viewed in this manner, it is apparent that multiple time-series analysis, stochastic learning models, and Markoff processes are all variations of the same fundamental phenomena where repeated measures through time are obtained on the single individual for the purpose of studying change.

Unfortunately from an inferential point of view, most multiple time-series are much more complex and involve larger systems of variables than is true of the learning model with only two variables in a highly controlled experimental situation. Take, for example, even a simple experiment involving presence or absence of a drug treatment as the exogenous variable and activity level as the endogenous or response variable. Unlike a series of learning trials which can be given in one session, the study of drug effects would take many months to build up enough observations to constitute a stable time-series since the time interval between changes in drug treatment must be a matter of days or weeks rather than minutes.

The alternative where one has a treatment variable to study in relation to the individual's behavior is to change the treatment less frequently, holding it constant for sufficient time to be reasonably sure that any possible effect has registered an impact on the endogenous variables in question. Of course it is not feasible to consider the treatment variable itself as a time-series since there are too few units of treatment as a variable to deal with it statistically.

When taken over the entire period of 245 days, the time-series in Figures 11.1–11.3 involve an exogenous treatment variable with long time intervals of 60 days between change. For the first 60 days, the patient received a daily placebo. During the second 60 days, chlorpromazine replaced the placebo. From day 120 to day 179, chlorpromazine was continued but with electroshock therapy superimposed. The final 65-day period consisted once again of placebo. Unusual precautions were taken by Mefferd and his colleagues, including nearly complete control of diet, physical environment, and other treatment variables in order to minimize the possibility of undesirable exogenous variables affecting the system. Consequently, the data presented in Figures 11.1–11.3 are probably as well controlled and carefully collected as it is reasonable to expect.

While it seems obvious from even a casual glance at Figures 11.1–11.3 that the several treatments had markedly different effects upon the patient, it is not easy to prove this hypothesis by statistical analysis. First, any other exogenous variables accidentally linked with these particular treatment phases—such as crises in the life of the patient, world events, or changes in the social organization of the psychiatric ward—could be influencing the endogenous system of variables in an important but unknown way. Although precautions can be taken to minimize such unwanted influences, they may still lurk in the background. Second, the amount of serial correlation in Series B, the last 145 days during which the most marked changes occurred, is sufficiently high, even when lagged for a number of days, to create real difficulties in applying such standard statistical tests as analysis of variance or regression analysis. A possible alternative to the standard procedures is to reduce the degrees of freedom in the error variance, adapting the work of Box (1954) or its extension by Geisser and Greenhouse (1958) to the adjustment of serially correlated error terms in the analysis of treatment effects on a single individual.

When all three of the time-series in our example are considered simultaneously, the question of cross correlations arises. To what extent can the variation in daily measurement of z be attributed to concomitant variation in x and y? Correlation coefficients between time-series can be computed in the usual manner. Whenever serial correlation is present in both variables, however, the ordinary tests of significance are no longer valid. If the two time-series being correlated consist of 30 or more pairs of observations, an approximate test suggested by Bartlett (1935) can be applied. See also Orcutt and James (1948). An estimate of the effective number of independent observations to be employed for testing a cross correlation can be obtained from the following formula:

$$N' = N/(1 + 2r_1r_1' + 2r_2r_2' + \cdots),$$

where N is the number of pairs on which r_{xy} is based, r_1, r_2, $\cdots$ are the serial correlations for x, and r_1', r_2', $\cdots$ are the corresponding serial correlations for y.

Consider the cross correlations among x, y, and z for Series A in Figures 11.1–11.3. Since z is a stationary time-series with no serial correlation present, r_{xz} and r_{yz} can be tested for significance using an N' of 100 as the number of independent paired observations—a total of 98 degrees of freedom. The correlation between x and y, however, requires adjustment of the degrees of freedom prior to testing its significance. Significant serial correlation is present in both x and y until a lag of 14 is reached. Applying Bartlett's formula, an N' of 16.3 is obtained—only 14 degrees of freedom. Cross correlations in Series B would have an even more serious shrinkage in degrees of freedom for testing their significance. Obviously, removal of the major trend before computing cross correlations among time-series has some definite advantages.

Lagged cross correlations among time-series can also be computed by systematically lagging x behind y and vice versa. Table 11.1 contains all possible correlations among x, y, and z from zero lag (the standard cross correlation) to a lag of five observations between paired measures. The principal diagonal of each submatrix in Table 11.1 contains the serial correlation of the variable indicated at the head of the column, lagged as indicated by the left-hand column of the table. Only the submatrix for lag zero is symmetric, the remaining five submatrices containing lagged cross correlations. For example, the correlation between creatinine, lagged one observation in time (x_1), and Perceptual Speed with no lag (y_0) is .17, while the reverse correlation between x_0 and y_1 is .13.

Any one of the correlations in Table 11.1 can be tested for significance from zero by the appropriate procedures indicated earlier, the particular method depending upon the degree of serial correlation present. In the present matrix, none of the cross correlations is significantly different from zero, simplifying considerably any further analysis or interpretation.

Frequently the cross correlations will be sizable and will vary considerably in the amount of lag needed to reduce them to zero. Where a particular cross correlation is of special interest, such as might be the case if one were to hypothesize that changes in creatinine should lag several days behind changes in Word Association, the cross correlogram can be plotted in the same manner as the correlograms in Figures 11.1–11.3.

Thorough analysis of a complete set of time-series presents some unusually difficult problems. On the basis of recent work, Quenouille (1957) has made some tentative suggestions for multiple time-series analysis. First, the complete set of correlation matrices, R_0, R_1, R_2, $\cdots$, R_{t-2}, R_{t-1},

TABLE 11.1

Cross and Serial Correlations up to a Lag of Five Days for Paired Observations on
Three Variables, Creatinine (x), Perceptual Speed (y), and Word Association
Relatedness (z) in Series A, the First 100 Days of Repeated Measurement on One
Schizophrenic Patient

lag (t)		x_0 C	y_0 PS	z_0 WA
0	x_0	1.00	.14	−.04
	y_0	.14	1.00	−.18
	z_0	−.04	−.18	1.00
1	x_1	.60	.17	−.04
	y_1	.13	.73	−.15
	z_1	.01	−.17	.19
2	x_2	.47	.19	−.03
	y_2	.05	.72	−.08
	z_2	.04	−.26	−.03
3	x_3	.44	.19	−.08
	y_3	.12	.72	−.07
	z_3	.02	−.21	−.08
4	x_4	.36	.16	−.05
	y_4	.14	.68	−.17
	z_4	.09	−.26	.00
5	x_5	.25	.16	.04
	y_5	.03	.69	−.17
	z_5	.03	−.13	−.19

R_t are computed as in Table 11.1, choosing t sufficiently large to encom-
pass safely the estimated order of Markoff scheme that is present. Second,
$R_t R_{t-1}^{-1}$ is calculated for each value of t to see whether a Markoff scheme is
operating. Third, the determinants of the resulting t submatrices are calculated and compared. If they vary considerably, the t difference-matrices,
$R_t R_{t-1}^{-1} - R_{t-1} R_{t-2}^{-1}$, are calculated to gain further insight into the reason
for the noted Markoff scheme. Proportionality of row elements in the
difference-matrices would indicate an unlagged relationship operating.
Fourth, the latent roots of the t quotients, $R_t R_{t-1}^{-1}$, are computed and arranged in a matrix with t rows and p columns, where p is the number of
time-series (variables) in the analysis. A stable, large root (column) indicates a strong trend component; a stable root changing sign with increas-

ing lag indicates an oscillatory component; and an erratically variable root suggests a relationship largely independent of trend.

Quenouille goes on to suggest several different approaches that can be tried out for elimination of trend and analysis of various smaller combinations of the original p time-series to learn more about the internal structure of the system. Since little is known about the reliability of this laborious approach to time-series analysis, and since intuitive judgment still enters into the picture rather strongly at several places in the analysis, Quenouille's methods should be used with a great deal of caution. Nevertheless, it represents a comprehensive approach to multiple time-series analysis that serves to point up the frustrating complexity and generally refractory nature of such systems.

Quite a different approach to multiple time-series analysis has been suggested by Cattell (1951*b*) who for years has been advocating the repeated measurement of a single individual across many occasions. By means of the methods of factor analysis, the zero-lagged intercorrelation matrix among the p time-series is factored in the usual manner. Known as P-technique, this method generally ignores the serial correlation and its effect upon the outcome of the analysis. Occasionally, however, the linear trend component due to time is removed by including a synthetic variable with regular, monotonically increasing values and rotating the linear time component out of the picture before dealing with the remaining factors.

That such a procedure leaves many serious problems unresolved, and may indeed obscure the interpretation still further in some instances, should be clear from the foregoing discussion. Of course where the amount of lagged cross correlation is small, as in the three time-series of Table 11.1, or where the amount of serial correlation is negligible, P-technique appears quite appropriate. But it is just those cases where appreciable cross correlation is present, often with sizable serial correlation, that are the most interesting from a theoretical or practical point of view in the study of the interrelations of different functional systems as they change through time within the single individual. The methodological issues in P-technique have been presented in detail elsewhere (Holtzman, 1962).

Concluding remarks

As psychologists become more and more interested in the study of change within the single individual or system, they will have to come to terms with many of the same problems that have plagued economists and meteorologists in dealing with multiple time-series. Foremost among these is the difficulty introduced into any analysis by the presence of appreciable serial correlation in such series of repeated measurements through time. The logical problems of statistical inference from the single case, though barely touched upon in this presentation, also require considerable thought to avoid jumping enthusiastically to unjustified generalizations.

For psychologists, many important variables are excluded from consideration because repeated measurement on the same person is unfeasible. For many psychological tests, only one or two forms exist and retesting with the same version of the test is of highly questionable validity. The simplest variables to study through repeated measurement are those which have low serial correlation, which can be measured repeatedly without marked change in meaning, and which show sufficient variability from one observation to the next to be interesting.

Although methods for the analysis of a single time-series have been rather highly developed, the more important problem of dealing with multiple time-series remains largely unsolved except for special cases. With the advent of modern computing facilities and increasing attention to time-series analysis by mathematicians, it is to be hoped that more adequate models and accompanying analytical methods will be developed shortly for handling repeated measurement on the single case.

Twelve

From Description to
Experimentation: Interpreting
Trends as Quasi-Experiments

DONALD T. CAMPBELL

The preparation of this paper has been made possible by the author's participation in Northwestern University's Carnegie Corporation supported program in psychology and education. Revision of it has been supported by U.S. Office of Education Project C-998, Contract 3-20-001, under provisions of Title VII of the National Defense Education Act.

Scientist as intruder or scientist as unintrusive observer: These two models compete for the loyalties of social scientists. In this conference on the measurement of change we have primarily focused upon our role as describers of processes that would be going on even had we not been present. We have examined the methodology of asking: "Did a change take place here?" "What attributes changed?" "What things tend to change together?" "What is the general, normal, change or growth pattern for this animal, this person, this group, this institution?" "How do change patterns vary as concomitants of social settings?" The problems encountered at this level are so formidable that it may seem gratuitous to ask a still more ambitious one. So frequently do data processing procedures mislead us in answering the question "Did a change occur?" that we should perhaps hesitate before jumping to ask "What caused the change?"

Yet in the literature, the methodology of which we are seeking to improve, this reticence is usually lacking. Few describe change without attempting to explain it. Most undertake the research assuming in advance that they know the causal agent, asking only the question of the degree of efficacy: be it of genetic patterns of maturation, Vassar College, military experience, psychotherapy, remedial reading, or what not. Correspondingly, our meta-science of methodology should stay with our clients over this interpretative hurdle too.

212

The present author accepts "true" experimentation as the optimal model for the interpretation of change in causal terms. With regard to the models of scientist as intruder (experimenter) versus scientist as unintrusive observer, I clearly prefer the first where it is possible, and would utilize the second only as a substitute where intrusion is not possible. Experimental design in the Fisher tradition is the optimal setting for the study of interpretable change. The magic of randomization is that it attenuates the causal threads of the past as they might codetermine both exposure to the treatment and gain scores. Randomization renders implausible innumerable rival explanations of the observed change by cutting the lawful relationships which in the natural setting would determine which person gets which treatment. This provides the persuasive "causal" interpretations, made possible by experiments involving randomization. Where he can, the social scientist interested in studying change should so intrude.

Yet we make assured causal inferences in many settings not involving randomization: The earthquake caused the brick building to crumble; the car's crashing into it caused the telephone pole to break; the language patterns of the older models and mentors caused this child to speak English instead of Kwakiutl. These are all potentially erroneous inferences, unproven, unsupported by deductive certainty. They are of the same type as experimental inferences, in that we are confident that were we to intrude experimentally, we could confirm the causal laws involved. Yet they are inferences available to the unintrusive observer. Cannot the social scientist as observer make some inferences as to sources of change on comparable grounds? The program of attempting quasi-experimental interpretation of observational sequences addresses itself to this problem.

Some slogans: Experiments *probe* theory, but do not *prove* theory. Any data that probe theory are worth looking at. The only uncontrolled variables that invalidate an experiment are those to which we are willing to attribute the status of empirical laws comparable in standing to the law under investigation. When we have an evidence of change and wish to interpret it causally, the only relevant threats to that interpretation are other plausible, probable, causal explanations.

Consider the inference as to crashing car and telephone pole. Our assurance of inference is due to the total absence of other possible causes. Combinations of termites and wind we have ruled out because the other data implications of these theories (e.g., termite tunnels and debris in the wood and wind records in nearby weather stations) do not occur. Spontaneous splintering of poles by happenstance coincident with the auto's onset does not impress us as a rival, nor would it explain the damage to the car. Analogously, in the quasi-experimental program, field observations will be given causal interpretation where (*a*) the interpretation in question squares with the data, and (*b*) other plausible rival hypotheses have been ruled out.

Does this let down the bars and give approval to the descriptive journalism which so often passes for science in our fields? I think not, if we vigorously attend to the specific plausible rival hypotheses appropriate to each situation. In particular, I find the plausible rival hypothesis of regression (R. L. Thorndike, 1942; Campbell and Clayton, 1961) so compelling as to rule out totally these well-established customs in the reported observations of natural change: Chapin's (1955) "ex-post facto experiments" in all forms; matching as a substitute for randomization in providing pretreatment equivalence of groups; sociology's "qualifier," "elaboration," "turnover table," and other complex cross-classifications with percentages for comparison computed to part-sample bases; partial or multiple correlation when used to reject the hypothesis of cosymptom in favor of the hypothesis of distinctive determinant; and the division of pretest scores into extreme subgroups for the assessment of differential rates of change as a function of initial level.

Check-list of factors jeopardizing internal and external validity

For the evaluation of data series as experiments or quasi-experiments, a set of twelve frequent threats to validity have been developed (Campbell, 1957; Campbell and Stanley, 1963). These may be regarded as the important classes of frequently plausible rival hypotheses which good research design seeks to rule out. While not all will be employed in the evaluation of the designs treated here, all will be presented briefly so as to provide continuity with the previous presentations.

Fundamental to this listing is a distinction between *internal validity* and *external validity*. *Internal validity* is the basic minimum without which any experiment is uninterpretable: Did in fact the experimental treatments make a difference in this specific experimental instance? *External validity* asks the question of *generalizability*: To what populations, settings, treatment variables, and measurement variables can this effect be generalized? Both types of criteria are obviously important, even though they are frequently at odds, in that features increasing one may jeopardize the other. While *internal validity* is the *sine qua non*, and while the question of *external validity*, like the question of inductive inference, is never completely answerable, the selection of designs strong in both types of validity is obviously our ideal.

Relevant to *internal validity*, there are eight different classes of extraneous variables which, if not controlled in the experimental design, might produce effects confounded with the effect of the experimental stimulus. These are:

1. *History:* the other specific events occurring between the first and second measurement in addition to the experimental variable.

2. *Maturation:* processes within the respondents operating as a function of the passage of time *per se* (not specific to the particular events), including growing older, growing hungrier, growing more tired, and the like.

3. *Testing:* the effects of taking a test upon the scores of a second testing.

4. *Instrumentation:* changes in the calibration of a measuring instrument or changes in the observers or scorers which may produce changes in the obtained measurements.

5. *Statistical regression:* regression operating when groups have been selected on the basis of their extreme scores.

6. *Selection:* biases resulting in differential recruitment of respondents for the comparison groups.

7. *Experimental mortality:* the differential loss of respondents from the comparison groups.

8. *Selection-maturation interaction,* etc.: in certain of the multiple-group quasi-experimental designs, such as the nonequivalent control-group design, such interaction is confounded with, i.e., might be mistaken for, the effect of the experimental variable.

The factors jeopardizing *external validity* or *representativeness* are:

9. The *reactive* or *interaction effect* of *testing,* in which a pretest might increase or decrease the respondent's sensitivity or responsiveness to the experimental variable and thus make the results obtained for a pretested population unrepresentative of the effects of the experimental variable for the unpretested universe from which the experimental respondents were selected.

10. *Interaction* effects between *selection* bias and the *experimental variable.*

11. *Reactive effects of experimental arrangements,* which would preclude generalization about the effect of the experimental variable for persons being exposed to it in nonexperimental settings.

12. *Multiple-treatment interference,* a problem wherever multiple treatments are applied to the same respondents, and a particular problem for one-group designs involving equivalent time-samples or equivalent materials samples.

In the presentation of the experimental designs, a uniform code and graphic representation will be employed to epitomize most, if not all, of their distinctive features. An X will represent the exposure of a group to an experimental variable or event, the effects of which are to be measured; O will refer to some process of observation or measurement; the X's and O's in a given row are applied to the same specific persons. The left-to-right dimension indicates the temporal order, with X's and O's vertical to one another being simultaneous. These are the simplest symbols needed to designate the different designs as they are usually presented. To make the important distinction between the "true" experimental control-group design and the nonequivalent control-group design, a symbol R indicating random assignment to separate treatment groups is necessary. This randomization is conceived to be a process occurring at a specific time, and is the all-purpose procedure for achieving pretreatment equality of groups, within known statistical limits. Along with this goes another graphic convention, in that parallel rows unseparated by dashes represent comparison groups equated by randomization, while those separated by a dashed line represent comparison groups not equated by random assignment.

Table 12.1 provides a check-off of the designs discussed against these threats to validity. In this table, and in the discussion, the designs for convenience are numbered as in Campbell and Stanley (1963). In this paper the main emphasis is upon the two time-series designs and the cross-lagged panel correlation. The two more traditional quasi-experimental designs are presented as background argument against which to contrast the others.

The one-group pretest–post-test design

The simplest two-stage measure of change is also one of the commonest experimental designs, although so weak when used in the social sciences as not really to justify being called an experiment. It can be diagramed as follows:

$$O_1 \ X \ O_2 \quad \text{One-group pretest–post-test design.}$$

One of the uncontrolled rival hypotheses for this design is *history*. Between O_1 and O_2 many other potentially change-producing events may have occurred in addition to the experimenter's X. If the pretest (O_1) and the post-test (O_2) are on different days, then the events in between may have caused the difference. To become a *plausible* rival hypothesis, such an event should have occurred to most of the subjects in the group under study, as in some other class-period or via a widely disseminated news story. In Collier's (1944) classroom study, while his students were reading Nazi propaganda materials, France fell; the obtained attitude

TABLE 12.1

Check-Off of Sources of Invalidity

Designs	Internal								External			
	History	Maturation	Testing	Instrumentation	Regression	Selection	Mortality	Interaction of selection and maturation, etc.	Interaction of testing and X	Interaction of selection and X	Reactive arrangements	Multiple-X interference
2. One-group pretest–post-test design $O\ X\ O$	−	−	−	−	?	+	+	−	−	−	?	
7. Time-series $O\ O\ O\ X\ O\ O\ O$	−	+	+	?	+	+	+	+	−	?	?	
10. Nonequivalent control-group design $O\ X\ O$ — — — — $O\quad O$	+	+	+	+	?	+	+	−	−	?	?	
14. Multiple time-series $O\ O\ O\ X\ O\ O\ O$ — — — — — $O\ O\ O\quad O\ O\ O$	+	+	+	+	+	+	+	+	−	−	?	
17. Cross-lagged panel r $X_1 X_2$ ⤢ $O_1 O_2$	?	?	?	+	+	+	+	−	−			

Note: A minus indicates a definite weakness, a plus indicates the factor is controlled, a question mark indicates a possible source of concern, and a blank indicates not relevant.

changes seemed more likely to be the result of this event than of the propaganda itself. *History* becomes a more plausible rival explanation of change the longer the O_1–O_2 time lapse, and might be regarded as a trivial problem in an experiment completed within a one-hour or two-hour period, although even here, extraneous sources, such as laughter, distracting events, etc., are to be looked for. Relevant to the variable *history* is the feature of *experimental isolation*, which can so nearly be achieved in many physical science laboratories as to render the one-group pretest–post-test design acceptable for much of their research. Such effective experimental isolation can almost never be assumed in social science. For these reasons a minus has been entered in Table 12.1 under *History*. We will classify with *history* possible effects of season or of institutional-event schedule, although these might also be placed with *maturation*. Thus optimism might vary with seasons and anxiety with the semester examination schedule (Windle, 1954; Crook, 1937). Such effects might produce an O_1–O_2 change confusable with the effect of X.

A second rival variable, or class of variables, is designated *maturation*. This term is used here to cover all of those biological or psychological processes which systematically vary with the passage of time, independent of specific external events. Thus between O_1 and O_2 the students may have grown older, hungrier, more tired, more bored, and the obtained difference may reflect this process rather than X. In social remediation or psychotherapy which focuses on exceptionally disadvantaged persons, a process of "spontaneous remission," analogous to wound healing, may be mistaken for the specific effect of a remedial X. (Needless to say, such a remission is not regarded as "spontaneous" in any causal sense, but rather represents the cumulative effects of learning processes and environmental pressures of the total daily experience, which would be operating even if no X had been introduced.)

A third confounded rival explanation is the effect of *testing*, the effect of the pretest itself. For achievement and intelligence tests it is usually the case that students taking the test for a second time, or taking an alternate form of the test, do better than those taking the test for the first time (Anastasi, 1958, pp. 190–191). These effects, as much as three to five IQ points on the average for naive test-takers, occur without any instruction as to scores or items missed on the first test. For personality tests, a similar effect is noted, with second tests showing in general better adjustment, although occasionally a highly significant effect in the opposite direction is found (Windle, 1954). For attitudes toward minority groups a second test may show more prejudice, although the evidence is very slight (Rankin and Campbell, 1955). Obviously, conditions of anonymity increased awareness of what answer is socially approved, and the like, all would have a bearing on the direction of the result. For prejudice items under conditions of anonymity, the adaptation level created by the hostile statements presented may shift the student's expectations as to what kinds of attitudes are tolerable in the direction of greater hostility. In a signed personality or adjustment inventory, the initial administration partakes of a problem-solving situation in which the student attempts to discover the disguised purpose of the test. Having done this, or having talked with his friends about their answers to some of the bizarre items, he knows better how to present himself acceptably the second time.

With the introduction of the problem of test effects comes a distinction among potential measures as to their *reactivity*. This is a most important theme in my overall program, accompanied by a general exhortation to use *nonreactive* measures wherever possible. It has long been a truism in the social sciences that the process of measuring may change that which is being measured. The test-retest gain would be one important aspect of such change, a threat to *internal* validity. The interaction of testing and X, which could occur without any main effect of testing, represents a serious threat to *external* validity. Such reactive effects can be expected whenever the testing process is in itself a stimulus to change rather than a passive record of behavior. Thus in an experiment on therapy for weight control, the initial weigh-in might in itself be a stimulus to weight reduction, even without the therapeutic treatment. Similarly, placing observers in the classroom to observe the teacher's pretraining human relations skills may in itself change the teacher's mode of discipline. Placing a microphone on the desk may change the group interaction pattern. In general, the more novel and motivating the test device, the more reactive one can expect it to be.

Instrumentation or "instrument decay" (Campbell, 1957) is the term used to indicate a fourth uncontrolled rival hypothesis. This term refers to autonomous changes in the measuring instrument which might account for an O_1–O_2 difference. These changes would be analogous to the stretching or fatiguing of a spring scales, or condensation in a cloud chamber. Where human observers are used to provide O_1 and O_2, processes of learning, fatiguing, etc., within the observers will produce O_1–O_2 differences. If essays are being graded, the grading standards may shift between O_1 and O_2 (suggesting the control technique of shuffling the O_1 and O_2 essays together and having them graded without knowledge of which came first). If classroom participation is being observed, then the observers may be more skillful or more blasé on the second occasion. If parents are being interviewed, the interviewer's familiarity with the interview schedule and with the particular parents may produce shifts. Similarly, a change in interviewers or observers between O_1 and O_2 could cause a difference.

A fifth confounded variable in some instances of the one-group pretest–post-test design is statistical *regression*. If, for example, in a remediation experiment, students are picked for a special experimental treatment because they are particularly poor on an achievement test (which becomes for them the O_1), then on a subsequent testing using a parallel form, or repeating the same test, O_2 for this group will almost surely average higher than did O_1. This dependable result is not due to any genuine effect of X or to any test-retest practice effect. It is rather a tautological aspect of the imperfect correlation between O_1 and O_2. Because of the great attention this or related problems have received at this conference, I shall not belabor this point here.

The interrupted time-series experiment

The essence of this experimental design is the presence of a periodic measurement process on some group or individual and the introduction of an experimental change into this time-series of measurements, the results of which are indicated by a discontinuity in the measurements recorded in the time-series. It can be diagramed thus:

$$O_1 \, O_2 \, O_3 \, O_4 \, X \, O_5 \, O_6 \, O_7 \, O_8 \quad \text{Time-series design.}$$

This experimental design might be regarded as typical of much of the classical, 19th century experimentation in the physical sciences and in biology, typified by the polygraph record for extended periods before and after a major change of conditions for a single specimen. Thus this experimental design is frequently regarded as valid in the more successful sciences even though it has no accepted status in the enumerations of available experimental designs in the social sciences. There are good reasons for this differential status, and a careful consideration of them will provide a better understanding of the conditions under which the design might meaningfully be employed by social scientists in the absence of the possibility of achieving more thorough experimental control.

Figure 12.1 indicates some possible outcome patterns for time-series into which an experimental alteration had been introduced as indicated by the vertical line X. For purposes of discussion it will be assumed that one will be tempted to infer that X had some effect in time-series with outcomes such as A and B and possibly in time-series such as C and D, but that one would not be tempted to infer an effect in time-series such as E, F, and G, even were the jump in values from O_4 to O_5 as great and as statistically stable as were the O_4 to O_5 differences in A and B, for example.

While the problem of statistical tests will be postponed for a few paragraphs, it is assumed that the problem of internal validity boils down to the question of plausible competing hypotheses that offer likely alternate explanations to the shift in the time-series other than the effect of X. A tentative check-off of the controls provided by this experiment under these optimal conditions of outcome is provided in Table 12.1. The strengths of the time-series design are most apparent in contrast with Design 2, to which it has a superficial similarity in lacking a control group and in using before and after measures.

When the list of problems of internal validity in Table 12.1 is scanned, it is immediately apparent that failure to control *history* is the most important weakness of Design 7. That is, the rival hypothesis exists that not X but some more or less simultaneous event produced the shift. It is upon the plausibility of ruling out such extraneous stimuli that credence to the interpretation of this experiment in any given instance must rest.

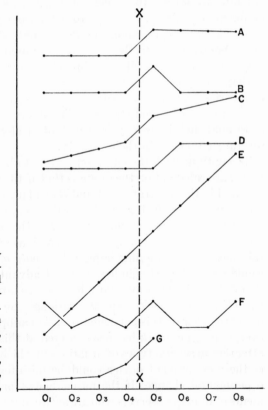

Fig. 12.1.—Some possible outcome patterns from the introduction of an experimental variable at point X into a time-series of measurements, O_1–O_8. (Except for D, the O_4–O_5 gain is the same for all time-series, while the legitimacy of inferring an effect varies widely, being strongest in A and B, and totally unjustified in E, F, and G.)

In many social science situations in which this design might be used, as in a factory or ship at sea, the experimenter might plausibly claim experimental isolation in the sense that he was aware of the possible rival events that might cause such a change and could assert that they did not occur in such a pattern as to provide an explanation of the results. It is on grounds such as these that Holmberg (1954) can refer to his experiences among the Siriono Indians as an experiment in culture change. Here was a tribe so isolated from contact with Europeans or other Indians that the anthropologist living among them for extended periods of time might well claim to be aware of the total impingement of novel stimulation. Observing as he was on a day-to-day basis, he might plausibly interpret in experimental terms the effects of his introduction of firearms and new crops. Insofar as his observations are to be fitted into an experimental paradigm at all, they would fit in best with the time-series design.

Among the other extraneous variables which might for convenience be put into *history* are the effects of weather and the effects of season. Experiments of this type are apt to extend over time periods that involve seasonal changes. In studies of worker output, the seasonal fluctuations in temperature and in the amount and quality of illumination available may be confounded with the introduction of the experimental change. Perhaps best also included under *history* would be periodical shifts in the time-series related to institutional customs such as the weekly work cycles, pay period cycles, and the like. The observational series should be such as to hold such known cycles constant or else be long enough to include several such cycles in their entirety.

To continue with the check-off factors to be controlled, *maturation* and *testing* are ruled out on the grounds that if the outcome is of such a nature as found in the illustrations *A* and *B* of Figure 12.1, *maturation* and *testing* do not provide plausible rival hypotheses to explain a shift occurring between O_4 and O_5 which did not occur in the previous time periods under observation. Had one only the observations at O_4 and O_5, as in Design 2, this means of rendering implausible *maturation* and test-retest effects would be lacking. Herein lies the great advantage of this design over Design 2. In a similar way, many hypotheses introducing changes in *instrumentation* would lack a specific rationale for expecting the instrument decay to occur on this particular occasion as opposed to earlier ones. However, a question mark has been entered at this point in Table 12.1 to call attention to several types of situations in which a change in the calibration of the measurement device could be misinterpreted as the effect of the experimental change. If the measurement procedure involves the judgments of human observers who are aware of the experimental plan, pseudo-confirmation of the hypothesis can occur due to the observer's expectations. Thus the experimental change of instituting a new police commissioner may produce a change in the reporting or logging of crime rather than in the crime rate itself. Trend lines illustrating the effect upon rate of industrial accidents of safety training sessions for foremen (Blum, 1949, p. 297) may have been produced by a change in the foreman's reporting standards as a result of the pressure placed upon him to have a good record, rather than by a reduction of actual incidents. *Regression* effects are also usually some orderly function of time and are likewise implausible as explanations of an effect at O_5 greater than the effects at O_2, O_3, and O_4. *Selection* and *mortality* are ruled out in both this design and in Design 2, if the same specific persons are involved at all points. However, if the observations consist of collective products, then a record of the occurrence of absenteeism, quitting, and replacement should be made to make sure that coincidences of personnel change do not provide plausible rival hypotheses to the effects of X.

Regarding external validity factors, it is clear that the experimental effect might very well be specific to those populations subject to repeated testing. However, this design is particularly appropriate to those institutional settings in which records are regularly kept and thus constitute a natural part of the environment to which one wants to generalize. Production records in many factories, efficiency reports and other records in the military setting, test performance in classrooms, and the like may represent measurement devices periodically available which would not be reactive, in the sense that they are typical of the universe to which one wants to generalize. On this point, some of Rice's (1931) comments on one of the Industrial Fatigue Research Board experiments introducing rest periods may be in order (Wyatt and Fraser, 1925). Even though they were working in a piece-work shop in which production records were a natural part of the payment procedure, in the actual experiment the interest in precision was such that for a three-week period prior to the experimental change, a group of specially trained observers equipped with stop watches were moved into the plant to record minute-by-minute production rates, to provide more precise data than the gross piece-work pay records would have provided. As Rice (1931) points out, this undoubtedly created a self-consciousness which made the measured behavior less typical of what one wanted to generalize to than it would have been without the additional measurement effort. It seems probable that in this instance the effort to achieve greater precision resulted in a less valid experiment than if the normal production records had been utilized without the workers' awareness of experimentation.

TESTS OF SIGNIFICANCE

If the more advanced sciences use tests of significance less than do psychology and sociology for example, it is undoubtedly because the magnitude and the clarity of effects with which they deal are such as to render tests of significance unnecessary; were our conventional tests of significance to be applied, high degrees of significance would be found. It seems typical of the ecology of the social sciences, however, that they must work the low-grade ore in which tests of significance are necessary. It also seems likely that wherever common sense or intuitive considerations point to a clear-cut effect, some test of significance is possible which formalizes the considerations that have gone into the intuitive judgment. Thus tests of significance must be possible which would distinguish between the several outcomes illustrated in Figure 12.1, judging A and B to be significant and E and F not, as far as possible effects of X are concerned. Such statistics are not fully developed, but a few approaches are available. Certain conceivable approaches must be rejected as inadequate. If the data in Figure 12.1 represent group means, then a simple significance of the difference between the observations of O_4 and O_5 is insufficient. If in series E and F, these provided t ratios that were highly significant, we would nonetheless not find them interpretable because of the presence of other similar significant shifts occurring on occasions for which we had no matching experimental explanation. Where one is dealing with data such as provided in national opinion surveys, it is common to encounter highly significant shifts from one survey to the next which are nonetheless random noise from the point of view of the interpreting scientist, inasmuch as they represent a part of the variation in the phenomena for which he has no explanation. The effect of a clear-cut event or experimental variable must rise above this level of shift in order to be interpretable. Similarly a test of significance involving the pooled data for all of the pre-X and post-X observations is inadequate, inasmuch as it would not distinguish between instances of type E and instances of type A. If one has theoretical expectations appropriate to using a series of points in the postexperimental period (an expectation of an instance like A rather than B in Figure 12.1), then one might use tests of difference in slope and intercept between the pre-X and the post-X series (e.g., Walker and Lev, 1953, pp. 390–395), although assumptions of independence of observations are a problem. Mood (1950, pp. 297–298) provides a t test, appropriate to effects of type B of Figure 12.1, for the significance of the first post-X observation from a trend extrapolated from the pre-X observations. Usually one would have insufficient data to justify other than a linear fit to the pre-experimental observations, and thus might be misled in an instance such as *G* of Figure 12.1, in which a systematic trend involving a rapid acceleration might be misinterpreted as an effect of the experimental variable except on visual inspection grounds. Since interpretation seems likely to continue to depend in part upon visual inspection, it seems imperative that the plot of the time-series be published. The usual positive autocorrelation for departures from the trend between adjacent points is computable, for a long enough time-series, and perhaps should be taken into account in some significance tests. This autocorrelation provides one reason for ruling out a test of significance for time-series hypothesized to be of type *A* of Figure 12.1, in which one would project the line of best fit from the pre-*X* observations into the post-*X* region, and test the significance of the difference between the predicted and the obtained post-*X* values, using degrees of freedom based upon the number of post-*X* observations.

If such time-series are to be interpreted experimentally, it seems essential that the experimenter specify in advance the expected time relationship between the introduction of the experimental variable and the manifestation of an effect. Were this to be done, the pattern indicated in time-series *D* of Figure 12.1 could be almost as definitive as that in *A*. Exploratory surveys opportunistically deciding upon interpretations of delayed effect would require cross validation before being interpretable. As the time interval between *X* and effect increases, the plausibility of the rival hypotheses of effects from extraneous events increases.

Since this presentation is inevitably exploratory, it seems desirable to look at some actual time-series from which research workers have attempted to infer causation. Figure 12.2*A* presents a long time-series from Farmer (1924), which was interpreted as showing an increase in production rate as a result of a change in work day from ten hours to eight hours in a bottle factory. There is in this time-series a systematic seasonal fluctuation, but the period of observation is long enough to enable us to take this into account to some extent. It perhaps exaggerates the apparent effect that the change was introduced during the summer slump (Farmer reports a correlation of −.35 between temperature and production). Note, however, that the summer slump fails to appear in the final summer. Were there more years' data available, one perhaps would do best to remove the seasonal change before proceeding further. This has not been done, however, in the analysis illustrated in Figure 12.2*B*. A model such as *A* or *C* of Figure 12.1 being assumed, separate linear trends have been fitted to the pre-*X* and to the post-*X* portions of the series. These are then compared with a single linear fit for the total series. Even the visual impression of effect is destroyed by the addition of these lines—the total series line obviously fitting the points almost as well as the two separate lines. For a test of significance, the following F-ratio has been computed: The numerator consists of the variance of the points predicted by the two part-series fits from the points predicted by the single linear fit; the denominator, the variance of the observed values from the part-series predictions. The resulting F-ratio is 1.07 with 1 and 27 degrees of freedom, a clearly insignificant result.

This analysis was suggested and carried out by Keith N. Clayton. For those who would like to check the computations or try alternate ones, the numerical values used in the computations were 9.10, 9.58, 8.73, 9.62, 9.20, 9.10, 9.10, 9.53, 10.00, 9.13, 9.62, 10.30, 10.30, 10.38, 9.61, 9.69, 9.52

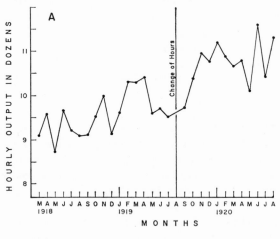

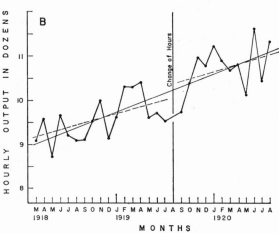

Fig. 12.2.—Change in hourly productivity as a result of shifting from a 10-hour to an 8-hour work day (after Farmer, 1924).

(experimental change), 9.72, 10.40, 10.98, 10.80, 11.23, 10.90, 10.70, 10.80, 10.13, 11.60, 10.43, 11.32. Mr. Clayton and others have expressed a reservation about the assumption of independence in tests of significance for time-series. To be sure, the time-series of repeated measurements differs from a plot of data in which each point represents a mean of a separate experimental population. One major effect of this difference is to reduce the random variability of points, and to reduce the error term. Since in the method illustrated, the shift is tested against the obtained variability of points, this effect is automatically taken into account. In general, homogeneous nonindependence, orthogonal to experimental treatments, is not the nonindependence to be avoided. The problem of nonindependence arises when it is fully or partially confounded with treatments (when, for example, all plots receiving fertilizer A are adjacent and separate from those receiving fertilizer B). The troubling nonhomogeneous nonindependence in time-series comes from the higher correlation of adjacent points than nonadjacent ones. As mentioned above, this makes unacceptable testing the departure of the whole set of post-X observations from the extrapolated trend line of the pre-X values.

Figure 12.3 takes from Vernon, Bedford, and Wyatt (1924) a set of time-series designed to test the effect of introducing a rest period upon the productivity of various kinds of factory workers. In all except the bottom series, for "Handkerchiefs," the original reporters judged that a positive effect was present. Without intending to discourage the use of time-series experiments, the present writer finds no convincing evidence of an experimental effect in any of them. For "Boots and Shoes," "Bicycle Chains," and "Grooves," there is insufficient pre-X data to establish a trend, particularly considering the manifest instability of production rates. For "Labeling" where the data seems most adequate, the previously illustrated parts-vs.-whole linear fit F-test was applied, resulting in an F of 16.19 with 1 and 35 degrees of freedom, $p < .005$. But visual inspection renders the linear fit implausible, the "effect" seeming to start three observations before the introduction of X, a simple curvilinear or sinusoidal trend being indicated.

There can be noted in all of these series, both before and after X, a general trend toward increased productivity. Perhaps this is just what one should expect of any viable social organization, particularly any organization which is interested in research on the conditions of productivity. Just as an animal always tends, through the many minor adjustments called learning, to a more and more efficient fit to his environment, so a factory is apt to be continually undergoing many minor changes of policy, equipment, and personnel, all having as their goal the correction of things that are not working right, most resulting in some slight improvement. These many sources of improvement are confounded with the X under study, as a form of *history*. This general ameliorative trend makes it particularly undesirable to express the effect in terms of mean production rates before and after X. It also makes one dubious of interpretations of delayed effects, for the longer the time interval between X and supposed effect, the more numerous the extraneous sources of improvement are likely to be.

In preparing our chapter for Gage's *Handbook of Research on Teaching*, Julian Stanley and I considered in detail several possible tests of signifi-

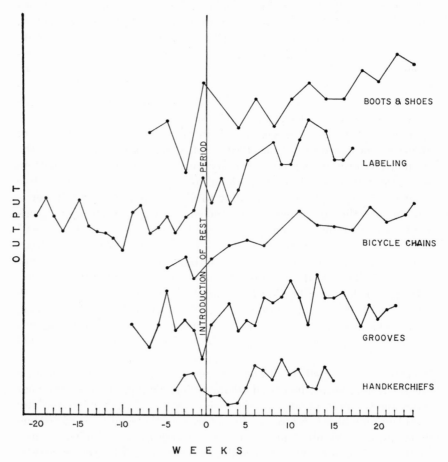

Fig. 12.3.—Effects upon productivity of the introduction of a rest period (after Vernon, Bedford, and Wyatt, 1924).

cance. In the end, equivocation between the alternatives of undesirable weakness and implausible assumptions led us to cut 90 per cent of our prepared discussion from the final manuscript (Campbell and Stanley, 1963). I hope that Professor Stanley will make available his unpublished work along this line, in particular his corrections and extensions of the mode of analysis suggested by the economist Quandt.

With regard to linear tests of changes in intercept and/or slope this general defense can be made: The linear test can be regarded as a minimum test. If the data cannot make random fluctuation an implausible rival hypothesis for explaining the effects under these conditions, then the hypothesis that X had an effect certainly should be held in abeyance. The linear hypothesis had this useful editorial function in most of the factory production time-series which we examined above. If a body of data passes this test (as did the data on "Labeling"), then comes the stage for ruling out lawlike curvilinear trends as hypotheses explaining the post-X gains.

CAN NONEXPERIMENTAL TIME-SERIES BE INTERPRETED AS EXPERIMENTS?

The social scientist, considering the puny nature of the experimental variables which he is likely to be able to manipulate, is ever on the outlook for validly interpretable natural experiments, particularly in situations in which time-series data are regularly available. Cantril (1944) has provided impressive time-series data on public opinion in the United States prior to and during the early years of World War II, in which such catastrophic events as the fall of France seem clearly to have affected public opinion, even though memorable speeches by Roosevelt provide effects of dubious demonstrability. If such interpretive efforts start with a hypothesis about the effect of the natural X prior to examination of the results, they are perhaps encompassable within the time-series experiment. But if, as is probably more usual, there is an opportunistic selection of both events to be regarded as X's and portions of the time-series to be interpreted as significantly shifting, one must withhold the precious label of *experiment*. However, if X be regarded as a continuously varying quantity, rather than something that occurs in only the two degrees of presence or absence, then the time-series experiment merges with the time-series correlation typical of economic studies. Causal interpretation of such data involves numerous difficulties, including the presence of long-term trends which are associated only by chance, the chance association being repeatedly resampled in the correlated sets of observations with the result of highly significant correlations if significance is based upon the N of sampled points. Yule and Kendall (1950) discuss such instances and the particular sampling problem that is involved. Mintz (1946) provides an excellent illustration of the problems involved, in correcting earlier work on the correlation between the rate of lynchings and the price of cotton. In addition, typical problems recur as to the direction of causation and the possibility of correlation without causation. However, through an absence of plausible rival hypotheses, in some cases a temporal correlation is unambiguously interpretable, such as the effect of rainfall upon the price of wheat: Causation is from rainfall to price and not from price to rainfall, or at least was prior to artificial seeding of rain clouds. Such interpretations may be helped by noticing the direction of the temporal lag which maximizes the correlation. But even where a clear-cut temporal lag is present, the interpretation in causal or quasi-experimental terms is a matter of having a plausible explanatory model for one interpretation, plus the absence of plausible rival explanations. Wold (1953, 1954, 1956) has provided valuable discussions of the utilization of causal interpretations of time-series correlations.

While the introduction of cybernetic or feedback models has been accompanied by a renewed willingness to speak in causal terms, it has also shown how compensatory mechanisms can cover up important causal connections. In a thoroughly adaptive system, only experimental intrusion of an unnatural or artificial sort can delineate the causal connections involved, as recent research in experimental biology shows. And on general grounds of avoiding capitalization on chance and post-hoc rationalizations, it seems well to give a separate status to the deliberate introduction of an experimental change into a continuing time-series of observations.

In conclusion, the time-series experiment, in the form in which an experimenter controls a deliberate intrusion of X into an otherwise uniform set of conditions, is one of the frequent research designs of the biological and physical sciences. While to date appropriate and successful applications may be lacking in the social sciences, the design should probably, nonetheless, be granted a position of semirespectability.

The nonequivalent control-group design

One of the most widespread experimental designs in social science research involves an experimental group and a control group, both of which are given a pretest and a post-test, but the control group and the experimental group do not have pre-experimental sampling equivalence. Rather, the groups constitute naturally assembled collectives such as classrooms, as similar as available but yet not so similar that one can dispense with the pretest. The assignment of X to one group or the other is ideally random and under the experimenter's control.

$$\frac{O \quad X \quad O}{O \qquad\quad O}$$ Nonequivalent control-group design.

Two things need to be kept clear about this design: First, it is not to be confused with a design in which experimental subjects are assigned *randomly* from a common population to the experimental and the control groups. Second, in spite of this, Design 10 should be recognized as well worth using in many instances in which true experimental designs are impossible. In particular it should be recognized that the addition of even an unmatched or nonequivalent control group reduces greatly the equivocality of interpretation over what is obtained in Design 2, the one-group pretest–post-test design. The more similar the experimental and the control groups are in their recruitment, and the more this similarity is confirmed by the scores on the pretest, the more effective this control becomes. When these desiderata are approximated, for purposes of internal validity the design can be regarded as controlling the main effects of *history, maturation, testing,* and *instrumentation,* in that the difference for the experimental group between pretest and post-test (if greater than that for the control group) cannot be explained by main effects of these variables such as would affect both the experimental and the control groups.

An effort to explain away a gain specific to the experimental group in terms of such extraneous factors as *history, maturation,* or *testing* must hypothesize an interaction between these variables and the specific selection differences that distinguish the experimental and control groups. While in general such interactions are unlikely, there are a number of situations in which they might be invoked. Perhaps most common are interactions involving *maturation.* If the experimental group consists of psychotherapy patients and the control group some other handy population tested and retested, a gain specific to the experimental group might well be interpreted as a spontaneous remission process specific to such an extreme group, a gain that would have occurred even without X. Such a *selection-maturation interaction* (or a *selection-history interaction,* or a *selection-testing interaction*) could be mistaken for the effect of X, and thus represents a threat to the *internal* validity of the experiment. This possibility has been represented in the eighth column of Table 12.1.

The illustration of psychotherapy applicants provides an instance in which the assumptions of homogeneous regression and of sampling from the same universe except for extremity of scores would seem likely to be inappropriate. The inclusion of normal controls in psychotherapy research is of some use, but extreme caution must be employed in interpreting results. It seems important to distinguish two versions of Design 10, and to give them different status as approximations to true experimentation. On the one hand, there is the situation in which the experimenter has two natural groups available, e.g., two classrooms, and has free choice in deciding which gets X or at least has no reason to suspect differential recruitment related to X. Even though the groups may differ in initial means on O, the study may approach true experimentation. On the other hand, there are instances of Design 10 in which the respondents clearly are self-selected, the experimental group having deliberately sought out exposure to X, with no control group available from this same population of seekers. In this latter case, the assumption of uniform regression between experimental and control groups becomes less likely, and *selection-maturation interaction* (and other selection interactions) becomes more probable. The "self-selected" Design 10 is thus much weaker. Nonetheless, it may provide information which in many instances would rule out the hypothesis that X has an effect. The control group, even if widely divergent in recruitment and mean level, assists in the interpretation. The equivocality produced by the assumption of homogeneity of regression becomes a particular problem if Design 10 produces seeming evidence of significant effect.

The scale used in quantifying measures can in some circumstances provide an inhomogeneity of regression misinterpretable as an effect of X in Design 10. Consider a case in which the control group and the experimental group differ widely in level, with the control group showing a slight gain, the experimental group showing a large gain. In such a case, a logarithmic transformation of the metric justifiable on other grounds might entirely remove the difference in slopes. In such a case, the character of the initial metric, combined with the difference in the initial levels of the groups, explains the effect. To assimilate this possibility into the check-off list, metric can be included as one of the aspects of *instrumentation*, this threat thus becoming a *selection-instrumentation* interaction. I am indebted to Dr. Leroy Wolins for this observation.

The multiple time-series design

While No. 10, the nonequivalent control-group design, is an experimental design worthy of more detailed discussion because of its ubiquitous availability, its discussion here has been introduced primarily as a transition to the multiple time-series design. Let us illustrate a transition from Design 2 through Design 10 to Design 14 with the content of E. L. Thorndike's classic quasi-experiments on formal discipline. Let us assume that Thorndike found a course in Latin associated with a significant gain in English vocabulary, as modern re-analysis with covariance might well show, for note the trends in Broyler, Thorndike, and Woodyard (1927). A pre-Thorndikian study might be graphed as in Figure 12.4A. Thorndike adds a control group, and in overcoming the pretest differential, at least partially avoids the matching fallacy by testing post-test scores against regressed pretest scores. The hypothetical results can be graphed as in Figure 12.4B. Adding this control removes Design 2's plausible rival hypotheses (sources of invalidity) of the main effects of *history*, *maturation*, and *testing*. Let us suppose that the sophomores taking Latin do gain in vocabulary over the course of the year significantly more than do the non-Latin-taking "controls." Is this attributable to the effect of

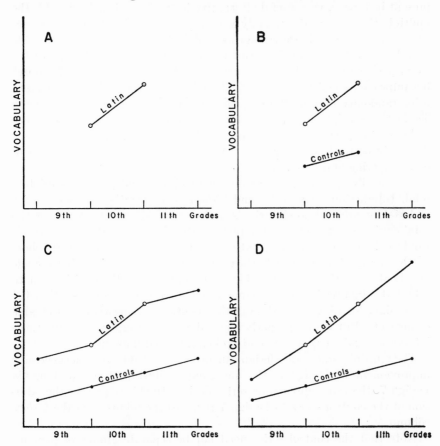

Fig. 12.4.—Forms of quasi-experimental analysis for the effect of specific course work, including multiple time-series.

Latin without plausible rival? Of course not, for it is very plausible that the students selecting Latin were not only above average in English vocabulary to begin with, but also differed from the others in usual annual rate of increase: i.e., that they would have shown greater gains than the controls even without Latin. Hence the minus in the eighth column of Table 12.1 for Design 10. But this assumption of differential slope or differential regression has implications which are themselves testable. And it is the very essence of the quasi-experimental program that all the data available be brought to bear on the problem of rendering implausible the uncontrolled factors, with, if necessary, "patched-up" designs of great inelegance resulting (viz., Campbell and Stanley, 1963, Design 15). In the present instance a very useful alternative is available, i.e., Design 14, the multiple time-series. Presumably we may have vocabulary tests for several previous years. If these data look like Figure 12.4D, then we decide that Latin has had no effect. But if the outcome is as in Figure 12.4C, we may conclude that Latin (here assumed to be a one-year course only) has improved English vocabulary. This is not as good as an experiment using randomization in assigning class schedules. Nonetheless, we have in Table 12.1 a solid row of pluses for internal validity. Each one of those eight rival hypotheses has been rendered implausible. The design is very distinctly better than Design 10, and is, in fact, one of the very best of quasi-experimental designs.

Technically speaking, the column-eight plus should not be completely solid. Interactions of *selection* and *history*, or of *selection* and *maturation* and *history*, are still possible rivals, and one would want to scrutinize the total environments to judge the plausibility of these. Such possible rivals would exist if those choosing Latin were transferred to a different school on that account, or even if Latin were a freshman course so that change of school for both groups coincided with Latin, or if the decision not to take Latin involved a formal renunciation of a college career, so that the vocabulary-learning motivation of the "controls" underwent a specifiable change, etc. But with a properly selected control group and setting, these interactions might very well end up being judged implausible.

The multiple time-series design can also be reached through a successive improvement of Design 2, the one-group pretest–post-test design, via Design 7, the interrupted time-series design. In this sequence, the addition of the control series to Design 7 removes the minus from the *history* column.

Note that the control series need not be separate groups of persons. Control series differing in contents sampled may be useful. Thus in the advertising evaluation of a novel and intense sales campaign, the sales of rival brands could provide the control series. Or in our case, the English vocabulary can be split into groups by root. If the plots for a "control group" of Anglo-Saxon roots showed no gains, while those of Latin did, the rival hypothesis of differential rates of autochthonous vocabulary growth would not be plausible. Thorndike (Thorndike and Ruger, 1923) used such a comparison, although in a single pretest-type design and for a different purpose.

At the present time tests of significance appropriate to this design have not been uncovered. The issues of autocorrelation or greater shared error for adjacent points (at least within experimental group or within control) are still present. A new feature, adding precision if usable, is the cross correlation of zero lag between experimental group and control. To estimate this correlation, it probably should be computed separately for the pre-X and the post-X series, and then averaged. The higher this value, the smaller the error term, presumably, for the jump in the experimental group at X. But such an error term has not been spelled out. Where it is plausible that the same secular and cyclical trends are present in both the experimental and control series (e.g., when both are simultaneous in time and under presumed control of the same exogenous variables except X), then the presence of the control series would seem to reduce the problem of selecting the appropriate trend to use for extrapolation. How to implement this is the problem.

One suggested approach is analogous to the economist's confident "removal" from the time-series of all "known" secular and cyclical trends before looking for novel effects. While in their studies this is done by extrapolating to a degree that will usually seem undependable in our settings (and that often involves regression artifacts, through providing an expectation that systematically lies closer to central tendency than will obtained extremes), the control-group data may serve a comparable function. Thus we can "remove" these trends by generating a series of difference scores (or if the absolute levels vary greatly, of ratios). This single time-series can then be tested by methods appropriate to Design 7, the single interrupted time-series. Assumptions of linear trend (or even of linear trend plus zero slope) will be much more frequently plausible for such difference scores than they would be for the raw data of the experimental series.

The cross-lagged panel correlation

In the discussion of the possibility of "natural" time-series experiments above, the use of lagged cross-series correlations was suggested as one means of deciding the direction of causation. Where two data series correlate, e.g., annual Norwegian harvest yields and numbers of marriages (Yule and Kendall, 1950), the direction of causation may be equivocal (given the universally hypothesized efficacy of fertility rites in increasing harvest yields, etc.). In such a situation, $r_{C_n E_{n+1}}$ should be greater than $r_{C_{n+1} E_n}$, where C stands for cause, E for effect. These cross-lagged series correlations can frequently differentiate the relative plausibilities of competing causal interpretations. When both variables are on both sides of the comparison, i.e., when relative correlation magnitude is used rather than the absolute level of $r_{C_n E_n}$, secular trends or long-term cycles are controlled.

The correlations involved in these analyses are correlations between two variables over a population of temporally distributed occasions. They are correlations of Cattell's type P, with lags (see the papers of Cattell and Holtzman in this volume). Rarely will we have data sufficient to justify these. Typically our situation is one of annual measurements repeated over a very few years. But typically also, we have data for each year on many individuals. In such a situation, the comparison of cross-lagged correlations computed over a population of persons seems useful. For the economist, these would be lagged cross-sectional correlations. In the harvest-marriage example, these would be correlations of marriage rates and harvest magnitudes across a population of nations. The cross-lagging would involve correlating harvest rates for one year with marriage rates for the next year, and vice versa, with an N of nations. Our criterion becomes $r_{C_1 E_2} > r_{C_2 E_1}$.

We have now moved into an area where social science data are more readily available. Longitudinal studies of child development, archives of school records, panel studies of voting and of consumer preferences, all provide appropriate settings, with an N of individuals, parent-child pairs, etc. Do adjustment problems cause poor school performance or vice versa? Does lack of parental love cause children to be behavior problems, or does a difficult child cause parents to love less? While in many such instances, the causal relations are doubtless in both directions, an index of relative preponderance would be very valuable, and where a preponderance is clear, the status of the dominant hypothesis is clearly enhanced, and the credibility of the weaker one must be based upon other bodies of data.

The cross-lagged panel correlation when applied to dichotomous data corresponds to Lazarsfeld's "Sixteenfold Table" (Lazarsfeld, 1947; Levenson, 1955; Lipset, Lazarsfeld, Barton, and Linz, 1954). Conversely, the cross-lagged panel correlation would seem to be the most feasible means of extending the "Sixteenfold Table" beyond the dichotomous situation.

Although Lazarsfeld has not seen fit to present this method publicly in spite of having an eminently publishable 24-page manuscript, I judge this to be the most usefully ingenious of his many methodological contributions. In selecting the name, I have employed the term "panel" to indicate the intellectual heritage of the analysis, as well as to distinguish it from the cross-lagged series correlation.

Let us illustrate the logic of Lazarsfeld's design with some hypothetical data typical of the setting in which Lazarsfeld first introduced it. In a political campaign, Own Vote Intention and Expectation as to the Winner

TABLE 12.2

Correlation Increase between Expected Winner and Vote Intention with Hypothetical Panel Data

July Survey

Expected Winner	Vote Intention Dem.	Vote Intention Rep.
Rep.	20	30
Dem.	30	20

September Survey

Expected Winner	Vote Intention Dem.	Vote Intention Rep.
Rep.	10	40
Dem.	40	10

are correlated. Is this due to wishful thinking, with Vote Intention causing Expectation? Or is it due to the bandwagon effect, with Expectation causing Vote Intention? Let us suppose that in two waves of a panel study we find this correlation increasing, as in Table 12.2. The equivocality of ordinary correlational data, and the ingenuity of Lazarsfeld's analysis, becomes apparent if we note that among the many shifts which would have made the transformation possible are the polar opposites shown in Table 12.3. Here we have presented only 8 of the potential 16 cells. We have neglected the other 8 which reduce the correlation. Lazarsfeld's type of presentation, for the bandwagon effect outcome, is shown in Table 12.4. The empty parentheses indicate the potential loci of the "wishful thinking" instances, nonexistent in this pure case. While it is obvious that we are observing a "causal" antecedence-subsequence relation only for those 20 cases that change, we probably have no grounds for expecting them to be different from those who on the first interview

TABLE 12.3

Two Modes of Shift for the Effect in Table 12.2

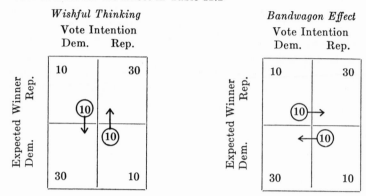

Wishful Thinking
Vote Intention
Dem.   Rep.

Bandwagon Effect
Vote Intention
Dem.   Rep.

already occupied the comfortable Dem.: Dem. and Rep.: Rep. diagonal corners where expectation and vote are in agreement.

Diagramed as cross-lagged panel correlations, the bandwagon outcome provides the two fourfold tables shown in Table 12.5.

Lazarsfeld's "index of mutual effects" is a complex combination of ratios of the determinants of changers to the base of changers, separating changers increasing the correlation from changers decreasing the correlation. Since I am unfamiliar with the mathematical techniques employed, and since these are unlikely to be usable for nondichotomous variables, I shall not duplicate them here, but will illustrate the present suggested analysis for the three bodies of data which Lazarsfeld presents in full. The first asks a question of the 1940 voting data (otherwise presented in Lazarsfeld, Berelson, and Gaudet, 1944): Did personal attraction to Willkie cause people to vote Republican, or did Republicanism rather cause people to like Willkie. The basic data are as shown in Table 12.6.

TABLE 12.4

Sixteenfold Table Presentation of Bandwagon-Effect Case of Table 12.3

July interviews	September interviews			
Vote:Expect.	Rep.:Rep.	Rep.:Dem.	Dem.:Rep.	Dem.:Dem.
Rep.:Rep.	30	0	0	0
Rep.:Dem.	(0)	10	0	10
Dem.:Rep.	10	0	10	(0)
Dem.:Dem.	0	0	0	30

TABLE 12.5

Cross-Lagged Panel Correlations for the Bandwagon-Effect Case of Table 12.3

Expectation-to-Vote   *Vote-to-Expectation*

Sept. Vote Intention   July Vote Intention

For these data, the correlation between vote intention and liking of Willkie moves from .53 on the first interview to .67 on the second. The cross-lagged panel correlations are $r_{V_1W_2} = .65$, whereas $r_{V_2W_1} = .51$. These differ significantly at the .015 level (two-tails, z transformation, intercorrelation of correlation arrays disregarded, $N = 266$). Lazarsfeld's index for this instance is .129. This index value, but not the mode of computing it, is presented in the chapter on voting in the *Handbook of Social Psychology* (Lipset, Lazarsfeld, Barton, and Linz, 1954). It is concluded that Republicanism causes more liking of Willkie than vice versa.

Earlier (Campbell and Clayton, 1961) I had argued that the differential in a cross-lagged panel correlation could be explained away in some instances by two concomitant plausible rival hypotheses, to wit: (*a*) That increased correlation ($r_{V_1W_1} < r_{V_2W_2}$) was required and could be due to extraneous sources such as the test-retest effect and other pressures for consistency; (*b*) that the asymmetry could be due to the higher reliability

TABLE 12.6

Lazarsfeld's Sixteenfold Table for Vote Intention and Attitude toward Willkie

First interview	Second interview			
Vote:Attitude	Dem.:Ag.	Dem.:For	Rep.:Ag.	Rep.:For
Dem.:Against Willkie	68	2	1	1
Dem.:For Willkie	11	12	0	1
Rep.:Against Willkie	1	0	23	11
Rep.:For Willkie	2	1	3	129

or stability of one of the variables. In cases where $r_{C_1E_2} > r_{C_2E_1}$ it may usually be found that $r_{C_1C_2} > r_{E_1E_2}$, if $r_{C_1E_1} < r_{C_2E_2}$ as in the pure case above. In the present data, $r_{V_1V_2} = .94$, while $r_{W_1W_2}$ is only .77. I no longer believe this lower reliability provides a plausible rival hypothesis however. The correlation shows test-retest stability for the period of change, and if taken as an index of reliability, should be generalized alike to both V_1 and V_2, or to both W_1 and W_2. Even though we know that various attitude topics vary greatly in their intrinsic reliability, and may find it plausible that Willkie attitude is less reliable than party preference, we would still normally assume that the reliability of Willkie attitude was equal on both interviews, and the same for party preference. Thus reliability differences

TABLE 12.7

Lazarsfeld's Sixteenfold Table on Vote Intention and Expectation

First interview	Second interview			
Vote:Expect.	Rep.:Rep.	Rep.:Dem.	Dem.:Rep.	Dem.:Dem.
Rep.:Rep.	59	10	1	0
Rep.:Dem.	13	14	0	4
Dem.:Rep.	3	0	1	3
Dem.:Dem.	6	3	7	69

between the variables, as reliability is normally conceived of, enter in to lower both $r_{V_1W_2}$ and $r_{V_2W_1}$ equally, and thus do not provide an explanation of one's being larger than the other. However, a shift in reliability of one of the variables (ascertained by other means than test-retest) may be in some instances a plausible rival hypothesis. A variable which increases in reliability from Time 1 to Time 2 will, *ceteris paribus*, show up as an "effect" rather than a "cause."

A second body of data presented by Lazarsfeld deals with the Bandwagon vs. Wishful Thinking hypothesis, and is shown in Table 12.7. In this case, the correlation between Expectation and Vote Intention remains nearly constant: $r_{E_1V_1} = .63$, $r_{E_2V_2} = .64$. However, in agreement with Lazarsfeld's analysis $r_{E_1V_2} = .62$ which is larger than $r_{E_2V_1} = .54$. The difference between correlations is significant only at the $p < .24$ level. Lazarsfeld's index is .084, and while he says "Thus we see that the 'bandwagon effect' predominates" (Lazarsfeld, 1947, p. 15), it is unlikely that the index would have been significant by the test provided by William S. Robinson in Appendix C of that paper. For the benefit of interest generated in this specific content problem, it should be noted that in the subsequent voting panel study (Berelson, Lazarsfeld, and McPhee, 1954, p. 289) they report that neither that study nor the one we have just considered showed a differential influence on the bandwagon effect vs. wishful thinking analysis.

These data do indicate, however, that it is possible to meet the criterion of $r_{C_1 E_2} > r_{C_2 E_1}$ even when $r_{C_1 E_1} \geq r_{C_2 E_2}$. How shall we interpret such instances? Note in this case that unlike the model initially presented, the stability of the "cause," Expectation, is lower (.60) than that of the "effect," Vote Intention (.82). The causal model would still be tenable for an intermittent unstable cause, and in instances like rainfall and wheat price, or harvest and marriage rate, we could accept the causal model

TABLE 12.8

Lazarsfeld's Sixteenfold Table on Seeing Ads and Buying

First interview	Second interview			
See:Buy	See:Buy	See:Don't Buy	Don't See: Buy	Don't See: Don't Buy
See:Buy	83	8	35	7
See:Don't Buy	22	68	11	28
Don't See:Buy	25	10	95	15
Don't See:Don't Buy	8	32	6	493

even where the general level of correlation did not increase year after year, and even where cause was less reliable than effect.

In a third case, Lazarsfeld examines the equivocal correlation between buying a product and seeing the ads for the product. As he points out, and as Festinger (1957) has more recently emphasized, it could well be that owning or using a product increases one's attentiveness to its advertisements. Lazarsfeld's data come from a two-wave panel study of advertising exposure and commodity purchase. These data are shown in Table 12.8. For these data, $r_{S_1 B_1} = .29$, $r_{S_2 B_2} = .32$. The cross-lagged panel correlations are $r_{S_1 B_2} = .37$, $r_{S_2 B_1} = .27$, this difference being significant at the .016 level. The reliabilities are $r_{S_1 S_2} = .59$, $r_{B_1 B_2} = .78$. Here again the "cause" is less stable than the "effect." The Lazarsfeld index is in this instance .077.

For this design in its dichotomous form, regression probably becomes a plausible rival hypothesis when the item marginals are extreme and differ for the two variables, both for the Lazarsfeld index and for the phi coefficients of the lagged cross correlation as they are differentially affected by the ceilings created by the uneven marginals. However, for continuous variables, no such limitation seems likely. The bugaboo to all correlational interpretation represented by third variable causation could possibly, in complex form, provide plausible rival hypotheses in some instances, and in any application these should be examined. A shift in reliability of one of the variables would lead to mistaken inference if it went unnoticed. In general, however, the design represents a welcome addition to our armamentarium of quasi-experimental analyses. Using it on the bodies of data available and exposing the interesting results to the criticisms of colleagues wise in the specific content areas will in the long run enable us better to fill out the check-list of plausible rival hypotheses.

Summary

The problem of moving from description of change to inferring the causes of change has been examined in terms of the threats to internal validity found in quasi-experimental designs. While change is most interpretable where the experimenter has intruded into natural processes, three designs available to the unintrusive observer have been found worthy of application and careful examination. These three are the interrupted time-series design, the multiple time-series design, and the cross-lagged panel correlation. In all such assemblies of nonexperimental data, quasi-experimental interpretation depends upon rendering implausible those explanations of the observed change which stand as rivals to the hypothesis that a designated experimental variable caused the change. A check-list of eight classes of frequently plausible rival hypotheses has been used in the examination of the data arrangements under discussion.

References

Index

References

Acton, F. S. 1959. *Analysis of straight-line data.* New York: Wiley.

Alexander, H. W. 1946. A general test for trend. *Psychol. Bull.*, **43**, 533–555.

Allport, G. W. 1938. *Personality: A psychological interpretation.* New York: Holt.

Anastasi, A. 1958. *Differential psychology* (3rd ed.). New York: Macmillan.

Anderson, N. H. 1961. Scales and statistics: Parametric and nonparametric. *Psychol. Bull.*, **58**, 305–316.

Anderson, R. L. 1942. Distribution of the serial correlation coefficient. *Ann. math. Statist.*, **13**, 1–13.

Anderson, R. L., and Bancroft, T. A. 1952. *Statistical theory in research.* New York: McGraw-Hill.

Anderson, T. W. 1958. *Introduction to multivariate statistical analysis.* New York: Wiley.

——. 1960. Some stochastic process models for intelligence test scores. In Arrow, K. J., Karlin, S., and Suppes, P. (Eds.), *Mathematical methods in the social sciences.* Stanford: Stanford University Press.

——. 1961. *The use of factor analysis in the statistical analysis of multiple time series.* Tech. Rep. No. 12, Contract AF 41 (657)-214, Sch. Aviat. Med., Brooks A. F. Base.

——. 1962. The choice of the degree of polynomial regression as a multiple decision problem. *Ann. math. Statist.*, **33**, 255–265.

Bargmann, R. 1957. *A study of independence and dependence in multivariate normal analysis.* Chapel Hill: University of North Carolina, Inst. Statist., Mimeo. Ser.

Bartlett, M. S. 1935. Some aspects of the time-correlation problem in regard to tests of significance. *J. Roy. Statist. Soc.*, **98**, 536–543.

——. 1951. The goodness of fit of a single hypothetical discriminant function in the case of several groups. *Ann. Eugen.*, **16**, 199–214.

Beck, S. J. 1953. The science of personality: Nomethetic or idiographic? *Psychol. Rev.*, **60**, 353–359.

Bereiter, C., and Freedman, M. B. 1962. Fields of study and the people in them. In Sanford, N. (Ed.), *The American college.* New York: Wiley.

Berelson, B. R., Lazarsfeld, P. F., and McPhee, W. N. 1954. *Voting.* Chicago: University of Chicago Press.

Blum, M. L. 1949. *Industrial psychology and its social foundations.* New York: Harper.

Bock, R. D. 1960. Components of variance analysis as a structural and discriminal analysis for psychological tests. *Brit. J. statist. Psychol.*, **13**, 151.

————. 1961. *Fixed-point subroutines for multivariate statistical computation.* Chapel Hill: University of North Carolina, Psychometric Lab., Res. Memo. No. 6.

————. 1962. *Programming univariate and multivariate analysis of variance.* Chapel Hill: University of North Carolina, Psychometric Lab., Res. Memo. No. 11.

BONEAU, C. A. 1960. The effect of violations of assumptions underlying the *t* test. *Psychol. Bull.,* **57,** 49–65.

BOX, G. E. P. 1950. Problems in the analysis of growth and wear curves. *Biometrics,* **6,** 362–389.

————. 1952. Multifactor designs of the first order. *Biometrika,* **39,** 49–57.

————. 1954. Some theorems on quadratic forms applied in the study of analysis of variance problems: II. Effects of inequality of variance and of correlation between errors in the two-way classification. *Ann. math. Statist.,* **25,** 484–498.

BOX, G. E. P., AND HAY, W. A. 1953. A statistical design for the efficient removal of trends occurring in a comparative experiment with an application in biological assay. *Biometrics,* **9,** 304–319.

BROWNLEE, K. A. 1960. *Statistical theory and methodology in science and engineering.* New York: Wiley.

BROYLER, C. R., THORNDIKE, E. L., AND WOODYARD, E. 1927. A second study of mental discipline in high school studies. *J. educ. Psychol.,* **18,** 377–404.

CAMPBELL, D. T. 1957. Factors relevant to the validity of experiments in social settings. *Psychol. Bull.,* **54,** 297–312.

CAMPBELL, D. T., AND CLAYTON, K. N. 1961. Avoiding regression effects in panel studies of communication impact. In *Studies in public communication,* No. 3. Chicago: University of Chicago, Dept. of Sociol.

CAMPBELL, D. T., AND STANLEY, J. S. 1963. Experimental and quasi-experimental designs for research on teaching. In Gage, N. L. (Ed.), *Handbook of research on teaching.* Chicago: Rand McNally.

CANTRIL, H. 1944. *Gauging public opinion.* Princeton: Princeton University Press.

CATTELL, R. B. 1946. *The description and measurement of personality.* New York: World.

————. 1951a. On the disuse and misuse of *P, Q, Q'* and *O* techniques in clinical psychology. *J. clin. Psychol.,* **7,** 203–214.

————. 1951b. *P*-technique, a new method for analyzing the structure of personal motivation. *Trans. N. Y. Acad. Sci.,* Ser. II, **14,** 29–34.

————. 1952a. *Factor analysis.* New York: Harper.

————. 1952b. The three basic factor-analytic research designs—their interrelations and derivatives. *Psychol. Bull.,* **49,** 499–520.

————. 1953. A quantitative analysis of the changes in the culture pattern of Great Britain, 1837–1937, by *P*-technique. *Acta Psychol.,* **9,** 99–121.

———. 1955. The chief invariant psychological and psychophysical functional unities found by *P*-technique. *J. clin. Psychol.*, **11**, 319–343.

———. 1957. *Personality and motivation structure and measurement.* New York: Harcourt, Brace, and World.

———. 1961*a*. Group theory, personality and role: A model for experimental researches. In Geldard, R. (Ed.), *Defence psychology.* New York: Pergamon Press.

———. 1961*b*. The theory of situational, instrument, second order, and refraction factors in personality structure research. *Psychol. Bull.*, **58**, 160–174.

———. 1962. *The theory of fluid and crystallized intelligence: A crucial experiment.* Urbana: University of Illinois, Lab. Pers. Assess. and Group Behav.

———. (Ed.). 1963. *Handbook of multivariate experimental psychology.* Chicago: Rand McNally.

CATTELL, R. B., AND ADELSON, M. 1951. The dimensions of social change in the U.S.A. as determined by *P*-technique. *Soc. Forces*, **30**, 190–201.

CATTELL, R. B., CATTELL, A. K. S., AND RHYMER, R. M. 1947. *P*-technique demonstrated in determining psycho-physiological source traits in a normal individual. *Psychometrika*, **12**, 267–288.

CATTELL, R. B., AND CROSS, K. 1952. Comparison of the ergic and self-sentiment structures found in dynamic traits by *R*- and *P*-techniques. *J. Pers.*, **21**, 250–271.

CATTELL, R. B., AND LUBORSKY, L. B. 1950. *P*-technique demonstrated as a new clinical method for determining personality and symptom structure. *J. gen. Psychol.*, **42**, 3–24.

CATTELL, R. B., AND NESSELROADE, J. 1962. *The IPAT seven factor state battery.* 1602 Coronado Dr., Champaign, Ill.: IPAT.

CATTELL, R. B., AND SCHEIER, I. H. 1961. *The meaning and measurement of neuroticism and anxiety.* New York: Ronald Press.

CATTELL, R. B., AND WHITE, O. 1962. *Confactor rotation: Some unsolved problems.* Urbana: University of Illinois, Lab. Pers. Assess. Group Behav.

CATTELL, R. B., AND WILLIAMS, H. F. 1953. *P*-technique, a new statistical device for analyzing functional unities in the intact organism. *Brit. J. prev. & soc. Med.*, **7**, 141–153.

CHAPIN, F. S. 1955. *Experimental designs in sociological research* (Rev. ed.). New York: Harper.

COLLIER, R. M. 1944. The effect of propaganda upon attitude following a critical examination of the propaganda itself. *J. soc. Psychol.*, **20**, 3–17.

CORNFIELD, J., AND TUKEY, J. W. 1956. Average values of mean squares in factorials. *Ann. math. Statist.*, **27**, 907–949.

COURTIS, S. A. 1950. *Maturation units and how to use them.* 9110 Dwight Ave., Detroit, Michigan: Author.

COX, D. R. 1957. The use of a concomitant variable in selecting an experimental design. *Biometrika*, **44**, 150–158.

———. 1958. *Planning of experiments.* New York: Wiley

CROOK, M. N. 1937. The constancy of neuroticism scores and self-judgments of constancy. *J. Psychol.*, **4**, 27–34.

DANFORD, M. B., AND HUGHES, H. 1957. Mixed model analysis of variances assuming equal variances and equal covariances. *USAF Sch. Aviat. Med. Rep.*, No. 57-144.

DANFORD, M. B., HUGHES, H., AND McNEE, R. C. 1960. Tne analysis of repeated measurements experiments. *Biometrics*, **16**, 547–565.

DAVIS, F. B. 1961. The assessment of change. In Marquette University, Reading Center, *Tenth yearbook, national reading conference.* Milwaukee: Marquette University.

DuBOIS, P. H., AND MANNING, W. H. 1961. *Methods of research in technical training.* St. Louis: Washington University, Tech. Rep. No. 3, ONR No. Nonr 816(02).

EDWARDS, A. L. 1960. *Experimental design in psychological research* (Rev. ed.). New York: Holt, Rinehart, and Winston.

EISENHART, C. 1947. The assumptions underlying the analysis of variance. *Biometrics*, **3**, 1–21.

FADDEEVA, V. N. 1959. *Computational methods of linear algebra.* New York: Dover.

FARMER, E. 1924. *A comparison of different shift systems in the glass trade.* Rep. No. 24, Med. Res. Council, Indus. Fatigue Res. Bd. London: His Majesty's Stationery Office.

FELDT, L. S. 1958. A comparison of the precision of three experimental designs employing a concomitant variable. *Psychometrika*, **23**, 335–353.

FERGUSON, G. A. 1959. *Statistical analysis in psychology and education.* New York: McGraw-Hill.

FESTINGER, L. 1957. *A theory of cognitive dissonance.* Evanston: Row Peterson.

FISHER, R. A. 1951. *The design of experiments* (6th ed.). New York: Hafner.

FISHER, R. A., AND YATES, F. 1957. *Statistical tables for biological, agricultural, and medical research.* New York: Hafner.

FLEISHMAN, E. A., AND HEMPEL, W. E. 1954. Changes in factor structure of a complex psychomotor task as a function of practice. *Psychometrika*, **19**, 239–252.

GAITO, J. 1958a. The Bolles-Messick coefficient of utility. *Psychol. Rep.*, **4**, 595–598.

———. 1958b. The single Latin square in psychological research. *Psychometrika*, **23**, 369–378.

———. 1958c. Statistical dangers involved in counterbalancing. *Psychol. Rep.*, **4**, 463–468.

———. 1959. Non-parametric methods in psychological research. *Psychol. Rep.*, **5**, 115–125.

———. 1960. Expected mean squares in analysis of variance techniques. *Psychol. Rep.*, **7**, 3–10.

———. 1961. Repeated measurements designs and counterbalancing. *Psychol. Bull.*, **58**, 46–54.

GARSIDE, R. F. 1956. The regression of gains upon initial scores. *Psychometrika*, **21**, 67–77.

GEISSER, S., AND GREENHOUSE, S. W. 1958. Extension of Box's results on the use of the *F* distribution in multivariate analysis. *Ann. math. Statist.*, **29**, 885–891.

GRANT, D. A. 1956. Analysis-of-variance tests in the analysis and comparison of curves. *Psychol. Bull.*, **53**, 141–154.

———. 1962. Testing the null hypothesis and the strategy and tactics of investigating theoretical models. *Psychol. Rev.*, **69**, 54–61.

GREEN, B. F., JR., AND TUKEY, J. W. 1960. Complex analyses of variance: General problems. *Psychometrika*, **25**, 127–152.

GREENHOUSE, S. W., AND GEISSER, S. 1959. On methods in the analysis of profile data. *Psychometrika*, **24**, 95–112.

GRENANDER, U., AND ROSENBLATT, M. 1957. *Statistical analysis of stationary time-series.* New York: Wiley.

GUILFORD, J. P. 1954. *Psychometric methods.* New York: McGraw-Hill.

GULLIKSEN, H. 1950. *Theory of mental tests.* New York: Wiley.

GUTTMAN, L. 1940. Multiple rectilinear prediction and the resolution into components. *Psychometrika*, **5**, 75–99.

———. 1953. Image theory for the structure of quantitative variates. *Psychometrika*, **18**, 277–296.

———. 1954a. A new approach to factor analysis: The radex. In Lazarsfeld, P. F. (Ed.), *Mathematical thinking in the social sciences.* Glencoe, Illinois: The Free Press.

———. 1954b. Some necessary conditions for common-factor analysis. *Psychometrika*, **19**, 149–162.

———. 1955. The existence of total least-squares images. Unpublished manuscript.

———. 1956. "Best possible" systematic estimates of communalities. *Psychometrika*, **21**, 273–286.

———. 1957. *Communalities that maximize determinacy.* Berkeley: University of California Res. Rep. 16, Contr. No. AF 41(657)-76.

HAGGARD, E. A. 1957. Socialization, personality, and academic achievement in gifted children. *Sch. Rev.*, **65**, 388–414.

———. 1958. *Intraclass correlation and the analysis of variance.* New York: Dryden.

HARMAN, H. 1960. *Modern factor analysis.* Chicago: University of Chicago Press.

HARRIS, C. W. 1955. Separation of data as a principle in factor analysis. *Psychometrika*, **20**, 23–28.

———. 1956. Relationships between two systems of factor analysis. *Psychometrika*, **21**, 185–190.

———. 1962. Some Rao-Guttman relationships. *Psychometrika*, **27**, 247–263.

HARTER, H. L., AND LUM, M. D. 1955. Partially hierarchial models in the analysis of variance. *WADC Rep.* No. 55-33, March.

HAVERLAND, E. 1954. Applications of an analytical solution for proportional profiles rotation. Doctor's Thesis, University of Illinois, October.

HEMPLE, C. G. 1952. *Foundations of concept formation in empirical science.* Chicago: University of Chicago Press.

HOLMBERG, A. 1954. Adventures in culture change. In Spencer, R. F. (Ed.), *Method and perspective in anthropology.* Minneapolis: University of Minnesota Press.

HOLTZMAN, W. H. 1962. Methodological issues in *P*-technique. *Psychol. Bull.,* **59,** 248–256.

HOOD, W. C., AND KOOPMANS, T. C. 1953. *Studies in econometric method.* Cowles Com. Monogr. No. 14. New York: Wiley.

HORST, P. 1961*a*. Generalized canonical correlations and their applications to experimental data. *J. clin. Psychol.,* Monogr. Supp. No. 14, 331–347.

———. 1961*b*. Relations among *m* sets of variables. *Psychometrika,* **26,** 129–149.

HUGHES, H. M., AND DANFORD, M. B. 1958. Repeated measurements designs assuming equal variances and covariances. *USAF Sch. Aviat. Med. Rep.,* No. 59-40.

JORDAN, N. 1962. Letter. *Amer. Psychologist,* **17,** 205–206.

KAISER, H. 1958*a*. *The best approximation of a common-factor space.* Berkeley: University of California Res. Rep. 25, Contr. No. AF 41(657)-76.

———. 1958*b*. The varimax criterion for analytic rotation in factor analysis. *Psychometrika,* **23,** 187–200.

———. 1961. A note on Guttman's lower bound for the number of common factors. *Brit. J. statist. Psychol.,* **14,** 1–2.

———. 1962. Scaling a simplex. *Psychometrika,* **27,** 155–162.

KELLEY, T. L. 1948. *Fundamentals of statistics.* Cambridge: Harvard University Press.

KEMPTHORNE, O. 1952. *The design and analysis of experiments.* New York: Wiley.

KENDALL, M. G. 1948. *The advanced theory of statistics.* London: C. Griffin and Co.

———. 1961. Natural Law in the social sciences. *J. Roy. Statist. Soc.,* Ser. A, **124,** 1–16.

KISH, L. 1953. Selection of the sample. In Festinger, L., and Katz, D. (Eds.), *Research methods in the behavioral sciences.* New York: Dryden.

LAWLEY, D. N. 1940. The estimation of factor loadings by the method of maximum likelihood. *Proc. Roy. Soc. Edinburgh,* **60,** 64–82.

LAZARSFELD, P. F. 1947. *The mutual effects of statistical variables.* New York: Bureau of Applied Social Research, Columbia University.

LAZARSFELD, P. F., BERELSON, B. R., AND GAUDET, H. 1944. *The people's choice.* New York: Duell, Sloan, and Pearce.

LEVENSON, B. 1955. *Panel analysis workbook*. New York: Planning Project for Advanced Training in Social Research, Columbia University.

LEWIS, D. 1960. *Quantitative methods in psychology*. New York: McGraw-Hill.

LINDQUIST, E. F. 1947. Goodness of fit of trend curves and significance of trend differences. *Psychometrika*, **12**, 65–78.

———. 1953. *Design and analysis of experiments in psychology and education*. Boston: Houghton Mifflin.

LIPSET, S. M., LAZARSFELD, P. F., BARTON, A. H., AND LINZ, J. 1954. The psychology of voting: An analysis of political behavior. In Lindzey, G. (Ed.), *Handbook of social psychology*. Cambridge, Addison-Wesley.

LORD, F. M. 1955. Sampling fluctuations resulting from the sampling of test items. *Psychometrika*, **20**, 1–22.

———. 1956. The measurement of growth. *Educ. psychol. Measmt.*, **16**, 421–437. See also Errata, *ibid.*, 1957, **17**, 452.

———. 1958. Further problems in the measurement of growth. *Educ. psychol. Measmt.*, **18**, 437–454.

———. 1959. Statistical inferences about true scores. *Psychometrika*, **24**, 1–17.

———. 1960. Large-sample covariance analysis when the control variable is fallible. *J. Amer. Statist. Ass.*, **55**, 309–321.

LUBIN, A. 1957. *Some rank-order tests for trend in a set of correlated means*. Washington, D.C.: Walter Reed Army Institute of Research.

———. 1958. *On the repeated measurements design*. Washington, D.C.: Walter Reed Army Institute of Research.

———. 1961. The interpretation of significant interaction. *Educ. psychol. Measmt.*, **21**, 807–817.

———. 1962. Statistics. In Farnsworth, P. R., and McNemar, Q. (Eds.), *Annual review of psychology*. Palo Alto, California: Annual Reviews, Inc.

McGREGOR, J. R. 1960. An approximate test for serial correlation in polynomial regression. *Biometrika*, **47**, 111–119.

McNEMAR, Q. 1955. *Psychological statistics* (2nd ed.). New York: Wiley.

———. 1958. On growth measurement. *Educ. psychol. Measmt.*, **18**, 47–55.

MEFFERD, R. B., JR., MORAN, L. J., AND KIMBLE, J. P., JR. 1958. *Use of a factor analytic technique in the analysis of long term repetitive measurements made upon a single schizophrenic patient*. Paper presented at a symposium on multivariate analysis of repeated measurements on the same individual, American Psychological Association, September 3, 1958.

MEFFERD, R. B., JR., MORAN, L. J., AND KIMBLE, J. P., JR. 1960. Chlorpromazine-induced changes in blood constituents in schizophrenia. *Transactions of the fourth research conference on chemotherapy and psychiatry*. Washington, D.C.: Veteran's Administration.

MEYER, W. J., AND BENDIG, A. W. 1961. A longitudinal study of the Primary Mental Abilities Test. *J. educ. Psychol.*, **52**, 50–60.

MINTZ, A. 1946. A re-examination of correlations between lynchings and economic indices. *J. abnorm. soc. Psychol.*, **41**, 154–160.

Mood, A. McK. 1950. *Introduction to the theory of statistics.* New York: McGraw-Hill.

Moran, L. J. 1959. *Repetitive psychological measures.* Austin: University of Texas, Hogg Foundation.

Moran, L. J., Mefferd, R. B., Jr., and Kimble, J. P., Jr. 1960. Standardization of psychometric and psychodiagnostic tests for daily measurements in psychopharmacological research. *Transactions of the fourth research conference on chemotherapy and psychiatry.* Washington, D.C.: Veteran's Administration.

Mosier, C. I. 1943. On the reliability of a weighted composite. *Psychometrika,* **8,** 161–168.

Myers, J. L. 1959. On the interaction of two scaled variables. *Psychol. Bull.,* **56,** 384–391.

Neuhaus, J. O., and Wrigley, C. 1954. The quartimax method: An analytical approach to orthogonal simple structure. *Brit. J. statist. Psychol.,* **7,** 81–91.

Noble, M., Gruender, A., and Meyer, D. R. 1959. Conditioning in fish (*Molliensia Sp.*) as a function of the interval between CS and US. *J. comp. physiol. Psychol.,* **52,** 236–239.

Orcutt, G. H., and James, S. F. 1948. Testing the significance of correlations between time series. *Biometrika,* **35,** 397–413.

Osgood, C. E., Suci, G. J., and Tannenbaum, P. H. 1957. *The measurement of meaning.* Urbana: University of Illinois Press.

Plackett, R. L. 1960. Models in the analysis of variance. *J. Roy. Statist. Soc.,* Ser. B, **22,** 195–217.

Potthoff, R. F., and Roy, S. N. 1962. *A generalized MANOVA model useful especially for growth cruve problems.* Chapel Hill: University of North Carolina, Inst. Statist., Mimeo. Ser.

Quenouille, M. H. 1952. *Associated measurements.* New York: Academic Press.

——. 1957. *The analysis of multiple time series.* New York: Hafner.

Rankin, R. E., and Campbell, D. T. 1955. Galvanic skin response to negro and white experimenters. *J. abnorm. soc. Psychol.,* **51,** 30–33.

Rao, C. R. 1955. Estimation and tests of significance in factor analysis. *Psychometrika,* **20,** 93–111.

Rice, S. A. 1931. Experimental determinations by S. Wyatt and J. H. Fraser of the effects of rest pauses upon repetitive work. In Rice, S. A. (Ed.), *Methods in social science.* Chicago: University of Chicago Press.

Robson, D. S. 1959. A simple method for constructing orthogonal polynomials when the independent variable is unequally spaced. *Biometrics,* **15,** 187–191.

Roy, J. 1958. Step-down procedure in multivariate analysis. *Ann. math. Statist.,* **29,** 1177–1187.

Roy, S. N., and Bargmann, R. E. 1958. Tests of multiple independence and the associated confidence bounds. *Ann. math. Statist.,* **29,** 491–503.

Roy, S. N., and Gnanadesikan, R. 1959. Some contributions to anova in one or more dimensions: I and II. *Ann. math. Statist.,* **30,** 304–317, 318–340.

Scheffé, H. 1959. *The analysis of variance.* New York: Wiley.

SHISKIN, J., AND EISENPRESS, H. 1957. Seasonal adjustments by electronic computer methods. *J. Amer. Statist. Ass.*, **52**, 415–449.

SNEDECOR, G. W. 1946. *Statistical methods.* Ames: Iowa State College Press.

STANLEY, J. C. 1956a. Fixed, random, and mixed models in the analysis of variance as special cases of finite model III. *Psychol. Rep.*, **2**, 369.

———. 1956b. Review of F. G. Cornell's "The essentials of educational statistics." *Educ. psychol. Measmt.*, **16**, 549–554.

STEEL, R. G. D., AND TORRIE, J. H. 1960. *Principles and procedures of statistics.* New York: McGraw-Hill.

THOMSON, G. H. 1924. A formula to correct for the effect of errors of measurement on the correlation of initial values with gains. *J. exp. Psychol.*, **7**, 321–324.

———. 1939. *The factorial analysis of human ability.* Boston: Houghton Mifflin.

———. 1951. *The factorial analysis of human ability* (5th ed.). Boston: Houghton Mifflin.

THOMSON, G. H., AND LEDERMANN, W. 1939. The influence of multivariate selection on the factorial analysis of ability. *Brit. J. Psychol.*, **29**, 288–306.

THORNDIKE, E. L. 1924. The influence of chance imperfections of measures upon the relation of initial score to gain or loss. *J. exp. Psychol.*, **7**, 225–232.

THORNDIKE, E. L., AND RUGER, G. J. 1923. The effect of first year Latin upon knowledge of English words of Latin derivation. *School and Society*, **81**, 260–270, 417–418.

THORNDIKE, R. L. 1942. Regression follows in the matched groups experiment. *Psychometrika*, **7**, 85–102.

TUCKER, L. R. 1959. Determination of generalized learning curves by factor analysis. In DuBois, P. H., *et al.*, *Factor analysis and related techniques in the study of learning.* St. Louis: Washington University, Tech. Rep. No. 7, O.N.R. Contract No. Nonr-816(02).

TUKEY, J. W. 1949. *Interaction in a row by column design.* Princeton: Princeton University, Memo Rep. 18.

VERNON, H. M., BEDFORD, T., AND WYATT, S. 1924. *Two studies of rest pauses in industry.* Med. Res. Council, Indus. Fatigue Res. Bd., Rep. No. 25. London: His Majesty's Stationery Office.

WALKER, H. M., AND LEV, J. 1953. *Statistical inference.* New York: Holt.

WEBSTER, H. 1957. *Consistency statistics from sampling variances of test scores.* Poughkeepsie, New York: Vassar College, Mellon Foundation Research Report.

———. 1960a. A generalization of Kuder-Richardson reliability formula 21. *Educ. psychol. Measmt.*, **20**, 131–138.

———. 1960b. *Use of a general variance model for estimating test reliability.* Berkeley: University of California, Center for the Study of Higher Education.

———. 1962a. Item sampling as a sufficient but unnecessary requirement for precise mental testing. *Educ. psychol. Measmt.*, **22**, 321–324.

254   *References*

——. 1962*b*. Reliability of the ordering achieved by tests: A lower bound for generalized KR 21. *Psychol. Rep.*, **10**, 59–63.
WEBSTER, H., AND ASPREY, W. 1958. *Forming groups that are homogeneous with respect to a large number of measures.* Poughkeepsie, New York: Vassar College, Mellon Foundation Research Report.
WHITTLE, P. 1951. *Hypothesis testing in time series analysis.* Uppsala: Almquist.
WILK, M. B., AND KEMPTHORNE, O. 1955. Fixed, mixed, and random models in the analysis of variance. *J. Amer. Statist. Ass.*, **50**, 1144–1167.
WILK, M. B., AND KEMPTHORNE, O. 1957. Non-additivities in a Latin square design. *J. Amer. Statist. Ass.*, **52**, 218–236.
WILLIAMS, J. R. 1959. A test of the validity of the *P*-technique in the measurement of internal conflict. *J. Pers.*, **27**, 418–437.
WINDLE, C. 1954. Test-retest effect on personality questionnaries. *Educ. psychol. Measmt.*, **14**, 617–633.
WISEMAN, S., AND WRIGLEY, J. 1953. The comparative effects of coaching and practice on the results of verbal intelligence tests. *Brit. J. Psychol.*, **44**, 83–94.
WISHART, J., AND METAKIDES, T. 1953. Orthogonal polynomial fitting. *Biometrika*, **40**, 361–369.
WOLD, H. 1953. *Demand analysis.* New York: Wiley.
——. 1954. Causality and econometrics. *Econometrica*, **22**, 162.
——. 1956. Causal inference from observational data. A review of ends and means. *J. Roy. Statist. Soc.*, Sec. A, **119**, 28–61.
WOODROW, H. 1932. Quotidian variability. *Psychol. Rev.*, **39**, 245–256.
——. 1939*a*. Factors in improvement with practice. *J. Psychol.*, **7**, 55–70.
——. 1939*b*. The relation of verbal ability to improvement with practice in verbal tests. *J. educ. Psychol.*, **30**, 179–186.
WYATT, S., AND FRASER, J. A. 1925. *Studies in repetitive work, with reference to rest pauses.* Med. Res. Council, Indus. Fatigue Res. Bd., Rep. No. 32. London: His Majesty's Stationery Office.
YULE, G. U. 1926. Why we sometimes get nonsense correlations between time series. *J. Roy. Statist. Ass.*, **89**, 1–64.
YULE, G. U., AND KENDALL, M. G. 1950. *An introduction to the theory of statistics* (14th ed.). New York: Hafner.
ZIEVE, L. 1940. Note on the correlation of initial scores with gain. *J. educ. Psychol.*, **31**, 391–394.

Index

For many of the topics, a page number following the entry refers to the beginning of a discussion that continues for several pages.